# Eyes of the God

*R. H. Barlow (center) with his students, 1949, on the patio of Mexico City College, where he was head of the department of anthropology.*

# Eyes of the God

## Selected Writings of R. H. Barlow

Second Edition, Revised and Expanded

Edited by S. T. Joshi, David E. Schultz, and
Douglas A. Anderson

Hippocampus Press

New York

Published by Hippocampus Press
P.O. Box 641, New York, NY 10156.
www.hippocampuspress.com

Cover illustration by R. Saunders, from *The Californian* (Winter 1936).
Frontispiece photograph and illustration on p. 62 courtesy of the
John Hay Library.
Cover design by Dan Sauer, dansauerdesign.com.
Hippocampus Press logo designed by Anastasia Damianakos.

Second Edition
1 3 5 7 9 8 6 4 2

ISBN 978-1-61498-385-9 (paperback)
ISBN 978-1-61498-386-6 (ebook)

*To an eminent Barlovian,*
*Kenneth W. Faig, Jr.*

# CONTENTS

# INTRODUCTION

This volume presents virtually the complete fiction, poetry, and essays of Robert Hayward Barlow (1918–1951). Many of the items herein have not been reprinted since their original appearances in amateur or fan magazines of the 1930s, and several are previously unpublished. This is not the place for an extended analysis of Barlow's achievements as a fiction writer, essayist, or poet; but we hope this volume provides the raw materials for such work.

Barlow's fiction writing clearly was inspired by his early readings in fantasy—notably Clark Ashton Smith and Lord Dunsany—and his association with H. P. Lovecraft, which began in the summer of 1931. Barlow was only thirteen at the time, and well before his fifteenth birthday he was soliciting Lovecraft's opinions on his stories. One was "The Slaying of the Monster," for which Lovecraft supplied the title and some revisions to the prose. In his comments on the story,[1] Lovecraft mentions two other pieces, "The Little Box" and "the tale of the man who became a satyr"; these may be segments I and VII of "Annals of the Jinns" and were composed no later than March 1933 (*OFF* 51). About this time Barlow must have written "Eyes of the God" (*Sea Gull*, May 1933) winner of the story laureateship of the National Amateur Press Association (NAPA).

Nearly all Barlow's early tales were published in amateur journals affiliated with the NAPA or in the emerging fantasy fan magazines. Nine episodes of "Annals of the Jinns" appeared in the *Fantasy Fan* from October 1933 to February 1935, when the magazine folded. A tenth appeared in the *Phantagraph* for August 1936, though it was surely composed much earlier. We include the unpublished "An Episode in the Jungle" as the eleventh "Annal." In an unpublished bibliography of Barlow's work, his literary executor

---

1. HPL to RHB, 18 February 1933, *O Fortunate Floridian: H. P. Lovecraft's Letters to R. H. Barlow*, ed. S. T. Joshi and David E. Schultz (Tampa, FL: University of Tampa Press, 2007), 51. Subsequently cited in the text under the abbreviation *OFF*.

George T. Smisor notes that a story of this title was "supposed to have appeared in *The Phantagraph*, Vol. 6, No. 1 (May 1937), but the edition was so mangled by the printe[r] that it was destroyed and only 4 pp. saved which did not contain Barlow's story." It is our conjecture that "An Episode in the Jungle" is that lost episode. On the manuscript above this title "Annals of the Jinns" has been typed, and both the series title and the story title (written in pen) are crossed out. The manuscript is dated February 1934.

The manuscript of "The Hoard of the Wizard-Beast" is dated September 1933, but Barlow did not show it to Lovecraft until December. Lovecraft revised it extensively, so that it can be classified as the second (of six) Lovecraft–Barlow collaborations. It remained unpublished until its appearance in a booklet in 1994. The third collaboration is the celebrated "Battle That Ended the Century," written in July 1934 when Lovecraft was visiting Barlow in Florida. We have supplied critical notes on the various characters in the tale, some not correctly identified heretofore. Little is known of the unpublished tale, "The Fidelity of Ghu," but it likely dates to June 1934, when Lovecraft began to address Barlow as "Lord Ghu" and such in correspondence. Two other works of 1934 exist only in their published appearances—"The Inhospitable Tavern" and "The Misfortunes of Butter-Churning"—so that we are uncertain of their date of composition. "'Till A' the Seas,'" another story revised by Lovecraft, may have been begun as early as January 1934, when Lovecraft mentions a "last man story" on which Barlow was working (*OFF* 207); but it was not completed until January 1935, when Lovecraft and Barlow went over the text in New York (*OFF* 201).

In 1935 Barlow conceived a lengthy episodic work, *From the Book of Garoth,* very much in the spirit of Dunsany's *Book of Wonder.* Two segments were published: "The Temple," containing chapters 3 and 4, and "The Adventures of Garoth," containing chapters 10, 11, and part of 12. A partial typescript of this text contains chapters 14, 16, and 18; it is unclear whether the intervening chapters were lost or whether Barlow never actually wrote them. An untitled fragmentary chapter that apparently belongs to this series has been appended to the text.

The lengthy and substantial tale, "The Experiment," appeared in the summer of 1935. During Lovecraft's second visit to Barlow that summer, the two collaborated on the incomplete spoof, "Collapsing Cosmoses," each writing alternating segments of the work. "The Bright Valley" is an unpublished tale dated by Barlow to July–September 1935. It was scheduled to appear in James Blish's fanzine *The Planeteer* but evidently did not. Three substantial tales—"The Summons," "A Dream," and "A Memory"—were published later in 1935, but their dates of composition are unknown. Also perhaps dating to this time is the whimsical tale "The Herbivorous God," which is set in ancient Assyria and features Gilgamesh as a minor character.

"Pursuit of the Moth" appeared in Barlow's own amateur magazine, the *Dragon-Fly,* for May 15, 1936. Our text is derived from an annotated copy of a clipping from the magazine on which Barlow has made extensive revisions. "The Root-Gatherers" is dated on the manuscript to November 1935, but it was not published for another four and a half years. "A Dim-Remembered Story" probably was written shortly before it appeared in the *Californian* for Summer 1936. Lovecraft does not appear to have seen it prior to publication, so he cannot have had any revisory hand in the work. His enthusiasm for the tale, recorded both in private correspondence and in his "Literary Review" (*Californian,* Winter 1936), is well known.

"The Night Ocean" as presented herein is slightly revised from previous appearances; moreover, the discovery of Barlow's original typescript, with revisions by Lovecraft, allows us to ascertain with precision the nature and extent of Lovecraft's contribution to this masterwork. We now see that Lovecraft did little more than smooth out the prose throughout, only occasionally rewriting a passage. His contribution probably amounts to less than 10 percent of the story. There is no question that this atmospheric marvel is almost solely Barlow's work.

Barlow's fiction career was interrupted in 1937 by a variety of circumstances, including the death of his friend and mentor Lovecraft (who had appointed Barlow his literary executor), and his own uprooting from Florida because of family troubles. Barlow published two issues of a superb amateur magazine, *Leaves,* in 1937 and 1938, the second of which contained his story "Origin Undetermined." Several brief prose poems—"The Swearing of an Oath," "The Artizan's Reward," and "The Questioner"—appeared in the fanzine *Polaris* in 1940. On tearsheets of these items Barlow dates all three to the spring of 1939. Also dating to this period is "Birthday," a delicate character sketch that points to Barlow's gradual move away from weird fiction. The fragmentary story "The Burrow" (1937) is a grim account of familial tragedy that provides glimpses of Barlow's view of his native Florida.

"Return by Sunset" was based upon a drawing by his erstwhile idol Clark Ashton Smith, who had abruptly broken off relations with him some years earlier. It appeared in the *Acolyte* for Summer 1943 but had been written between August 1938 and June 1939 in Mexico City and San Francisco. Three mainstream stories of a humorous or satirical sort appeared in the *California Pelican* (1941–42), presumably dating to the time he spent at the University of California at Berkeley. By 1943 Barlow had moved permanently to Mexico, and in 1948 he became chairman of the anthropology department of Mexico City College. His work in Meso-American anthropology is of pioneering significance, and his collected anthropological papers are in the process of publication in Mexico. It appears that several mainstream stories—"The Hat," "Cousin Anna," and "Fine Bindings"—date to this period, or perhaps slightly earlier.

Toward the end of his life Barlow translated a play, *The Sombreron* (1931), by the Mexican writer Bernardo Ortiz de Montellano (1899–1949).

"A Dim-Remembered Story" and "The Night Ocean" stand out as Barlow's chief triumphs in weird fiction, but at least half a dozen other tales are nearly as substantial. If Barlow's collected weird fiction is far lesser in quantity than that of others of the Lovecraft circle, its consistently high quality should earn it a place of respect as a compact but choice contribution to modern weird fiction.

Barlow's poetry is no less significant than his fiction. His poetry conveniently falls into two main types. One is formal and traditional in style and probably derives from his close association with Lovecraft. Many of the early poems—frequently sonnets—appeared in various amateur publications. The formal verse was in the main written between the spring of 1936 through the fall of 1939. The remainder of Barlow's poetry is modern and experimental, and its imagistic language is especially interesting. The modern phase of Barlow's poetic development began in the autumn of 1939 when he encountered Lawrence Hart and the "activist" poetry movement and adopted the activist approach. Hart (1901–1996) had begun the activist movement only three years earlier with other poets of the San Francisco Bay region, including his wife Jeanne McGahey (1906–1995), and Rosalie Moore (pen-name of Gertrude Elizabeth Moore Brown, 1910–2001). Activism derives from the notion that the language of poetry could be made more alive so as to better communicate the emotional aspect of poetry. In the May 1951 issue of *Poetry,* Hart articulated the activist intent as follows:

> The words of the poem are not the poetry, the poem being a series of emotions produced by detail in the mind of the reader, the words being the score, and no more poetry than the musical score is music. Therefore, one could not afford to write a poem which was not poetry in every detail. . . . The smallest unit of meaning was conceived to be, not the word, but the phrase, the words not having any more true poetic meaning in themselves than the letters of a word have logical meaning. . . . The effort required to raise the detail above certain levels was very great until methods were worked out for reaching accuracy and intensity through automatic writing, random usages and the like.

Barlow's activist poetry certainly begins with these aims and attains some wonderful effects. Through the 1940s and early 1950s the activist movement achieved some notable successes. McGahey's work was included in *Five Young American Poets* (1941), published by New Directions. Rosalie Moore's first collection, *Grasshopper's Man* (1949), with an introduction by W. H. Auden, appeared in the prestigious Yale Series of Younger Poets, and she received a Guggenheim award for poetry in 1950.

Hart noted that the activists "came to consider poetry as the adventure of the writer into the hidden springs of his own action and emotion—his work in poetry being parallel in some ways to that done through psychology," and in this aspect certain details of Barlow's personal life help to inform the reading of a number of his poems. For example, knowledge of Barlow's homosexuality not only suggests certain interpretations but also helps to explain Barlow's evasion of gender in his love poems, and his use of cryptic initials rather than full names. Yet to Barlow and the other activists this biographical method of interpretation might be entirely offbase—for the emotion in a poem, not incidental details that may have inspired it, gives the poem vitality.

We present Barlow's poetry in six sections. His declarative statement about poetry appears in the nonfiction section. The statement originally appeared in the Berkeley magazine *Circle* (1945), in a section titled "Ideas of Order in Experimental Poetry" (with contributions by Hart, Moore, and others) that was also issued as a small booklet. The groupings *Poems for a Competition* and *View from a Hill* contain the texts of Barlow's small-press booklets with those titles. *Poems for a Competition* was published in 1942, while *View from a Hill* appeared in 1947. Section V, "A Stone for Sisiphus" (we retain Barlow's unusual spelling of Sisyphus), comes from George T. Smisor's typescript, made after Barlow's death, of a collection Barlow assembled and dated 1949. Sections I and VI are based on posthumous collections assembled and typed by Smisor, entitled "Poems 1936–1939" and "Unfinished Poems," the latter here called "Miscellaneous Poems." Other uncollected poems have been added to both sections to make the collection as complete as possible.

Barlow's essays comprise a modest but highly significant branch of his output. He began by contributing brief letters and bibliographical articles to the *Fantasy Fan* (1933f.). He had the foresight to make extensive jottings in a diary about Lovecraft's lengthy visit to his Florida home in 1934. In the summer of 1935, when Lovecraft visited Barlow for a second time in Florida, the two authors apparently jotted down notes told by Barlow's father, E. D. Barlow, on the subject of national defense. These notes correspond to a published article, "National Defense" (*Californian*, Winter 1935), attributed to E. D. Barlow. Both the notes and the published article can be found in the Appendix. The editorial "Obiter Scriptum" (*Leaves*, Summer 1937) shows him reflecting Lovecraft's devotion to sincere, non-remunerative self-expression in weird fiction.

Following Lovecraft's death in 1937, Barlow was essentially shunned by leading figures in weird fiction, who derived the false impression that he had stolen items from Lovecraft's home (even though he had been named Lovecraft's literary executor and had clear ownership of the material—much of which he later donated to the John Hay Library of Brown University). But he continued to publish short pieces in the amateur press, as well as finding the time to edit a posthumous collection of George Sterling's later poetry, *After Sunset* (1939). By the time he had settled in Mexico in the 1940s, he had made peace with some former colleagues and even contributed to the Lovecraft-oriented fanzine, the *Acolyte* (1943f.). He also wrote a significant introduction to Henry S. Whitehead's *Jumbee and Other Uncanny Tales* (1944) for Arkham House, as well as the significant memoir of Lovecraft, "The Wind That Is In the Grass." Around this time he also wrote, at the urging of a psychiatrist, a compelling autobiography of the previous five or six years of his life.

But his nonfictional writings in Mexico, several of them apparently unpublished, testify to the depth of his interest in native cultures and his keen perception of the social and physical topography of that nation. "Journey to the Place of the Fish-Masters" is a remarkable account of his visit to the state of Michoacan, and his vivid description of a bullfight he witnessed is comparable to Hemingway. "Parícutin" relates a visit to a volcano in that same state.

H. P. Lovecraft once stated: "Barlow . . . refuses to adopt popular tricks & formulae. But he'll probably get into *W[eird] T[ales]* on his own terms sooner or later."[2] This comment seems true in perhaps a broader way than he intended. Robert Hayward Barlow both lived and wrote on his own terms, and it is chiefly because he did so that he is still remembered when many other writers of his time and place have been deservedly forgotten.

—S. T. JOSHI and DOUGLAS A. ANDERSON

The editors are grateful to staff at the John Hay Library, Providence, and of the University of Wisconsin–Madison Library Special Collections Department. They also extend thanks to Steven Black of the University of California–Berkeley, Alistair Durie, Kenneth W. Faig, John Hart, Derrick Hussey, Marcos Legaria, Vincent Martini, Charles D. O'Connor, III, Jordan Smith, and David Tribby for assistance in the preparation of this edition.

*Abbreviations*

*AB*      *Accent on Barlow*

A.Ms.   autograph manuscript, signed

HPL    H. P. Lovecraft

JHL     H. P. Lovecraft Collection, John Hay Library, Brown University (Providence, RI)

*OFF*    *O Fortunate Floridian*

*PC*      *Poems for a Competition*

RHB    R. H. Barlow

S         microfilm of Barlow material assembled by George T. Smisor

*SS*       *A Stone for Sisiphus*

T.Ms.   typed manuscript, signed

*VH*     *View from a Hill*

---

2. HPL to Robert Bloch, 12 August 1936, *H. P. Lovecraft: Letters to Robert Bloch and Others,* ed. David E. Schultz and S. T. Joshi (New York: Hippocampus Press, 2015), 173.

# Eyes of the God

*H. P. Lovecraft, "High," and "Doodlebug" (entering from behind),*
*6 May 1934, on a visit to the Barlow's in Florida*

# FICTION

## The Slaying of the Monster

*With H. P. Lovecraft*

Great was the clamour in Laen; for smoke had been spied in the Hills of the Dragon. That surely meant the Stirrings of the Monster—the Monster who spat lava and shook the earth as he writhed in its depths. And when the men of Laen spoke together they swore to slay the Monster and keep his fiery breath from searing their minaret-studded city and toppling their alabaster domes.

So it was that by torchlight gathered fully a hundred of the little people, prepared to battle the Evil One in his hidden fast-hold. With the coming of night they began marching in ragged columns into the foothills beneath the fulgent lunar rays. Ahead a burning cloud shone clearly through the purple dusk, a guide to their goal.

For the sake of truth it is to be recorded that their spirits sank low long ere they sighted the foe, and as the moon grew dim and the coming of the dawn was heralded by gaudy clouds they wished themselves more than ever at home, dragon or no dragon. But as the sun rose they cheered up slightly, and shifting their spears, resolutely trudged the remaining distance.

Clouds of sulphurous smoke hung pall-like over the world, darkening even the new-risen sun, and always replenished by sullen puffs from the mouth of the Monster. Little tongues of hungry flame made the Laenians move swiftly over the hot stones. "But *where* is the dragon??" whispered one—fearfully and hoping it would not accept the query as an invitation. In vain they looked—there was nothing solid enough to slay.

So shouldering their weapons, they wearily returned home and there set up a stone tablet graven to this effect—"BEING TROUBLED BY A FIERCE MONSTER THE BRAVE CITIZENS OF

LAEN DID SET UPON IT AND SLAY IT IN ITS FEARFUL LAIR SAVING THE LAND FROM A DREADFUL DOOM."

These words were hard to read when we dug that stone from its deep, ancient layers of encrusting lava.

## Eyes of the God

The thief moved quietly in the vast dim room. It was late and although he was certain all the Museum guards were gone—save for the unconscious watchman he had slugged—he was careful to shield his pocket flash-light. The many carven figures cast twisted and fantastic shadows on the wall as he shifted it about. Idols from the ends of the earth were gathered in that exhibition. Crude eikons from Africa that were but roughly shipped logs, and elaborately ornamented monstrosities from India. Squat, grotesque pottery images of ancient Mexico sat cheek by jowl with delicate translucent figurines of amber and jade from China. But among these he wandered stealthily in search of the last acquisition—a god of ebony with two enormous diamonds for eyes. He had exact duplicates of paste; it would be easy to substitute them and make his get-away before they were discovered. Thoughts of the peculiar death of its donor, who had surreptitiously carried it away from its devout followers at the height of their unpleasant power, and of the deep foot-prints in the garden on the night that man so queerly died; passed through the thief's mind as he methodically searched face after face. What was it the full moon was supposed to do to it? Oh yes . . . bring it to life. Odd what those natives believed.

In time a growing apprehension made him pause to wonder if his visit had been anticipated and the jewels moved to a place of safety. This he thought was improbable. So new and highly interesting an exhibit would surely be accessible to the public for a time at least. His light flashed on a heavy wooden base with a circle of dust showing it had been recently vacated. Dragging scratches faintly showed the course of the vanished occupant through the doorway. If that occupant were the god he sought, these scratches would lead him to its hiding-place. Indecisively he traced the marks. Odd the curator had moved the effigy. Perhaps, he thought nervously, a policeman awaited him on the other side of the archway. As he stepped into the adjoining room he noticed a full moon over the sky-line. . . .

Clipping from the *Daily Express:*

". . . The man, evidently a marauder seeking the jeweled eyes, was found dead this morning in the Hall of the American Indian with the idol on top of him.

"Police are as yet uncertain how he moved it, for it weighed six hundred pounds. . . ."

# Annals of the Jinns

". . . Thither Ganigul often retired in the daytime to read in quiet the marvelous annals of the Jinns, the chronicles of ancient worlds, and the prophecies relating to the worlds that are yet to be born."

Wm. Beckford
—"Story of Prince Barkiarokh"

## I. The Black Tower

At the head of the winding river Olaee, nearby the fragrant forest, stands the Black Tower of the Southlands. High into the air rise its bleak stone walls, piercing the sunset with slender spire. For eternity it has been there, by the sluggish waters on which float great bloated crimson lillies, and for eternity will it be there. The peasants of the nearby village know not whence it came nor why 'tis there, and wisely avoid it when the moon is on the wane. Few dare visit the colourful forest of evil or the treacherous river, for strange and unholy things dwell therein.

Some tell of how on the dark of the moon there comes from the great star Sirius a growing speck of flame ultimately losing itself in the eternal midnight of outer space. However this may be, it is certain strange and alien beings built this ebon tower in the dawn of the world, for purposes not understood by mortals; sealing the door long ages since.

There is a tale the old wives spin, saying: One of the adventurous villagers, Castor by name, took undue interest in the tower and was frequently seen slipping furtively to and from it in the dusk. Of all the people of the town he had the least savoury ancestry, his father being a satyr, his mother a witch-woman. True, others mated with the people of the glen, yet it is not considered a thing to be proud of. The very Burgomaster had a gnome none too far back in his lineage, which was expressed in the coarse features of his evil countenance. But a satyr! The righteous citizens avoided Castor scrupulously, and the dislike was mutual. So it was he continued on his silent trips unheeded.

What he did there so often was not known but the seasons came and went and the winter merged into spring and in time it was Walburgas Eve. That night the town gates were tightly closed and bolted and all cowered behind locked doors. Strange shapes flew screeching through the air and sniffed most horribly at the doorsteps.

That night Castor went to the tower as had become his habit, though his better sense warned him to stay home abed. His satyr ancestry openly rebelled, but the witch proved stronger. As he stole timorously through the wood he heard sounds of high revelry from within the castle. Therefore, he was quiet as he hesitated before the foot of the long unopened door. Queer things were abroad. Though he dared not return home alone through the forest, still more did he fear to remain within reach of the Things of the tower. As he deliberated on the course to take the great door swung silently open and a crab-like claw lovingly encircled his waist and drew him in.

And he was seen no more by the villagers.

## II. The Shadow from Above

A midsummer day in the hamlet of Droom. The villagers went about their various tasks, and within the tiny market-square the spice-vendors and the people from the hills with their exotic burdens of gay fruits created a pleasant hum of busy occupation. Sleeping dogs lay contentedly in the warm sunlight, and the squat beasts of burden ambled about peacefully upon their six clawless paws, their grotesque faces slit with toad-like grins. All was, no one could have denied, entirely calm.

Then one of the dogs lying in a doorway sprang suddenly and emitted a sharp bark. At the same moment a dark cloud apparently obscured the sun. In a short time it had passed unnoticed save for the dog. But his owner—an old crone in a voluminous black hood—peered intently at the clear and vacant sky, and started chattering in an excited tone. Soon the whole population was out of doors looking upwards at that which could not be seen yet which cast a deep shadow. Nothing was to be perceived in the expanse of blue, yet upon the square cobblestones of the quaint little village an irregular black form wavered back and forth. Then it grew larger. Whatever it may have been, it was settling. The people drew back affrighted. Slowly the swinging motion ceased, and the thing drew near. A deep, heavy panting was distinctly audible, much like that of a great beast, and with a dull impact as though it was of great weight, it alighted upon a grassy plot before the Chancellor's house. For a long time it lay there, resting. And still nothing could be seen save the indentation of the grass nor aught heard but the heavy breathing.

Then, to the terror of the white-faced and nervous citizens, it rose on giant feet and trampled down a lane. Thud . . . Thud . . . Thud . . . Thud . . . The sound grew monotonous in its deliberation. Before its path lay a sleeping hound. It was lifted as if in a vast claw, and vanished among horrid rending sounds. A single drop of blood flecked the earth. . . . Its taste momentarily sated, the thing paused and turned.

It took some moments for reason to replace the stark terror of the townsfolk. Then there was a mad and frantic rush for the nearest houses. Those to first gain entrance barred the doors upon their comrades. In a moment the street was apparently bare—save for the unseen monster.

All that afternoon and night it pried at doors, scratched at roofs, muzzled windows and upset fruit-carts inquiringly. But the people of Droom had built well. It did not gain entrance during the night, although few slept, when they heard the constant breathing before their homes, and the dull thumping sounds as it wreaked its malice upon the shops of the market-place.

It was high noon before any dared unbar their doors and venture forth. Nothing unusual greeted their blanched faces, and silently, apprehensively they stole to their tasks. Soon all activity again commenced.

The horror had gone.

## III. The Flagon of Beauty

The Princess drooped her long eyelashes. She was really quite pretty when she did this.

"And you have brought it?" she asked softly, her hand stealing into his. He coughed. This being spokesman was a delicate task.

"Yes, your Highness," said the man. "It is here." He touched a small parcel beside him on the divan.

"And you will give it to me?" she breathed.

Steeling himself, he replied, "Their terms are the freedom of the people."

She sprang to her feet. "Never!"

"Not for the Flagon?" he queried harshly.

"Not even for that." Reconsidering, she spoke softly. "Five years ago I sent a band in search of this fabulous drug, into the low-lying jungle that cloaks the Ancient Cities, the Cities that no man knows who built, there in the steaming swamps. Men have said that I was beautiful, yet, ironically, he for whom I have wrecked my empire scorned me. It was then I bethought me of this flask made in the immemorial years agone, which figured in legend as containing the essence of Beauty. Perhaps, I thought, with this I might win him from my rival. Today you have returned; successfully, I grant you; and demand yield of my power for that which I desire. I have been told bitter things—that I have ruled mercilessly and tyrannically. That I have, but I cared little for affairs of state since I became enamoured of my prince. He has neglected no indignity to impose upon me, but I cannot forget him. On the night of my Feast of Peacocks he sneered at the priceless dishes and fed his monkey from the plate. The gutter-rat he has an infatuation for entertains him most skillfully, but he shares her with the soldiers. He prefers her florid charms to me. This I do not understand, but I command you, *give me that flagon.*"

He slowly shook his head. "No, Majesty, I cannot betray their faith. Fever took many lives in those crumbling ruins."

"I warn you, I am desperate," she said imperiously, "give, or I shall take."

He lowered his gaze and remained silent. Seeing he was adamant, she made a gesture with her head, and a slave stepped from the curtained alcove. "Take this man to the Room of Pain," she ordered. In consternation, he sought to dash the frail vessel to the tiles, but it was dexterously twisted from his grasp by the blackamoor.

The princess laughed insanely.

---

"My men did well to steal you from under his nose, my wench," she sneered to the helpless woman at her feet. "Let me see those carmine lips smile at this!" she added contemptuously, breaking the ancient seal covered with writing none could interpret. "You are startled? Yes, it is the Flagon! Watch, if you wish, for you may not see when I am finished with you." She drained the very dregs, and flung the stopper in her captive's face. For a long moment there was no change apparent in her flushed countenance. Then she noticeably paled. Her hair swiftly grew leaded and grey, her lips assumed a ghastly pallor, and a score of tiny wrinkles appeared on her smooth skin.

She became an old hag, quite out of place in the splendour of the throne-room.

## IV. The Sacred Bird

There appeared one day in the market-place of Ullathia a most peculiar fowl which fell exhausted from the skies. Its plumage was of brilliant hue, and despite its confusion, a wise and knowing look was seen within the orange eyes. After resting a moment, it fluttered about the square, entering the various shops in a proprietary manner and finally settled in that of a sweetmeat dealer. Soon all the trades-folk hurried across the cobblestones to see this gaudy visitor and to feed it many tid-bits. Not in the least bothered by its admiring audience, it permitted its head to be scratched and petted as it ate.

In time, the news spread through the thatched houses to the ears of the Imperial Council, all of which laid down their pens and came in a body to view it. It was discovered by them greedily eating a preserved orange-rind, a meal varied by occasional pecks at a nut. Having already devoured odds and ends of all sorts, it was no longer hungry, and even as they panted in, it fell asleep. When the crowd drew aside to admit the rotund Council, it complained loudly.

"Gwarn arf 'n chase y'self!" commanded the half-awake bird. "Gwarn arf," it repeated, fluttering its wings and adjusting for a nice nap. It then uttered a rasping incoherency and dozed off placidly. The people drew back whispering excitedly. "A demon!" averred one. This brought a chorus of dissension among the others. "An angel . . . Just a trick . . . Who ever heard of a bird talking? . . . A magician in disguise . . . What has happened? . . . Still thy tongue, neighbor . . ."

. . . The head of the Council, a greybeard notoriously superstitious, cleared his throat and a silence fell over all present. "My friends," he gurgled happily, "My *dear* friends and fellow citizens!

This is an occasion of undoubted significance in the annals of our fair city, equalled only by that of, as you doubtless will realize, early in the reign of—rather; to continue: In other words, my dear friends," he began over, unable to sustain the sentence any longer, "To make it clear to all concerned, this is, I believe, and no one, I hope, would contradict me, I have occasion to think—" Here his voice lowered to a whisper and ended in a shout, "A *Messenger* sent to guide us!" He leered cheerfully at the mob. "Therefore, let us convey it in state to the City Hall to rule us as it sees fit!"

Which was forthwith done amid much celebration, and the chattering of the escaped parrot from that day guided the fortunes of the city of Ullathia, interpreted by the Ruler and his Council as they desired.

## V. The Tomb of the God

For four days, the band of explorers from Phoor had been excavating the ancient and immemorial tomb of Krang on the edge of the desert. The sands had been blowing ceaselessly, even as they had done since before the coming of man to that far land. The tomb was built long before any human walked the face of the world, built by evil powers that had reigned unchecked in that unthinkably ancient day, when all the desert had been a verdant garden through which stalked great yellow giants of small intelligence, but of prodigious strength, that had built the tower and the city of the ancient and most powerful Lord Krang. And even before that Krang had been; he had been for aeons, and in turn had come from a strange planet, it was told in tradition and runes inscribed in a dead language, the language of Old Gods, and in the time when dark magical powers had battled for possession of the universe. And Krang had won, Krang the old one, the monstrous brown leathern thing that planned and ruled and malefically twisted the futures of worlds. But the time came that none had foreseen and Krang the ancient fell into a semblance of death, though his flesh rotted not, nor did his aspect change. So the people of the earth gathered together and conveyed him in a giant funeral procession to the enormous tomb carven from living blue stone in the side of the mountain, and they sealed him in and forever departed from his company. And the years and the decades and the centuries and the aeons unthinkable came and went, and the sands swirled over the mouth of the tomb, and the door was obliterated, and none knew where Krang the Elder God lay in stupendous slumber.

Then audacious mortals had unwittingly found traces of this mausoleum that even legend had discredited, and they had resolved to open it and seek the great body of the old thing that had lain unmoving since the world was young and green, lain while the prolific vegetation died and the sand crept upon the land and laid it into barrenness.

It was said that there had been sealed up in Krang's tomb treasures that made avarice pale and gems the like of which no longer existed, jewels from far worlds of the dawn of time, worlds that had died and burned again—and the strange manuscripts with the Hsothian chants upon them, and other equally desirable objects. Therefore, many had set out to reach the far site of the old tomb, but few had reached it. Some had perished, slain by the hateful green devilthings that lay beneath the surface of the sand in wait for unwary persons, and that sprang up to drag their victims to a horrible death. Some reached their goal and scratched and chipped the tight sealed entrance, but it was as the gnawing of rats, and before they could do more, they had mysteriously vanished from human ken, nor had they ever been heard of afterwards. Yet this did not discourage others from amulting, [sic] for the desire for power will lead men far, and power there was in the tomb.

So again men were engaged in laboriously chipping away the obstruction and making slight headway, when one of their members chanced upon an orifice in the rock into which he thrust his arm curiously. Beyond he touched something, and lo! The great door grated outwards, inexorably, ruthlessly, and ground him horribly into the stone hill, leaving naught save an unpleasant smear of brown and a dank smell came forth, and the door was opened. Paralyzed, the survivors did not act until it had swung firmly back into place and was immovable save by a repetition of the catastrophe. So, though they could spare him ill, the others forced one of their brown slave-men from distant Leek to do this suicidal act; and he whimpered, and would have not, but they discouraged this by subtle and hastily improvised tortures, and he eventually complied.

They stepped delicately over the smear and caught the door; placing an obstruction in the way, so that it might stay open. And then they entered, the first living things in that place since their race had appeared.

The air was foul with the odor of a newly dried sea bed, and the stench was unlike that of anything within their ken. All about the giant vault were great chunks of richly coloured gems cut in curious facets, with cryptic inscriptions upon each. But the central object was the tomb of Lord Krang, where his great body reposed upon a slab of figured chalcedony. He was terrible to gaze upon, for even after the immense period, he still held semblance of the horrifying aspect that was traditionally assigned unto him.

And the explorers that had entered gathered around him for a moment in awe, but they were distracted by the infinite wealth that lay carelessly about. They became affected by it, into a type of madness, and with repulsive amour and fetishism, they stroked the jewels and clung unto them.

But what happened then none can tell, for their two fellows standing guard beyond the entrance heard a peculiar sound that seemed as a slither then a scream, then the door shut again, and although the obstructing block was not touched by them, it had moved.

———————

And Krang's tomb was again covered by the drifts; nor even after that brief glimpse of infinite wealth did any man of Phoor venture near.

For the Lord Krang had roused from his long sleep, and feasted.

## VI. The Flower God

Alair, the ruler of Zaxtl, sent a present unto his enemy, the neighboring King Luud. Now such an act was unlike Alair, and had not pleasant omens. For more than a decade they had waged bitter warfare, and therefore Luud was not a little surprised to see the crimson lotus on a field of *argent* displayed before his gates. The messengers came unguarded in their glittering robes, and when the portcullis was withdrawn, they ascended the steps before the throne and made obeisance. The guards of Luud would have fain drawn wary swords, but the king signalled withdrawal, that he might hearken unto the emissaries.

Their gift was brought in by swarthy slave men. It proved a many-coloured flower of alien aspect, whose aromatic perfumes spread languorously through the room. Alair had sent no message save to state cryptically that here was the ruler of plants, the Flower-God, and Luud preferred not to ask the reason for this strange and lovely gift. So it was he made a long and eloquent speech of surpassing insincerity, claiming friendship between the countries, and when they had left, he set artizans constructing a dais. When this had been done, the Flower-God was set upon it in a jewel-encrusted trough; where he might lift his eyes from affairs of state and gaze upon it. And it was admired by the entire court. Only Gra, the counsellor, would have been unwilling to accept it, but he was not heeded.

But the land soon found there was something amiss, for gossip spread throughout that a madness had come upon the king. He would lock himself in with the flower for days in succession and be oddly exhilarated upon resuming his customary life. Whispers were that he was drugged or hypnotized by the strange plant, that he performed odd and ancient rites before it—rites that were not good and were avoided by even necromancers. Truly, he had developed an abnormal passion for it, and there were obviously mysterious happenings afoot. In time, he was observed to make unwise decisions after he had been alone with the Flower-God, and he would pause in the midst of trite affairs and go over to it, lovingly stroking the tendrils and closing his eyes as if listening. But there was nothing audible save the rustle of the vibrant petals.

The country did not improve through these unusual activities. Affairs assumed a turbulent state; lawlessness prevailed. After a time, the traitorous openly denounced Luud, and there were few who did not sympathize. Those bolder even went so far as to suggest that Alair, the adjacent ruler, rule in his stead. But the king seemed entirely apathetic regarding this, or anything save the Flower-God and its unholy lure.

Meanwhile, Alair waited, smiling.

Had not the venerable Chancellor, Gra, chosen to intervene, the land would have fast gone to ruin. But he was wise, and took heed of the ultra-sensual lure the blossom held for his ruler. Therefore, he saw the futility of attempting to restrain or interfere in any ordinary manner, and consequently resolved upon action that would forever break the reign of the unholy plant. In fine, he determined to destroy the Lord of Flowers.

Having made his plans, the following day he noiselessly entered the throne-room, with a long grim knife concealed beneath his scarlet robe. The king did not heed him, for he was enthralled, beyond human affairs. But the plant sensed the presence of the intruder, and perhaps it half-knew his purpose, for the fleshy leaves writhed animatedly, and the green spines stood erect. Yet it did not arouse the entranced supplicant, and the hundred little viper tongues could not ward off the blows of the blade that Gra wielded so judiciously. The swollen blossom was rent and gashed in numberless places before the emperor became aware of it. It was too late then, for great yellow drops of sickening ichor slowly coursed down the drooping vines and the bloom itself was purpling fast.

Then it was the king staggered a moment and stared long at his Chancellor in a dazed manner. And Gra was thankful, for the light of madness was dying out, even as the plant faded.

The Flower-God was dead.

## VII. The Little Box

On the planet called Loth, in the Seventh City, there lived a semi-savage known as Hsuth. He had been captured in his youth by the fearless raiders of Phargo, but popular demand later caused the release of all the beings that once formed an interesting collection of the larger animals. So it was that one might have had for a neighbor anything from one of the reddish parrot-people from the far-away isle of Hin to a pale blue octopus-thing from the dried sea-bed of Innia. Hsuth, it is to be stated, was neither, being merely one of the commonplace brown tailed men from Leek. He was, as are most savages, very inquisitive, and one day after returning from the rid-na-zat works (wherein were manufactured first class ornaments to be worn in the nose) he espied a small black box in the window of a money-lender—a box whose curious carvings and tightly closed lid brought up many questions. When the dealer refused to open it for him his curiosity was doubly whetted, so that he purchased it (after unavoidable delay and expected haggling) thereby parting with the earnings of a week.

Returning home with his prize he managed to slip past a street-brawl and get inside his house—a three-towered affair resembling an ill-fitted layer cake, each successive story being smaller than the one upon which it reposed.

Bolting the door he then tried to force the lid open. But it resented this move on his part, and showed it by pinching his finger violently. This caused him to fling it against the wall. It came to the floor with a dull thud and the top fell off after a moment's silence. A squeaky voice issued from the interior. "—press the control marked A and the machine will come to him no matter where it is. I am making three boxes similar to this and hope that someone will gain some benefit, for I haven't. Anyone finding this is directed to press the control marked A and the machine will come to him no matter where it is iammakingthree-e-e-E-EEE Yah psuhutthush!" declared the little box. As Hsuth did not understand what was said, it is to be feared the directions were lost upon him, yet some demon directed his finger to the control marked A. Perhaps it was because all the other buttons were hopelessly jammed into the wood.

Nothing happened, and Hsuth disappointedly threw the box through the window where it landed upon the head of a prominent citizen, causing that worthy unwonted irritation.

And Hsuth forgot about the box and the fraudulent control marked A, not knowing that ten million miles away the machine was battering ceaselessly at its bonds, striving to escape and answer the long-awaited call—which it never quite managed to do.

But the Leerians gathered round with frightened eyes to watch the reanimation of the god of the forefathers on that far continent, and offered up sacrifices in the form of decrepit inhabitants and those who would have had them doubt their deity.

## VIII. The Fall of the Three Cities

Far to the south of Phoor and bordering upon Yondath extends the vast jungle-land. The River Oolae enters it at several points, making travel by boat difficult between Phargo on the desert, its outlet in the unnamed land. Where the jungle ceases it gives way abruptly to a vast and mighty plain. This open country is now desolate and entirely uninhabited. Nothing but the six-legged and grotesque monster-things called *rogii* roam its interminable fields of waving grass. Yet once this lower south-land was a populous and fertile plateau, from the swampy morasses of Yondath even unto the mountains and Zath, where dwell the fungi-masters. How it came to be so barren is told in antique myth, and when people hear the fate of the land beyond the jungle they shudder and make prayers in the air with the small finger.

This then is the tale of the fall of the cities of the plain—they that were called by men Naazim, Zo, and Perenthines.

Naazim lies now a waste, nor is there any trace of Perenthines. But one can yet find ancient ruins of Zo, and the vandals of Time have not entirely effaced the elaborate carvings of amber which lie half-buried in the concealing grass near where the vast pool was once constructed in the center of the city.

The whole thing started when the magician Volnar refused to leave Perenthines. He had been a most successful and prosperous sorcerer until the deplorable case of the fishwife whose hair all fell out and took root in the ground before her house. This the people took to be an evil omen, and it was really quite difficult for them to break into his low, strange house after his refusal to depart. They were all disappointed he had gone. They did not know of the black tunnel beneath where he kept his magical supplies. So after searching hopefully around the house someone set it afire, and they made merry by the embers, diverting themselves lustily during the pale night while he fled with only his vengeful thoughts for company. The curious manner of his attire together with the black-edged mantle of crimson caused him to resemble a great moth flapping across the wasteland between the cities. By the time the last flagon of wine lay untidily upon the paving before where his house once was, and while yet his pet *mondal* moaned inconsolably about the ashes, for his persecutors had been unable to capture the highly edible pet, Volnar arrived at the gates of Zo.

The brilliance had begun in the northern sky, and the three suns were nearly risen. Soon would the far mountains be illuminated in yellow light, and Zath shine his metal towers like the armor of a weary knight sprawled upon the hills. The black stone of the precipice directly under the fasthold served only to set it off. Soon too would the rich rice fields of cultivated vegetation gleam pleasingly and the jungle come to animated life. But not yet were the gates open, for it had been the rule in Zo to keep them fast-closed till full dawn, ever since the Night of The Monster in neighboring Droom, close unto the mountains. There was a smell of spice hanging in the air, for the breeze was small, but this loveliness was wholly wasted upon the angry little sorcerer as he chaffed before the giant gate. His robe was bedraggled from the mud and he was wearied of no sleep.

"Ho, guard!" he shouted irritably, "can you not let an honest traveler within your cursed village before high noon?"

This was on the whole a misrepresentation for his traveling was unintentional and he was by no means honest but he did not consider the moral aspect of the matter.

After a time sounds of distant shuffling reached his ears, and after prodigious squeakings and bangings a sleepy-faced man gave him entrance. Volnar entered the handsome city and made his way along the vast paving-stones of yellow and brown, and at length arrived at a lodging-house, the lighted lantern yet glimmering in the shadow of the sleeping town.

For a long time none saw the bearded little sorcerer upon the streets of Zo. He purchased an old house with curious artificial gold of his own contriving—a secret of wizardry he held to be pleasingly unique—and busied himself most industriously in the dank, ill-lit cellar. Twice he ventured forth, after nightfall, to obtain certain odd ingredients from a man to whom he was known, and the man (who had no ears, but patches of fur that he concealed beneath his head-gear) saw what was up, and left the city straightway. Volnar worked on with his charms and spells, occasionally sighing for his abandoned *mondal,* and frequently pondering upon his revenge.

He pottered amidst his instruments. The thin cold light streaming through a crack in the rocky ceiling was aided by that of the small fire beneath the pot of bulging iron. Yet though with even these the gloom was little dispelled, Volnar did not care, for his eyes were familiar with darkness, in which his long apprenticeship had been spent. That students of the dark lore were not appreciated had become increasingly clear to him, ever since the night of his departure from Perenthines. Consequent discretion called for subterranean quarters. These he had obtained, and thus did he work upon the Doom for Perenthines. And before he had completed the strange substance that bubbled so obscenely and which cast off the odor of fresh blood mingled with some nauseating aroma, Volnar sent a messenger for Sarall, the Lord of Worms, to obtain a certain ingredient most accessible to maggots. Frequently did he consult the parchments that were said to have been copied from the Hsothian manuscripts by a slave of the Lord Krang very long ago, and elaborate care was exercised upon the concoction.

Then, at last, it was completed, and Volnar gazed speculatively about the cellar, thinking for some time. He arose from his lengthy vigil, and poured the contents of the pot into a cylinder of unglazed pottery, deftly sealing it with enchanted gummy material of moist black. While the stuff was inside it continued to seethe audibly, although it had been off the fire for some time. And this jar he bore with extreme caution as he turned the immense iron key in the cellar door.

The sky was a starless void when he entered into the street, intent upon his mission. As he hurried through the silent city, accompanied only by his shadow, a successive lifting of vapor-mists revealed the moon of ashen blue, but it was quickly obscured again. The air was chill and in ceaseless motion, faintly disturbing his crimson robe. His footsteps echoed hollowly upon the paving, and he felt that everyone must surely hear him, but he was not accosted. A lone pedestrian abroad for no good purpose emerged from the mist abruptly, but passed Volnar unseeing and soon was lost in the fast-gathering dimness. It was very late now, and he was relieved when he approached the central part of the city with the cylinder beneath his arm, for it was increasingly heavy and the contents unruly with new animation.

Soon he reached the handsome marble pool that was the center of Zo and the marvel of the three towns, but which is now but a faint indentation in the waving grass. The water was very still, and he let the thing in the urn slide noiselessly into the pool. It sank unhurryingly to the bottom, expanding, more solid now, and drifted away in the dimly-hidden water. Whether it had moved of its own volition or was borne by a current, none but the inscrutable little man could have told. Volnar gazed after it, and apparently satisfied, departed.

He did not return to his lodging, but made directly for the mountains upon a stolen *rogii* which attained a remarkable speed for its bulk. And while the fate of the three cities moved slowly about the pool, the magician traveled ceaselessly towards Mt. Boriau. After the man and his steed had approximated the nearer peaks, they stopped, and Volnar knew he was within safety. Therefore he watched searchingly the far dim mass that was the grouped cities. Nothing could be discerned, but the watcher knew evil forces were at work, forces none could halt or evade save by direct flight, and who was to wake the sleeping towns? He chuckled grimly, and hoped his pet *mondal* was not within the doomed area. Then he made his way more slowly toward the crags of Boriau.

During this while the strange substance grew and distended in size and weight until it restlessly filled the large pool. It had assumed no definite shape, but life was unquestionably within the vast prehensile tissue that groped at the edge of its confines. It was as yet unable to release itself and venture in search of food, but the time was not distant. A chance pedestrian, with his moth-like cloak that was of the type common in those days, went slowly by and did not fully realize what was happening when he saw the thing droolingly emerge from the pool. The hundred evil eyes peered loathsomely as it extended an awful limb and seized him, intent upon the process of absorbing nutrition.

Nor was that the end, for it roved the streets unsated, growing, devouring throughout the night, and in a few horrible hours had depopulated the cities that were so hostile to sorcerers . . .

Volnar, it is told, went unto the black crags near Zath, though discreetly distant from the inhabitants of that fearful place, and with occult aid constructed for himself a castle of black stone in a very short period, wherein he dwelt the remainder of his existence. This was not long because of his ungrateful creature's abnormal longevity and appetite.

## IX. The Mirror

Upon a certain day in the year of the Plague of Dragons, the Emperor of Yondath held court in his ancient palace above the crypts.

Many of his subjects had come from sheer curiosity, and when he cast sentence upon Khalda, at least two of the more squeamish shuddered. For he had condemned the sorcerer Khalda to the tortures of the Green Fungi, and of course every one knew what that meant. Even if they had been obtuse or ignorant of the ways of the torturers in the subterranean rooms, the austere and saturnine look upon the face of His Majesty would have implied much that was not pleasant.

But Khalda, the only pupil of the wise one Volnar, stood scornfully before the throne and gave no sign of terror, although his doom was a fabled and terrible one. He even contrived an ironic obeisance before they took him away. The two ugly slaves that held him exchanged significant looks as they silently led him out of the gorgeously-hung room. Then those who had gathered began to depart, and many resolved not to anger their ruler after that.

Khalda's crime, it had been proclaimed, was that of high sacrilege. Not only had he sought through ancient and unwholesome magic the creation of artificial life, but he had spat upon the green stone feet of the great idol in the market-place, and asserted that the deity was impotent and its priests humbugs. Perhaps this iconoclastic behavior was regretted by Khalda, since his destination was not pleasant to contemplate, but he gave no sign as the slaves led him through a series of connected chambers. Each of these dimly-lit rooms was more ancient in appearance than the one preceding, and after he had traversed some dozen, the very bricks of the wall were so slimy with old moss that they emitted a noxious odour. Likewise the passages grew steadily darker.

Legend told of the things that lay beneath the palace, and of the Head Torturer Malyat that had dwelt in his crypt for untold years without being seen by man. It was said that his face was obscured from even his victims, by an ancient and grotesque mask. On this Khalda reflected as the guards paused to light their tapers at a sconce tipped by a pool of sulphurous flame that seethed and boiled endlessly. He wondered at this, for no tracks disturbed the settled dust, yet the torch was as if newly kindled. Guided now by this melancholy light, they descended again, their torch but little dispelling the gloom. In this manner they made their way toward the lower chambers. Khalda wondered at the labor that must have gone into chiseling these chambers from the rock, and at the ponderous ornamental masonry that remained yet immovable after so long a time.

At length they came to an ultimate passage fronting a huge door of iron curiously decorated and covered with the patina of aeons. This appeared most formidable to the prisoner. It was upon this ancient portal that the guards smote with their clanging brazen swords and then retired, leaving Khalda alone. He wondered what evil thing would appear as he saw the door slowly opening.

Then, in a terrible silence that his shrieks did not wholly dispel, a metal projection not unlike a tentacle rhythmically emerged, swayed a moment, and wrapped itself about him.

And he was drawn into the chamber of Malyat.

---

Four cycles of the crimson moon elapsed before rumors found their way to the ears of the Emperor. A tale was told of the last creation of the sorcerer, a masterpiece of malign sorcery, that had escaped destruction by the zealots of the green stone god.

It was said that all the work of Khalda was evil, but that this last creation was supreme. Even unto his last days he had labored and expended his talents upon a certain mirror of strange design. No man knew the purpose for which it was shapen; but it was certain that Khalda had not constructed it for the dubious vanity of reflecting his withered visage. The polished glass in it had come from the subterranean artizans of Saaldae, and it was polished and silvered by devious means. And the frame was of ebony strangely wrought with a monstrous carving. Great skill had gone into this, yet none knew its precise whereabouts, and the tales could find no definite origin.

So the Emperor had scrolls lettered in the hieroglyphs of the land, and these were posted about the capital and all the outlying provinces. And they said that any man that could produce this mirror would have a reward bestowed upon him.

At first there came many with false claims, but a supplementary proclamation was issued, to the effect that imposters would be painfully disposed of, and thereafter the ruler was little annoyed.

But in time there came an ancient one, unbelievably filthy, and clad in garments of odorous antiquity. His face was hideously wrinkled, yet it held a certain inscrutable wisdom. This repulsive being came unto the palace gates and demanded entrance. And the guards at first laughed, and then grew angry, and would have run him through with their long lances, had not the Emperor intervened and called upon his men to desist. For he had heard the commotion and became curious. Thus admittance was granted to the beggarly person, and he entered as if he had expected this from the start.

In dignity he went, and bowed before the throne, strangely incongruous amid the richly clad servants that shrank from him in repugnance. The Emperor's dwarf sought to make mock of the foul being, and rolled completely off his cushion in gales of false amusement; but he saw the eyes of the stranger and straightway climbed back, mumbling in a surly tone to himself.

The Emperor bade him state his mission, and the old one spoke in a manner remarkable for one so uncouth, saying, "I have brought the object you desire."

With great interest, the Emperor bade him display it, but the old one refused, stating in tones of certainty that he wished to make a few observations first.

"I might press my claim," observed the Emperor, somewhat amused by this effrontery.

"I believe I have likewise the right of naming my price," suggested the old man.

"Truly," assented his majesty, "but first tell me, what is this mirror?"

"It is the mirror of Truth," was the reply.

"A pretty allegory," remarked the Monarch, and settled back.

So it was, the unclean person spoke freely in the court of the ruler.

"You will recall that this mirror was constructed by a certain sorcerer," he began in an unpleasant tone. "And you will also recall that this sorcerer did you a great service once . . . did he not, Majesty?"

The Emperor looked startled, and then very grave.

"He did . . . but how came you to know of this?"

"I shall elucidate when the time has come. Likewise, did you not promise certain things to this sorcerer in return for his labors?"

The Emperor's eyes smoldered with secret fury, but he said nothing.

"This you ignored, and some moons agone had the wonder-worker—I believe he was referred to as a blasphemer in the sentencing—this man you had brought before you and sent to the terrible tortures of Malyat. Am I not correct?"

"That is common knowledge," asserted the ruler, uneasily.

"And he was taken to his doom?"

"My slaves seldom fail me."

"I am grateful to your majesty, for truth was essential. I have the mirror here," said the old one, abruptly.

"What wish you in return?"

"It is yours—my payment will be given me in due time."

And as the Emperor leaned forward, the man announced his identity and drew back his tattered robe, revealing the horror that lay beneath.

Then as the Emperor gazed in fascinated repulsion, Khalda drew forth the mirror, with its strangely shapen handle, and held it up that all might see.

And when the ruler looked therein, no man may know what was reflected, for a strange and terrible thing occurred. Some dire magic was at work, for the doom that came unto his majesty was alien to all accepted lines of death.

## X. The Theft of the Hsothian Manuscripts

Entering the tall, arched building of jet stone, the youth called Morla beheld a vast and impressive expanse. The mighty roof was a dozen times the height of a man, and the walls admitted great distance between themselves. No carpet was upon the floor, and everywhere was the bleakness of chiselled rock. Many curiously peaked arches permitted sight of yet other rooms equally large, and at the end of the hall seven low steps gave entrance into a dim and gloomy passage. To this Morla made his way, his sword clanking hollowly against his bronze armor in the emptiness of the place.

As he strode unhesitatingly across the paving of great blocks, he saw on either side of the steps an exceedingly ugly man rigidly holding a double scythe that spread its winged sharpness high against the wall. Morla regarded these green-clad men for a moment, but they did not heed him in the least. Presently he laughed, and unsheathing his sword, struck it against the petrified corpses that were so lifelike. Then he continued on his way, and mounting the stair, followed the path his mission had prescribed.

Dark was the long passage he fearfully went through and sounds of strange nature came from the darkness. Once a vast fluttering thing fled snortingly from his path, and he was afraid, but Morla did not show his fear. The mission upon which he had been sent by all his city was terrible indeed; for the facing of the ancient sorcerer Khalda in his secret palace was no wholesome task. People told him of what had happened to the Emperor of Yondath, and this curious fate was by no means conducive to optimism. Morla had experienced little difficulty in traversing the forest of orange fungi, and the toad-god he had slain with a minimum of trouble. The jewel within its head spoke odd things to Morla, and its voice was unpleasant to hear; yet had it saved him from other things far less bearable and describable.

So Morla had left the slain and bloody mass of pulp upon the ground, and because the sons of the toad-god feared him, they did not seek revenge. The slow river Oolae entered this exotic jungle, but it was never navigated, so Morla was forced to construct a raft of light wood, and cross the broad river.

Thus far his travel had been easy, but when he saw the giant angular walls of Khalda's black home he had been half-tempted to go no farther. This temptation he had resisted, and scaled the wall which no portal broke, entering then through a tiny *door* upon the roof. This eccentric and inconvenient arrangement was well-suited to the only pupil of Volnar, who had reared this hidden place after his lamentable encounter with Malyat. That doors should be placed in such a situation struck Morla as extremely odd, but he assumed it a whim of the old one, and descending through the opening, had found himself within the hall of the unliving guards.

Now he was in the penultimate chamber. Before him loomed a tremendous door; beyond which, rumor said, dwelt Khalda. The young man halted a moment, confronting the portal. No sound came from within, and only a crack of light crept beneath this ponderous barrier which he must so soon open. Morla tried the massive bronze latch, and found it yielding. Then, hesitantly, he pushed, and the great door swung forward, creaking on its twisted hinges.

He entered the last chamber, and saw a pale greenish figure slumped in a chair of antique carving. The wrinkles of the flesh, and sundry other vague subtleties of physiognomy and contour, made it clear that the sorcerer Khalda was no longer entirely human. This was distinctly moral, thought the youth in fright, and was doubtless attributable to Malyat. But the old one did not move, and Morla thought his fortune fine indeed. Something else, however, interfered with the contemplated robbery, for even as Morla gazed, a monstrous creature, one of the pets of the old man, arose hissing, and launched its brilliantly striped body at the intruder. Morla struck out with his sword, and battled for many seconds before he had severed the awful head, which continued hissing even after it had been detached and rolled beneath a table in the corner. It was only then that he was able to view the hideous creature which merged something of the dog with something of the winged snake;

whose mouth, extending into a pair of writhing tentacles, yet softly snarled.

Brilliant were the markings of the thing, immense the evil that lurked in its beady eyes. But however it may have fascinated him, Morla had not time to examine it. Softly treading, lest he should wake the sleeping figure, the invader went to the carven red chest that bore no lock, for who should dare to molest that which belongs to Khalda? Still fearful of some hidden snare, Morla did that of which no other had thought. Forbearing to open the box by its readily-lifted top, he inserted his sword and pried the three hinges from their firm grasp. Thus he escaped the clutch of the spiked and needle-like arm of enchanted metal which lay in the front portion.

From the interior of the chest Morla extracted a scroll of tattered papyrus on which was written that which he desired. Then, turning, he thought to leave while Khalda yet slumbered.

But Khalda, it would appear, was no longer asleep.

*May 1934*

## XI. An Episode in the Jungle

In the centre of the jungle Yondath gnarled branches tangle themselves so as to almost obscure the purple sky. Ancient tree-things overgrown with plants rise at every hand, and brilliant flowers of alien beauty spring amid the interwoven vines of the ground. On hot summer days when there is peace in Yondath, innumerable pinkish spiders run gaily about the glades, scuttling and dropping among verdant branches like petals fleeing the wind; and save for the warmth beating downward and the buzz of insects, quiet is lord there.

It was thus when Loman mistook his path and stumbled into one of the infrequent clearings. He and twenty others, laden with spears, had gone into the forest hunting beasts; and since they were young men, got rich trophies. Among these were elk and leopards, but no one had even seen a *mondal*, let alone slay it. Since none wished to return without a specimen of this rare and delectable beast, three of his party had set out hunting in the cold radiant dawn, and in an hour were far apart. Loman searched eastward, following a set of tracks until they were lost, and when he would have rejoined his fellows, saw that he could not. Vines hampering his feet were tangled about the boles of fern-trees wonderfully high, and nothing familiar was to be seen in the trackless undergrowth. Unbroken thickets circled the glade and its carpet of spangled moss. Blossoms—a vivid incredible blue, like hot metal—crept on the sward, broken by no foot. Here was the sanctuary of nature, resentful of the intruder. Even with luck his chances were few of regaining the camp before evening. His stout linen garments would protect him from the night's chill, but his knapsack was empty. Cursing the epicurean desires that had led him afield, Loman searched the clustered bushes for both his quarry and his path. He liked it ill, this being lost in the ancient wood, for there were tales of monsters within it.

His thoughts were less quiet than the jungle, for somehow even the silence was disturbing. The head came down and steam rose up from minute clustered green masses, and the forest did not heed him, but he was uneasy. Yondath was an ancient forest and there were things within it no man could explain, even if he wanted to. In a year when records were crumbled shreds and men no longer cared about the past, knowing there was no future, tales were the sole histories of the race. Narrated at twilight by pungent wood-blazes, these dealt with Yondath. There, old people said; looking back to earlier aeons in the crumbling fire; man was born. It was long tens of centuries since he made his towers there and built cities in the jungle; and now he was a long time away, spreading in a hundred tribes over earth's face, and growing less strong as he dispersed. His dawn was nearly forgotten, but early things grow dear when the end of memory approaches, and no one doubted but that the old race had greater towers than any which came after; and richer cities and markets. Prodigious stones of these cities lay hidden in little-explored places, and there were many ruins in Yondath though her cities had nearly perished. There is always magic in old things, and it was not odd that the vanished people of Yondath had been named wizards after they were all gone. What save wizardry could have built the monumental walls and dead places in which the children of a later age were astonished to wander? What save wizardry, and the consequences thereof, could have crowned a people with mightiness and then slain them in their glory? No one could even tell whence they had gone, though Loman's people were assuredly their descendants, but their doom was thought likely frightful and a punishment for power.

Dim stories of this people, whose tradition was on the distant side of an aeonian gulf, linking nowhere with his people's, had come to Loman; and with his fellows he had twice glimpsed buttresses crouching against the yellow sky beyond leagues of uninvaded jungle. He felt small and brief in the presence of such things, and yet was proud that men had once attained the heights defiant of the message of the stars. Now, as he clambered through natural snares of vine and bush, he felt that he was once more near a ruin of the old race, though why he felt this was doubtful. There was no sign of masonry through the jungle's patterned leaves. Instead, the place was teeming with scornful growing things which had never been cut or restrained by human implements; and these fought eagerly to the sky.

Then Loman stepped between certain bushes and saw an object not made by nature. In the centre of the clearing, dark with the patina of extreme antiquity, was a stone image. It was hewn from a squarish block, and the legs and arms were drawn close to its sides, so that it postured erect and frog-like. Much of the face had worn away, and it was of neither sex, though naked. The heavy base had carvings, but Loman could not read. Forgotten a long while, and unexplained now, it looked at him with the eyes of centuries. A sculptor who had beheld the thousand-year departed sun had chiseled it, and what he made was more permanent than memory. Yondath had grown and rotted and blossomed anew, but this idol was separate from the confused strife. No part of its existence was the battle around—moons had shone their ghost-beams upon it and suns had warmed it like warm flesh, but the assailing weather was powerless to wipe out the statue of a dead craftsman. Austerity clung to it like a veil; and knowing it a god, Loman knelt as was the custom of his race. His companions were a moment forgotten, and in their place was a mingled wonder and respect. He scrutinised the base, fascinated by the marks written upon it. There was no one now in all the world to read them. The scholar was dead, and the hunter had lost his lore, so that all the writings on statues and monuments and broken tombs was destined for no future reading, even unto the death of eternity. Silent, with no ears trained to receive their message, they would henceforth be fingered only by the rain.

Although Loman did not reflect on this, he wondered at the idol, and dug about with his foot to uncover a buried grotesque decorating the base. Dirt clogged it, and his interest was too casual to admit cleaning. The god would not object—his devotions were made, and it had grown accustomed to neglect. He would come back, if there was time to do it; but now the business of finding his companions faced him.

With no further interest, the barbarian stood by the image and gazed about, indecisive as to the way he would take; and the idol which would outlast him sat fixed in immemorial stone.

*February 1934*

# The Hoard of the Wizard-Beast

*With H. P. Lovecraft*

There had happened in the teeming and many-towered city of Zeth one of those incidents which are prone to take place in all capitals of all worlds. Nor, simply because Zeth lies on a planet of strange beasts and stranger vegetation, did this incident differ greatly from what might have occurred in London or Paris or any of the great governing towns we know. Through the cleverly concealed dishonesty of an aged but shrewd official, the treasury was exhausted. No shining *phrulder,* as of old, lay stacked about the strong-room; and over empty coffers the sardonic spider wove webs of mocking design. When, at last, the *giphath* Yalden entered that obscure vault and discovered the thefts, there were left only some phlegmatic rats which peered sharply at him as at an alien intruder.

There had been no accountings since Kishan the old keeper had died many moon-turns before, and great was Yalden's dismay to find this emptiness instead of the expected wealth. The indifference of the small creatures in the cracks between the flagstones could not spread itself to him. This was a very grave matter, and would have to be met in a very prompt and serious way. Clearly, there was nothing to do but consult Oorn, and Oorn was a highly portentous being.

Oorn, though a creature of extremely doubtful form and nature, was the virtual ruler of Zeth. It obviously belonged somewhere in the outer abyss, but had blundered into Zeth one night and suffered capture by the *shamith* priests. The coincidence of Its excessively bizarre aspect and Its innate gift of mimicry had impressed the sacred brothers as offering vast possibilities, hence in the end they had set It up as a god and an oracle, organising a new brotherhood to serve It—and incidentally to suggest the edicts it should utter and the replies It should give. Like the Delphi and Dodona of a later world, Oorn grew famous as a giver of judgments and solver of riddles; nor did Its essence differ from them save that It lay infinitely earlier in Time, and upon an elder world where all things might happen. And now Yalden, being not above the credulousness of his day and planet, had set out for the close-guarded and richly fitted hall wherein Oorn brooded and mimicked the promptings of the priests.

When Yalden came within sight of the Hall, with its tower of blue tile, he became properly religious, and entered the building acceptably, in a humble manner which greatly impeded progress. According to custom, the guardians of the deity acknowledged his obeisance and pecuniary offering, and retired behind heavy curtains to ignite the thuribles. After everything was in readiness, Yalden murmured a conventional prayer and bowed low before a curious empty dais studded with exotic jewels. For a moment—as the ritual prescribed—he stayed in this abased position, and when he arose the dais was no longer empty. Unconcernedly munching something the priests had given It was a large pudgy creature very hard to describe, and covered with short grey fur. Whence It had come in so brief a time only the priests might tell, but the suppliant knew that It was Oorn.

Hesitantly Yalden stated his unfortunate mission and asked advice; weaving into his discourse the type of flattery which seemed to him most discreet. Then, with anxiety, he awaited the oracle's response. Having tidily finished Its food, Oorn raised three small reddish eyes to Yalden and uttered certain words in a tone of vast decisiveness: *"Gumay ere hfotuol leheht teg."* After this It vanished suddenly in a cloud of pink smoke which seemed to issue from behind the curtain where the acolytes were. The acolytes then came forth from their hiding-place and spoke to Yalden, saying: "Since you have pleased the deity with your concise statement of a very deplorable state of affairs, we are honoured by interpreting its directions. The aphorism you heard signifies no less than the equally mystic phrase 'Go thou unto thy destination' or more properly speaking, you are to slay the monster-wizard Anathas, and replenish the treasury with its fabled hoard."

With this Yalden was dismissed from the temple. It may not be said in veracity that he was fearless, for in truth, he was openly afraid of the monster Anathas, as were all the inhabitants of Ullathia and the surrounding land. Even those who doubted its actuality would not have chosen to reside in the immediate neighbourhood of the Cave of Three Winds wherein it was said to dwell.

But the prospect was not without romantic appeal, and Yalden was young and consequently unwise. He knew, among other things, that there was always the hope of rescuing some feminine victim of the monster's famed and surprising erotic taste. Of the true aspect of Anathas none could be certain; tales of a widely opposite nature being commonly circulated. Many vowed it had been seen from afar in the form of a giant black shadow peculiarly repugnant to human taste, while others alleged it was a mound of gelatinous substance that oozed hatefully in the manner of putrescent flesh. Still others claimed they had seen it as a monstrous insect with astonishing supernumerary appurtenances. But in one thing all coincided; namely, that it was advisable to have as little traffic as possible with Anathas.

With due supplications to his gods and to their messenger Oorn, Yalden set out for the Cave of Three Winds. In his bosom were mixed an ingrained, patriotic sense of duty, and a thrill of adventurous expectancy regarding the unknown mysteries he faced. He had not neglected such preparations as a sensible man might make, and a wizard of old repute had furnished him with certain singular accessories. He had, for example, a charm which prevented his thirsting or hungering, and wholly did away with his need for provisions. There was likewise a glistening cape to counteract the evil emanations of a mineral that lay scattered over the rocky ground along his course. Other warnings and safeguards dealt with certain gaudy land-crustaceans, and with the deathly-sweet mists which arise at certain points until dispersed by heliotropism.

Thus shielded, Yalden fared without incident until he came to the place of the White Worm. Here of necessity he delayed to make preparations for finding the rest of his way. With patient diligence he captured the small colourless maggot, and surrounded it with a curious mark made with green paint. As was prophesied, the Lord of Worms, whose name was Sarall, made promise of certain things in return for its freedom. Then Yalden released it, and it crawled away after directing him on the course he was to follow.

The sere and fruitless land through which he now travelled was totally uninhabited. Not even the hardier of the beasts were to be seen beyond the edge of that final plateau which separated him from his goal. Far off, in a purplish haze, rose the mountains amidst which dwelt Anathas. It lived not solitary, despite the lonely region around, for strange pets resided with it—some the fabled elder monsters, and others unique beings created by its own fearful craft.

At the heart of its cave, legend said, Anathas had concealed an enormous hoard of jewels, gold, and other things of fabulous value. Why so potent a wonder-worker should care for such gauds, or revel in the counting of money, was by no means clear; but many things attested the truth of these tastes. Great numbers of persons of stronger will and wit than Yalden had died in remarkable manners while seeking the hoard of the wizard-beast, and their bones were laid in a strange pattern before the mouth of the cave, as a warning to others.

When, after countless vicissitudes, Yalden came at last into sight of the Cave of Winds amid the glistening boulders, he knew indeed that report had not lied concerning the isolation of Anathas' lair. The cavern-mouth was well-concealed, and over everything an ominous quiet lowered. There was no trace of habitation, save of course the ossuary ornamentation in the front yard. With his hand on the sword that had been sanctified by a priest of Oorn, Yalden tremblingly advanced. When he had attained the very opening of the lair, he hesitated no longer, for it was evident that the monster was away.

Deeming this the best of all times to prosecute his business, Yalden plunged at once within the cave. The interior was very cramped and exceedingly dirty, but the roof glittered with an innumerable array of small, varicoloured lights, the source of which was not to be perceived. In the rear yawned another opening, either natural or artificial; and to this black, low-arched burrow Yalden hastened, crawling within it on hands and knees. Before long a faint blue radiance glowed at the farther end, and presently the searcher emerged into an ampler space. Straightening up, he beheld a most singular change in his surroundings. This second cavern was tall and domed as if it had been shapen by supernatural powers, and a soft blue and silver light infused the gloom. Anathas, thought

Yalden, lived indeed in comfort; for this room was finer than anything in the Palace of Zeth, or even in the Temple of Oorn, upon
which had been lavished unthinkable wealth and beauty. Yalden
stood agape, but not for long, since he desired most of all to seek
the object of his quest and depart before Anathas should return
from wherever it might be. For Yalden did not wish to encounter the
monster-sorcerer of which so many tales were told. Leaving therefore
this second cave by a narrow cleft which he saw, the seeker followed
a devious and unlit way far down through the solid rock of the plateau. This, he felt, would take him to that third and ultimate cavern
where his business lay. As he progressed, he glimpsed ahead of him a
curious glow; and at last, without warning, the walls receded to reveal a vast open space paved solidly with blazing coals above which
flapped and shrieked an obscene flock of wyvern-headed birds.
Over the fiery surface green monstrous salamanders slithered, eyeing the intruder with malignant speculation. And on the far side
rose the stairs of a metal dais, encrusted with jewels, and piled high
with precious objects; the hoard of the wizard-beast.

At sight of this unattainable wealth, Yalden's fervour well-nigh
overcame him; and chaffing at his futility, he searched the sea of
flame for some way of crossing. This, he soon perceived, was not
readily to be found; for in all that glowing crypt there was only a
slight crescent of flooring near the entrance which a mortal man
might hope to walk on. Desperation, however, possessed him; so
that at last he resolved to risk all and try the fiery pavement. Better to
die in the quest than to return empty-handed. With teeth set, he
started toward the sea of flame, heedless of what might follow.

As it was, surprise seared him almost as vehemently as he had
expected the flames to do—for with his advance, the glowing floor
divided to form a narrow lane of safe cool earth leading straight to
the golden throne. Half dazed, and heedless of whatever might un-
derlie such curiously favouring magic, Yalden drew his sword and
strode boldly betwixt the walls of flame that rose from the rifted
pavement. The heat hurt him not at all, and the wyvern-creatures

drew back, hissing, and did not molest him.

The hoard now glistened close at hand, and Yalden thought of how he would return to Zeth, laden with fabulous spoils and worshipped by throngs as a hero. In his joy he forgot to wonder at Anathas' lax care of its treasures; nor did the very friendly behaviour of the fiery pavement seem in any way remarkable. Even the huge arched opening behind the dais, so oddly invisible from across the cavern, failed to disturb him seriously. Only when he had mounted the broad stair of the dais and stood ankle-deep amid the bizarre golden reliques of other ages and other worlds, and the lovely, luminous gems from unknown mines and of unknown natures and meanings, did Yalden begin to realise that anything was wrong.

But now he perceived that the miraculous passage through the flaming floor was closing again, leaving him marooned on the dais with the glittering treasure he had sought. And when it had fully closed, and his eyes had circled round vainly for some way of escape, he was hardly reassured by the shapeless, jelly-like shadow which loomed colossal and stinking in the great archway behind the dais. He was not permitted to faint, but was forced to observe that this shadow was infinitely more hideous than anything hinted in any popular legend, and that its seven iridescent eyes were regarding him with placid amusement.

Then Anathas the wizard-beast rolled fully out of the archway, mighty in necromantic horror, and jested with the small frightened conqueror before allowing that horde of slavering and peculiarly hungry green salamanders to complete their slow, anticipatory ascent of the dais.

## The Deplorable Voyage

The events culminating in the curious fate of the heretic Khalda are in aspect more moral than savory. It is known that he had done many sinful and unholy deeds, and escaped the great Malyat, slaying his Emperor. Other tales, too, are told of the terrible things within his windowless castle where he later retired from the world, and it has been noted that while there were no normal apertures within his secret house, a singularly suggestive *door* opened on the roof—

But the surprising use of this curious opening is not commonly known, though some have half-surmised the purpose.

Of a highly religious nature are the inhabitants of xxxxx, [*sic*] and though his supplication was not to the usual deities, Khalda made offerings to certain of the more obscure and dreadful gods in the years before his peculiar fate. It was through these affiliations that he obtained the charm hidden in this deadly mirror; and they were the same powers that had assisted him in even more repulsive rites.

It was known, among other things, that he possessed a small and battered image of the curious god Zotog-Ua. It was said that this had been handed down through generations of wonder-workers and their apprentices, straight from the anthropophagous deity himself, who had given it in return for the grandmother of an ardent devotee. This had been in the possession of the ill-fated Volnar (who was wholly consumed by his voracious monster), and it was said that Khalda had crept back during the night and stolen from his dead master.

Now Krang was great, but greater than he was the furred god Zotog-Ua, and when the mighty one had stopped for a year or two of rest in his travels, Krang had crawled beneath a mountain, and restively waited for the departure of his enemy, and he had rejoiced when Zotog-Ua continued his travels, going next to the far planet of Cykranosh.

This had been ages before the birth of Khalda, but when, as a student of the dark lore he discovered this historical detail, Khalda devoted no more time to the worship of Krang, but spent his time in the service of the more ancient gods, although they did not acknowledge his devotion. He had tried a number of times to estab-lish communication with certain of the Old Ones, and while once a little wisp of brown hair appeared in his magic pentacle, Khalda was uncertain of its origin.

Although astronomically the people of xxx [*sic*] were somewhat backwards, they had learned much of their universe through devious means; and everyone was aware that the small satellite of Gleer was devoid of abundant vegetation though inhabited by small pale green things that worshipped a tremendous thousand-year-old robot-machine. The bleakness of the landscape was commonly realized, and if it had not been for the sub-lunar caverns, existence upon this place would have been surpassingly difficult. Yet because of subterranean springs populated by pulpy fish-things, and on the outer coast the sparse but edible fern-grasses, it was generally conceded that man could live upon this place. Through their magic lenses necromantic adepts had viewed the barren landscape and examined the strange machine-god. There had been a time when its rusted arms had waved madly and fear was in the hearts of the watchers, and they saw the Gleerian folk prostrate themselves and make sacrifices, but it had ceased as if, being constructed of clockwork, it had run down.

Khalda, like many others, knew of this, although none had actually come closer than a spy-glass could bring them to the tiny satellite. It was his habit to sit in an inner room, his greenish face swarthily inscrutable as he surveyed a magic model of the heavens, and solemnly scrutinized it with a telescope. Within this chamber were all manner of wonderful appliances: there were, for example, three and a half pages copied from the Hsothian manuscripts, with dire and powerful chants upon them. Also, there was a small block of crystal containing embedded in its heart a perfectly formed young man who was there preserved for all eternity. This was the youth Morla, who had sought to steal the papyrus scroll containing the chants, and nine years before been terribly slain and thus oddly pickled. And there were many worn volumes of hideous books, as well as various strangely shapen stones and idols. Altogether a motley heap of objects filled the room where Khalda was wont to study and ponder upon diverse secrets.

*On Cykranosh*
*July 30, 1934*

Khalda dwelt not alone, for he had, with fine arts, constructed sentient creatures, and one of his favorite pets was a terrible thing that was soft and red-striped on its writhing yellow body. It resembled most a dog, but a dog with two trunk-tentacles like writhing arms that served as lips. This thing was created by Khalda from the blood of a spider and other ingredients; and he called it Barlykous. The creature showed no affection for its master, and once, when a strange slithering was heard upon the roof during the invocation of a particularly horrible deity, Barlykous set up an ululation that frightened it away. Khalda's rage knew no bounds, and he opened a very old flagon, pouring the contents down the throat of his animal. After that Barlykous could make no sound for a long time, and it broodingly lurked in the corners, glaring at its creator.

For a long time the master and his pet lived fairly peacefully, until the day came that Khalda resolved to try, with suitable conditions, the Chant of Shista. An essential to this charm was a *bait* of meat, or offering and trap, for the thin-limbed god, called Shista, whose multiple eyes were exceeded in number only by the sundry oddly-placed mouths that lay scattered upon its evil torso.

Shista was a very ancient deity, and the hermaphroditic grandparent of Selth, the Black One. It bore six thin rubbery arms; and the smouldering orange eyes were fearsome to behold. No garment was worn by Shista, for what could protect It against the outer cold of nothingness? But if It went obscenely unclad, yet Shista wore wide bracelets of pale green metal from which it derived its supernatural powers.

Khalda did not wish contact with this leering god for the purpose of absconding with its wonderful ornaments; and for this reason he set about certain preparations. There was, however, when all other requisite matters were attended to, yet the matter of flesh for bait. Now even the resources of wizards are not infallible, and Khalda perceived that he had neglected to provide for this contingency. Casting his gaze across the littered room, he seized upon the idea of using Barlykous as a suitable substitute. Thus he dragged the protesting creature to the strange design upon the floor, and tied his unfortunate pet to a heavy silver ring.

The upshot of the affair was that on a Tuesday evening long gone by the turbaned Khalda was visited by the god-thing called Shista. When the light began to glow in the center of the gemstoned place, and the unnatural *smell* began to develop, Barlykous, who had been chained as bait, began to howl in a hissing shriek. Before the eyes of the sorcerer began the materialization, and in a speedy time was Shista within the room. It did not bargain, but promptly sank satisfied teeth into the vegetable-like flesh of Barlykous, who bled not at all. When a portion or the creature had been somewhat unpleasantly devoured, he had lifted its eyes from the feast; and spied Khalda, its attention no longer upon the damaged beast, which no longer struggled, but permitted the imposition without protest.

Now Khalda had prepared an enchanted zone where he might be entirely safe; and it was guarded by four bowls of curious and brown liquid which had been strangely obtained. And nothing supernatural— as was Shista—could harmfully approach the devotee while he was thus protected. Shista knew this; and therefore was willing to parley most conservatively with the little sorcerer. Squatting with its greasy jowls; the deity held discourse to make bargainings with Khalda, yet protected by his barrier.

*never completed.*

## An Immorality

There was once a cavern wherein all was dark and chill, like a great tomb, and everywhere Cold was Lord, but in the center of this cavern a lake of flame one day chanced to bubble up like a cauldron, above hot coals from deeps that none could sound. This flame was warm, so that after the first aeons of ice and darkness, and before the ultimate aeons of ice and darkness; there grew in the chance light a race of green insects.

## II

These insects were very small, being unnoticed in the vastness by the Great Things which dwelt there. Yet to them the flaming pool was an infinity, and they crept about it, and one said:

## III

"How pleasant is the flame," as he sat with a pious companion in the reflected light. "Is it not fortunate that chance placed it here?"

But the other turned on him saying, "Heretic! Well you know that Yopp created the Flame, to nurture us, and that he formed us of an over-ripe fig; to honour him."

## IV

When time passed, and the observer of accuracy was also dust, the flame began to ebb, bubbling no longer like a cauldron above hot coals but like one which is upon ashes. And though many were sacrificed, and though pious ones brought incredible things to please their fickle deity, Yopp did not intervene.

So the chance-born flame vanished; and Cold stole out from ice-coated fissures, and was Lord again, bringing with him the night wherein all insects must perish.

But Yopp did not ever seem to concern himself with his race.

*Fall 1935*

# The Battle That Ended the Century

*(MS. Found in a Time Machine)*
*With H. P. Lovecraft*

On the eve of the year 2001 a vast crowd of interested spectators were present amidst the romantic ruins of Cohen's Garage,[1] on the

---

1. Kelly's Stables, a night club in New York "where there was some celebrated case of fisticuffs . . . movie folks involved maybe" (T. O. Mabbott to August W. Derleth,

former site of New York, to witness a fistic encounter between two renowned champions of the strange-story firmament—Two-Gun Bob, the Terror of the Plains,[2] and Knockout Bernie, the Wild Wolf of West Shokan.[3] [The Wolf was fresh from his correspondence course in physical training, sold to him by Mr. Arthur Leeds.[4]] Before the battle the auguries were determined by the venerated Thibetan Lama Bill Lum Li,[5] who evoked the primal serpent-god of Valusia and found unmistakable signs of victory for both sides. Cream-puffs were inattentively vended by Wladislaw Brenryk[6]—the partakers being treated by the official surgeons, Drs. D. H. Killer[7] and M. Gin Brewery.[8]

The gong was sounded at **39** o'clock, after which the air grew red with the gore of battle, lavishly flung about by the mighty Texas slaughterer. Very shortly the first actual damage occurred—-the loosening of several teeth in both participants. One, bouncing out from the Wolf's mouth after a casual tap from Two-Gun,[9] described a parabola toward Yucatán; being retrieved in a hasty expedition by

---

3 December 1949; ms., State Historical Society of Wisconsin).

2. Robert E[rvin] Howard (1906–1936) of Cross Plains, TX, a regular contributor to *Weird Tales* and other pulp magazines.

3. Bernard Austin Dwyer (1897–1943) of West Shokan, NY, an unseemly "champion of the strange-story firmament," for he published little if any fiction. The story acknowledges Dwyer's stout frame.

4. Arthur Leeds (1882–1952) of New York, Kalem Club member, once connected with the Home Correspondence School of Springfield, MA.

5. William Lumley (1880–1960) of Buffalo, NY, mystic and revision client of HPL.

6. H[arold] Warner Munn (1903–1981) of Athol, MA. HPL alludes to Munn's "cream-puff vending" in his letter to RHB of 1 September 1934 (*OFF* 174).

7. Dr. David H. Keller (1880–1966) of Stroudsburg, PA, prolific science fiction author and a physician.

8. Miles G. Breuer (1889–1947) of Lincoln, NE, author of "The Man with the Strange Head" and "Paradise and Iron."

9. The beginning of this sentence, as originally written by RHB, read: "One was picked up by James Ferdinand Morton, Esq., for preservation in the mineralogical hall of the Paterson Museum, while another—bouncing out from the Wolf's mouth under a casual tap from Two-Gun—described a . . .".

Messrs. A. Hijacked Barrell[10] and G. A. Scotland.[11] This incident was used by the eminent sociologist and ex-poet Frank Chimesleep Short, Jr., as the basis of a ballad of proletarian propaganda with three intentionally defective lines.[12] Meanwhile a potentate from a neighbouring kingdom, the Effjay of Akkamin (also known to himself as an amateur critic), expressed his frenzied disgust at the technique of the combatants, at the same time peddling photographs of the fighters (with himself in the foreground) at five cents each.[13]

In round two the Shokan Soaker's sturdy right crashed through the Texan's ribs and became entangled in sundry viscera; thereby enabling Two-Gun to get in several telling blows on his opponent's unprotected chin. Bob was greatly annoyed by the effeminate squeamishness shewn by several onlookers as muscles, glands, gore, and bits of flesh were spattered over the ringside. During this round the eminent magazine-cover anatomist Mrs. M. Blunderage portrayed the battlers as a pair of spirited nudes behind a thin veil of conveniently curling tobacco-smoke,[14] while the late Mr. C. Half-

---

10. A[lpheus] Hyatt Verrill (1871–1954), prolific author whose work included the Boy Adventurers series and also science fiction.

11. George Allan England (1877–1936), explorer and author of science fiction novels.

12. The beginning of this sentence, as originally written by RHB, read: "Between rounds this dental damage was repaired by Dr. Frank Belknap Long, Sr., while his gifted son and namesake incorporated the incident into a ballad of . . .". Frank Belknap Long, Jr. (1901–1994) of New York City, Kalem Club member and writer of weird and science fiction; his father was a dentist. When HPL and RHB printed and published a collection of Long's verse entitled *The Goblin Tower* (Cassia, FL: Dragon-Fly Press, 1935), HPL mentioned to correspondents that he and RHB not only organized the contents of the book but also revised the poems somewhat, to Long's indifference. Cf. HPL to RHB, 10 July 1936: "You don't want to follow Belknap's example of intentionally defective lines" (*OFF* 352).

13. Forrest J Ackerman (1916–2008), science fiction fan. HPL skewered Ackerman with the epithets "slimy effjeh weeds" and "akman" in "In the Walls of Eryx" (1936), written with Kenneth J. Sterling. A vitriolic debate between Ackerman and various weird tale enthusiasts (including HPL and RHB) was published in *The Fantasy Fan* in a column called "The Boiling Point" (Sept. 1933–Feb. 1934). Ackerman was known for shamelessly selling photographs and autographs, even of writers whose work he denigrated.

14. Margaret Brundage (1900–1976) of Chicago, referred to as an "anatomist" be-

Cent provided a sketch of three Chinamen clad in silk hats and galoshes—this being his own original conception of the affray.[15] Among the amateur sketches made was one by Mr. Goofy Hooey, which later gained fame in the annual Cubist exhibit as "Abstraction of an Eradicated Pudding".[16]

In the third round the fight grew really rough; several ears and other appurtenances being wholly or partially detached form the frontier battler by the Shokan Shocker. Somewhat irritated, Two-Gun countered with some exceptionally sharp blows; severing many fragments from his aggressor, who continued to fight with all his remaining members. At this stage the audience gave signs of much nervous excitement—instances of trampling and goring being frequent. The more enthusiastic members were placed in the custody of Mr. Harry Brobst of the Butler Hospital for Mental Diseases.[17]

The entire affair was reported by Mr. W. Lablache Talcum;[18] his copy being revised by Horse Power Hateart.[19] Throughout the event notes were taken by M. Le Comte d'Erlette for a 200-volume novel-cycle in the Proustian manner, to be entitled *Morning in September*,[20] with illustrations by Mrs. Blunderage. Mr. J. Caesar Warts[21] fre-

---

cause of her notorious cover art for *Weird Tales* depicting nudes (in scenes not described in the stories) adorned as described here.

15. C. C. Senf (1873–1949), illustrator for *Weird Tales*. HPL frequently accused Senf of providing illustrations that did not depict scenes from stories (as Senf's illustration of Chaugnar Faugn in Long's "The Horror from the Hills").

16. Guy L[incoln] Huey (1912–2001), an illustrator for *Marvel Tales*, another artist whose art did not match the contents of the publication it adorned.

17. Harry K. Brobst (1909–2010), a friend of HPL, was a nurse at Butler Hospital in Providence.

18. Wilfred Blanch Talman (1901–1986) of New York, Kalem Club member. HPL revised some of his work.

19. H. P. Lovecraft.

20. August W. Derleth (1909–1971) of Sauk City, WI. Derleth, alluded to as Comte d'Erlette, author of *Cultes des Goules*, in HPL's fiction, had ambitious plans for a very long fictional work about Wisconsin that he called the "Sac Prairie Saga." HPL had read Derleth's oft-revised *Evening in Spring* in manuscript many times.

21. Julius Schwartz (1915–2004) of New York. Schwartz edited *Fantasy Magazine*. Acting

quently interviewed both battlers and all the more important spectators; obtaining as souvenirs (after a spirited struggle with the Effjay) an autographed quarter-rib of Two-Gun's, in excellent state of preservation, and three finger-nails from the Wild Wolf. Lighting effects were supplied by the Electrical Testing Laboratories under the supervision of H. Kanebrake.[22] The fourth round was prolonged eight hours at the request of the official artist, Mr. H. Wanderer, who wished to put certain shadings of fantasy into his representation of the Wolf's depleted physiognomy, which included several supernumerary details supplied by the imagination.[23]

The climax came in round five, when the Texas Tearer's left passed entirely through Battling Bernie's face and brought both sluggers to the mat. This was adjudged a finish by the referee—Robertieff Essovitch Karovsky, the Muscovite Ambassador—who, in view of the Shokan Shocker's gory state, declared the latter to be essentially liquidated according to the Marxian ideology.[24] The Wild Wolf entered an official protest, which was promptly overruled on the ground that all the points necessary to technical death were theoretically present.

The gonfalons sounded a fanfare of triumph[25] for the victor, while the technically vanquished was committed to the care of the official mortician, Mr. Teaberry Quince.[26] During the ceremonies

---

as HPL's agent, he sold *At the Mountains of Madness* to *Astounding Stories*.

22. H. C. Koenig (1893–1959) of New York, a weird fiction enthusiast who lent HPL his books and gave HPL a tour of the Electrical Testing Laboratories, where he worked.

23. Howard Wandrei (1909–1956) of St. Paul, later New York, known for his intricately detailed pen and ink drawings. He illustrated his brother Donald's volume of poetry *Dark Odyssey* (1931).

24. Robert S[pencer] Carr (1909–1994), like Long, espoused Marxism. He visited the Soviet Union in the early 1930s.

25. In drafts of the story "The Scarlet Citadel," Robert E. Howard misused the word *gonfalon* though he corrected it (per HPL's advice) for publication (*WT*, January 1933). He thought a gonfalon is a musical instrument (as misused here), but it is a banner or pennant, especially one with streamers, hung from a crossbar.

26. Seabury Quinn (1899–1966) of Brooklyn, lawyer and editor of the mortician's

the theoretical corpse strolled away for a bite of bologna, but a tasteful cenotaph was supplied to furnish a focus for the rites. The funeral procession was headed by a gaily bedecked hearse driven by Malik Taus, the Peacock Sultan, who sat on the box in West Point uniform and turban,[27] and steered an expert course over several formidable hedges and stone walls. About half way to the cemetery the cortège was rejoined by the corpse, who sat beside Sultan Malik on the box and finished his bologna sandwich—his ample girth having made it impossible for him to enter the hastily selected cenotaph. An appropriate dirge was rendered by Maestro Sing Lee Bawledout on the piccolo;[28] Messrs. De Silva, Brown, and Henderson's celebrated aria, "Never Swat a Fly", from the old cantata *Just Imagine*,[29] being chosen for the occasion. The only detail omitted from the funeral was the interment, which was interrupted by the disconcerting news that the official gate-taker—the celebrated financier and publisher Ivar K. Rodent, Esq.—had absconded with the entire proceeds.[30] This omission was regretted chiefly by the Rev. D. Vest Wind, who was thereby forced to leave unspoken a long and moving sermon revised expressly for the celebration from a former discourse delivered at the burial of a favourite horse.[31]

---

journal, *Casket and Sunnyside,* as well as prolific contributor to *Weird Tales.*

27. E[dgar] Hoffmann Price (1898–1989) of Redwood City, CA. HPL referred to Price, a West Point graduate, as "The Peacock Sultan" because of Price's affinity for peacocks and because of his interest in the Middle East. (Price could speak Arabic, according to HPL.)

28. F. Lee Baldwin (1913–1987) of Asotin, WA, fantasy fan and amateur musician.

29. George Gard ("Buddy") DeSylva (1895–1950), Lew Brown (1893–1958), and Ray Henderson (1896–1970), a song-writing team. They did write "Never Swat a Fly" and "Just Imagine."

30. Hugo Gernsback (1884–1967), science fiction magazine editor. Gernsback was notorious for late payment for stories he published, earning from HPL the epithet "Hugo the Rat" (hence "Rodent"). Like Ackerman, HPL lampooned Gernsback in "In the Wall of Eryx" in reference to "ugrats" and obliquely in "scificlighs" (i.e., Science Fiction League, founded by Gernsback).

31. Rev. Wind appears to be Rev. David Van Bush (1882–1959), a motivational speaker and HPL's revision client. His poem "Vy Not Keep A-Going?" mentions the

Mr. Talcum's report of the event, illustrated by the well-known artist Klarkash-Ton (who esoterically depicted the fighters as boneless fungi),[32] was printed—after repeated rejections by the discriminating editor of the *Windy City Grab-Bag*[33]—as a broadside by W. Peter Chef.[34] This, through the efforts of Otis Adelbert Kline,[35] was finally placed on sale in the bookshop of Smearum & Weep,[36] three and a half copies finally being disposed of through the alluring catalogue description supplied by Samuelus Philanthropus, Esq.[37]

In response to this wide demand, the text was finally reprinted by Mr. De Merit in the polychromatic pages of Wurst's *Weakly Americana* under the title "Has Science Been Outmoded? Or, The Millers in the Garage".[38] No copies, however, remain in circulation; since all which were not snapped up by fanatical bibliophiles were seized by the police in connexion with the libel suit of the Wild Wolf, who was, after several appeals ending with the World Court, adjudged not only officially alive but the clear winner of the combat.

---

death of a horse.

32. Clark Ashton Smith (1893–1961) of Auburn, CA, addressed by HPL as Klarkash-Ton in correspondence, and mentioned as such in "The Whisperer in Darkness." HPL delighted in Smith's paintings of unearthly, fungoid vegetation.

33. HPL considered Farnsworth Wright, editor of *Weird Tales*, to be capricious in his selection of material for publication.

34. W. Paul Cook (1880–1948) of Athol, MA. Cook published Donald Wandrei's *Dark Odyssey* and printed (but did not bind or distribute) HPL's *The Shunned House*. RHB received the printed sheets (by way of Walter J. Coates) but bound only a few copies.

35. Otis Adelbert Kline (1891–1946), literary agent and author. HPL and Kline participated in "Cigarette Characterizations" (*Fantasy Magazine* 3, No. 4 [June 1934]).

36. Dauber and Pine, the bookstore at which HPL's friend Samuel Loveman worked.

37. Samuel Loveman (1887–1976) of Brooklyn, poet and Kalem Club member.

38. The allusions are as follows: A[braham] Merritt (1884–1943); Hearst's *American Weekly* (where Merritt worked); Henshaw Ward's "Science Has Not Gone Mystical," *Atlantic Monthly* 152, No. 2 (August 1933): 186–94; and Merritt's "The Dwellers in the Mirage."

## The Fidelity of Ghu

The Lord Ghu—last of the priests that had served Krang in the days before the sudden and inexplicable pseudo-demise of that horrid monster—gazed reflectively across the bright desert. For fully two moons his master had been sealed within his mighty tomb, and after proper lamentations, Ghu had begun to ponder upon his own fate, now that there was no further need of his services. The yellow slave-people were witless, and had for some time been wandering about in idle destructiveness, treading all over the vegetable garden behind the palace, in their clumsiness, and quite ruining, Ghu realized with a sigh, his crop of new pease.

The plight of the High Priest was typical of all those who had devotedly relied upon the infinite knowledge of their strange master for all directions. Now that he had been interred with due solemnity, none knew where next to turn. Clearly, things were in a deplorable state, and being the least stupid of them all, the withered Ghu sat sniveling upon a rock, and gazed vaguely across the hot dry sands to where the mountains of blue rock rose in distant majesty. The sun was rising gloriously, and a nearby insect chirped audibly. No wind disturbed his scanty locks, and the morning was quite peaceful and calm.

Ghu rose, shook the sand from his robe, and slowly walked into the desert. His resolution was both suitably dramatic and heroic, for Ghu had determined to perish by the tomb of his master, in noble sacrifice. He had thought all night upon the matter, and had concluded that this would, in the end, entail the least trouble, and yet at the same time serve his vanity, for it would cause his example to be pointed out by others with envious and admiring pride. Thus musing, he went slowly into the waste that stretched before him.

He had made his sorrowful way some distance into this uninhabited region, and was not far distant from the tomb of his master, when a strange thing occurred. From behind a rock, that but a moment gone had most assuredly not been there, stepped a terrible creature, shapen like a five legged spidery crab, and this tall creature was mottled with purple and green. It had upon its limbs four metal bracelets, and because of this fact, Ghu at once recognized that it was Shista, in one of the more or less original avatars that the god affected.

Now when Krang had yet lived, the worship of Shista had fallen into disuse, and the baffled deity had retired into seclusion. But when news of the death of Krang was brought to Shista, the recluse was mightily pleased, and had set out afoot toward the Old One's gleaming tower. Tremendous was the palace of Brown Krang, and coveted by all the evil powers of the universe. And as Shista was not unlike the others, this small god had determined to dwell therein.

The meeting with Ghu, it must be related, was purest accident, but finding this surprised, ogling priest upon the desert promptly suggested various uses to Shista, so that it spoke to him, and asked what his mission might be. This Ghu stated, in a voice heavy with sentiment, and he did not detect the amusement in the sundry orange eyes of the deity. Then, when he would have turned his feet again upon the goal of his pilgrimage, Shista spoke, and its voice was deep and strange. . . .

What was said unto Ghu in that far lonesome place is not recorded; but it is narrated in old scripts that on Tuesday week, following the interment of Krang, came the Lord Ghu back to the vacant temple, and beat upon the spotted drum hanging near an arched portal; by this summoning all the strange monsters that had been servitors of the Dead One. Then he spoke to this gathered multitude, saying, "Lo! I went into the desert to seek my master's tomb, and there I thought to perish. But as I was upon this mission, there came to me a messenger from the gods; and a demi-god itself, that spake to me, and tore away the veil of ignorance from my eyes. And now do ye bow, for I am possessed by the will of our dead Lord, and great Shista is come to rule in his stead. So I have returned to make ready for the One who shall follow when we have suitably prepared his temple."

Thus did Ghu remain faithful to his master.

## Loneliness

The thin road wound ahead between the silhouetted trunks of spectral trees and vanished in the mist. Darker yet the way became, and still we hurtled on the path. Wild fancies came to me and I was troubled by the thought of this dim path. I thought that it might [lead?] nowhere, but lead away to regions void and infinite. The maggot-moon within the rotting sky crept off, devoured in turn by evil clouds; and now the greyness that remained was terrible past any darkness more complete. A chill gloom everywhere prevailed, until the very trees were lost in nothingness, but scatteredly, dark monoliths rose ruined tiers throughout the murky sky. Enigmatic beacon-lights shone cryptically through slimy mists as if they sought a thing unseen. Within the sinister night all sense of up and down and distances departed, and hurtling thus upon the ancient road, we came at last upon the waiting doom.

## The City in the Desert

Vast and obscure is the lore of the world called Loth, and many the legends of things and places that are no more. Chief among these vanished places was Phargo, The City In The Desert. Now there is only a great expanse of hot and dry earth, from the river Oolaee even unto Zath. Somewhere in this lies buried the tomb of the Lord Krang, though many say that he is no longer in his tomb. Men opened the mighty sepulcher, and dire things happened. What then became of the lord is not known. Some have told that he died again and that his living corpse is yet there, but this is doubted by many, and the tale is made that the Great One joined his distant cousins, they that are named Khut-Lu, Zatog-Ua and Iog-Zodot. And it is said that the broad leather wings of the lord were lifted in flight, and that his shadow passed over many cities, and that he disappeared forever from the ken of man. These say that between the star-spaces circle strange things, and of them is Krang now one.

Though their ruler was gone yet remained those who had served him; and it is said that these retired in part to the mountain called Zath. In the earth were the First Things that hated Krang, and waged battle with the Great One when Loth was new.

And when the Lord had been gone from man's thought, who can tell what brought the news to the strange and plastic monsters in their buried lair?

In the center of the vacant desert-space a tremendous crater filled with seething grey lava is known to exist, and from this place come nauseous bubbles that burst unctuously. Here is set down the tale made of the place of charred earth, and none knoweth if they be true or false.

A number of miles distant from the deep river of ebon that men named Oolaee, but yet so situated as to be enabled to use it for navigation and trading in slaves from distant Leek, rise the numberless towers of the old city called Phargo. This town was built of yellow stone, beyond the hills, wherein strange remains form curious designs known to students of palaeolithic sorcery. Because of whispered fables that drift from none knows where, strangers were loath to approach the strange town except for business, and travelling merchants took great care to secrete their profits within their turbans (which, though it is really the obvious place for robbers to look, has been a convention for so long no one would think of changing). The markets were quite empty by dusk, and if any evil things took place, it was the concern of only the inhabitants of Phargo, who men say have always numbered three thousand, since none ever die, and all have been aged for eternity.

And men said the City did not grow as do others, but that it was found suddenly to be there, with its people and things. And its folk were old when men first saw them. An odd place, surely, was Phargo, and the vast commerce transacted, and the wealth of the dour citizens was held nigh sinful by the envious. Yet although it had an evil name, the mud-coloured fine sand of the desert was always thronged with persons travelling towards it or away. Since none had ever stayed willingly the city contained none of the green-lanterned rooming-houses which were so common in lands adjacent.

Everyone had warned Rian against remaining after dusk, but upon the arrival of his caravan of ape-tusks that had cost so many lives in the feverish jungles of Phoor, he had a great curiosity about the old city, and determined to spend a night within its confines, despite all the warnings, and the habitual barring of the huge gate after the traders had left. So it is always . . . what is told to be forbidden and terrible, we seek. What there is so intriguing about mystery and horror none can say—but because of the tales he had heard whispered, Rian stayed after sunset in the ancient town.

His cargo of prime ivory—obtained through the deaths of innumerable slave-men and even three of his companion-explorers—sold readily, and at a good price, to the artizens that know how cunningly to carve and filigree it. His proceeds secreted, Rian determined to traverse other parts of the city before the market square was evacuated. This he did to a fair extent, for the city was not large; and though the twisted streets wound confusingly, he obtained a fair conception of the principal landmarks. As evening came on he made plans to hide in the grove of odd and alien trees that stood near a certain temple. The branches were enmeshed nearly impenetrably, and when he had made his way well into the central thicket he found his vantage point commanded an unobscured view of the strange rounded temple with its numberless low towers that were somehow awry. This building, he had been told, was the center of the strange nocturnal occupations of the inhabitants of Phargo; they that are reputed to be so old.

Empty were the heavens, and all crossed over with strange bars of light that had as source the indefinite moon. A multitude of distant croakings served only to accentuate the prevailing silence.

Had he not slept strange things would have appeared unto Rian, things that would have seared his soul forevermore. Yet he did doze, and was not awake when the foul rites took place there in the court paved with great blocks upon each of which is a prayer graven. And during the ceremonies his flesh remained, but he was not blasted, so that when he awakened Rian knew not of the doings of the night.

So he was annoyed, oblivious of the fortunes that had been his, and when he saw the day was new, Rian returned to the square where was tied his beast. And he took the halter from it, and led it to the opened gates, showing the creature the desert beyond, bidding it go, for Rian had resolved not to leave the city until its mystery was clear. The animal nuzzled him with its giant mouth, and unhurryingly departed, ambling slowly towards the horizon.

Then Rian returned to the city gates, and made bargainings with a certain ancient peddler. And the old man peered over his spectacles of square green diamonds, wondering sadly, and finally sold the drug Rian desired.

And what then Rian did is not narrated, though it is certain he somehow made drunken a member of the race of the Old Ones. What inquiries he made concerning the origin of the city, man does not know, but terrible things must have been told him that day.

When he had done Rian looked with terror at the Old One, and unpausing ran through the streets screaming. None turned to regard him, for strange happenings were common in Phargo, and though an awful formless tentacle reached for him from a gloomy doorway, the youth evaded it and was soon beyond the gates. The elder ones knew at once their secret was told, and terrible things pursued Rian as he recaptured his reluctant mount, but he rode away into the desert unharmed.

Thus the Old Ones barred up their gates, and during the night the City sank amid rumblings into the earth where it had emerged nine hundred years before, at the departure of the mighty enemy.

And a vast crater in the heated sand is all that remains of Phargo. From this come sighing great bubbles that moistly burst.

## The Cavern of Fear

In the central part of the verdantly lush jungle of Yonath the gnarled branches and strange pulpy growths are so entangled as almost to obscure the purple sky. Ancient tree-things overgrown with peculiar plants rise on every hand and brilliant flowers of alien beauty spring prolifically amid the interwoven vines of the ground. On hot summer days when all the tiny life is quiet and there is peace in the forest, the pinkish spider-men scamper gaily about the glades and gambol by the still tarns. And save for the warmth beating with continual steadiness from the distant sun, and the rasping buzz of some busy insect, all is inanimate.

On such a day Loman lost his way and stumbled into one of the infrequent clearings. The fellow-members of his hunting party were far to the east, but he knew it not. He was completely lost when he took the precisely wrong direction after his vain pursuit of the delectable but allusively agile mondal. Cursing the epicurean desires that had led him afield, Loman searched he thick growths uselessly for both his quarry and his path. Great vines were tangled about the boles of fern-trees wonderfully high, and they hampered his way. Nothing was visible but the trackless undergrowth. He liked it not, this being lost in the ancient wood, for tales were narrated of the fierce and insatiable monsters that dwelt within its confines. Also did he realize that the chances were small for his erstwhile companions to find him—rather would he have to seek them and he knew not what direction to take.

The tough fabric of his encasing suit protected him from the intense heat and the thorny branches, but he carried little food, at best enough for three days.

So it was that after his prey had vanished and Loman knew what had happened he attempted logical exploration of his surroundings. This took little time and was fruitless in result. The unbroken thickets rose impenetrably on all sides, and the quite glade with its carpet of flower-spangled moss seemed the sole departure from entangled vegetation. Not even the primitive birds, those with green-scaled wings and harsh cry, frequented this secluded spot, and the exotic purple orchid-flowers nodded aloofly.

In the center of the clearing, overgrown with ancient vines and covered with the patina of extreme antiquity, he perceived a strangely shaped image. So curious did Loman become that he forgot his angered weariness and made his way to this obscure object. And though the grotesque features were nearly obliterated, while unthinkably long exposure had marred the carven perfection of detail, he stood in awe for this statue of some female deity unknown to him. What hands had shaped and graved the curious glyphs upon the base, and how it had come to be in this hidden place he knew not, but he saw that he was confronting an idol of incalculable age—a relique of the early race that had dwelt in Yondath before ever the jungle flourished. It was told that once a mighty civilization had flourished in the old years after Lord Krang was sealed in his mausoleum, and their colossal towers were greater than those of any who came after, and their accomplishments mightier and their gods infinitely more powerful than those of any people that lived in later aeons. How true this may have been Loman knew not, but it was said that prodigious blocks of stone lay half-hidden in little-explored places and odd ruins sprawled in isolated portions of his world. None could say where this mighty elder race had vanished, although some narrated hideous legends of its doom in the forgotten years.

Austerity clung to it like a veil, and knowing that it was a god, Loman dwelt as was the custom of his race. Then he half-turned; and his foot slipped into an unseen hole, so that he fell twistedly upon the ground. Examining the earth beneath the rotting leaves and moss, he saw that it had crumbled away at the base of the statue. Small bits of fresh soil clung to his boot as he gained his feet, and a sizeable hold was revealed from which came an intangible aroma.

He scooped away the covering dirt, and found beneath him a cave of no mean size. That a natural orifice should exist in the region of the statue seemed scarcely probable, so he set to work and enlarged the opening until he might descend into the cave below.

Into what the other end of the tunnel emerged, Loman could not fathom. He felt that the passage had been there for some purpose of concealment—perhaps by even that fabled race of Yondath, whose treasures might well be hidden in such an obscure place. But for the accidental manner in which he had discovered the clearing and the hollow, he might have easily gone past, never conceiving that such a mystery lay so close at hand.

With no small excitement and curiosity he slid awkwardly into the opening that he had made, and discovered, upon reaching the hard packed floor, that the roof was far enough above to permit his standing erect. The fresh moisture of the upper strata did not reach the earth lower on the walls. Long-undisturbed dust lined the tunnel. Because it was extremely dark within, and his vision could penetrate but little before him, Loman drew from his knapsack a small device that showed the way before him. After a moment of hesitation, he followed the rough corridor beneath the forest floor.

For a timeless period he groped through blackness. His light pierced it in a narrow, brilliant streak, but there was no change in his surroundings. That the passage was artificial he could no longer doubt, for there was evidence of the chisel, and other primitive digging implements. As he progressed the hard clay was supplanted by outcroppings of peculiar rock. The point at which he had entered appeared to be the topmost level in the whole tunnel, for thereafter his way led continually downward.

After he had traversed perhaps eighty yards of the difficult and uneven way, Loman cast his light directly upon a vast and rugged opening. Beyond, it was as black as Yuggoth. This place seemed the natural mother-cave, from which branched many artificial labyrinths. No breath of air disturbed the deep-piled dust, nor did his light reveal anything but incalculable decay and disintegration. The very rock seemed weary with age, and during the prevailing darkness, many cracks had developed, so that in places the walls had partly collapsed into heaps of rubble.

Before him, in the great cavern, was a maze of fantastic stalagmites formed of hard and twisted rock. Making his way cautiously amid the forest of erect and sharpened points, Loman followed a well-defined trail. The path he trod was as if worn away by centuries of footsteps, and he wondered at the usage that had eroded the hard floor to such a degree.

For an illimitable time he followed this course, and then he came to a last, small cave. And here were no coloured pinnacles, but only a drab, uneven rock.

Swinging his light about, he saw that the path ended. It was apparent that his destination had been reached. What he would discover was as much a mystery as the reason for the artfully concealed chamber. Was there perhaps a treasure there—the jewel of the old race? Or a secret temple of some strange and terrible deity?

He speculated on this, toying with wild notions for a moment. Then his light revealed certain strange objects. Against the wall, half-shrouded by the darkness, he perceived a long row of tall bulky objects. He crossed to these, and saw in shocked surprise that each upright case held a curious mummified body, wrapped in ancient and crumbling gold cloth that had nurtured a nauseous green fungus in the dragging years. Was this place, then, only a repellent burying ground? What people had placed their dead in this inaccessible crypt? Perplexed and mystified, Loman he gazed in a fearful awe upon the strange corpses. Abiding wonder lingered here—a wonder more ancient than the forest or the ruins therein. He felt that there was something odd in the fact that no burial trappings lay beside the shrivelled bodies—no slender tear-jugs or urns bearing ash of sacred herbs.

Then to his horror and consternation a strange and hideous animation came upon those awesome beings in the upright sarcophagi. The cool moist breeze, impregnated with the light of the jungle, blew freshly through the corridors, by some caprice of chance, and played steadily upon the row of coffins. Softly and ceaselessly it blew—bearing life! Before the terrified eyes of the watcher the row of figures sagged a long moment and then almost imperceptibly moved. What foul image was this? Has the wind borne new life to those age-old bodies? They seemed to writhe—to live! And their rotting golden rags crumbled into shreds as the beings slouched into new, free postures. Then, to make the horror supreme, Loman's light flickered slightly. As he frantically fumbled with it the foul creatures unsteadily spread about, surrounding him. Could he but have gone starkly, gibbering mad then it would have been infinitely more merciful than that which happened, for a long-unused voice issued from the throat of one of the creatures, as revolting as the miasma that clung to its ancient wrappings.

"This being has intruded upon our slumber, brethren," it spoke. Loman closed his eyes, too weak with fear to gaze upon the ghastly sight of those living mummies.

The others nodded with the rustle of dead branches in a storm.

"What shall we do with him, my comrades?" asked the speaker.

A restless quiver ran through their encircling ranks.

"He must die," was the reply.

"Slowly . . . and painfully" said another.

"Yes," answered the first. Then there was silence. Loman opened his eyes; forced himself to look upon his captors.

"Let us take him to the cave of the Black Water," suggested one of the beings, and the others nodded. He will look different when his flesh is . . . like ours," saiod one. And an unspeakable chuckle came from beneath the concealing wrappings.

Then the one who had spoken first stepped towards Loman, and extended a stinking paw towards his shrinking arm. It clutched him firmly, and the grip was that of fleshless bone rather than human hand.

But something intervened, for the fast-fading pocket-light completely blinked out. The unexpected dark confused Loman for a moment, but then he dimly saw a light made by tiny fungi set upon the dripping roof. This illumination had been hidden by the more brilliant artificial rays. And he saw, too, that his captors were more disconcerted than he, for the peculiar construction of their unseen eyes prevented their perceiving the fungoid light.

"What has happened?" inquired a hollow voice. "It is black again."

"The flame of the human has been extinguished," said another.

"Then let us make flame of our own."

One of the creatures returned to the coffins and took from between two a bundle of gnarled purple faggots that appeared as if brightly stained. It set these upon the rocky floor, and fumbled with some primitive device. Loman thought wildly, frantically, and as the light flared up he was ready. Before his guard could tighten his loosened grip the man had sprung forward and caught up a blazing brand of the strange oily wood.

"Stop him," called his captor, but with the others drew back in fear.

"Aye, dead ones, stop me!" he jeered with mad assurance. "I shall find if your bodies are impervious to flame!" Then a whim struck him, and he laughed insanely. "Get back into your catacomb, O creatures of the dark! Ye are dead, and it is not fit that ye shall walk beside the living! Thou art the intruders, not I!" And he swore an hideous blasphemy, and hurled the torch into their midst. Then, with an ineffable reek striking his nostrils, he ran. Back, back through the caves, and past the numberless stalagmites. His shadow was oddly distorted on the walls, as if a monstrous thing accompanied his flight.

Behind him awful sounds pierced the cloud of pungent smoke, as he ran blindly on until his muscles wearied. How he found his way back into the tunnel beneath the idol he knew not, but after a time he saw light streaming from the hole, and with failing strength pulled himself up through the opening into the blessed and welcome day.

## Chant

In ancient years before our glories were forgotten, when yet the land was young and vast and wondrous to see, there lived a man called Nyarlathotep. Strange and terrible he was, and wise in mystic ways. The people of the land found oddness in his eyes, for they were cold and dark like secret caves of Yugot.

Thus for many years he dwelt and then was made into a semblance of death. From whence it came no man of Egypt knew, and it was a strange death, for he perished not or shrivelled, although cunning herbs were not put into him. Corruption touched him not, or rottenness. There were none who mourned when, by the light of many torches, he was borne into the caverned earth. Within the ancient silences his body lay in curious vestments of the tomb, and thus reposed while all the pyramids grew old.

*It is thus he shall be found. Or hath he been found? for time is timeless and eternity a circle. There is neither form nor shape when the hiding mists are blown away, for only Emptiness remaineth.*

And from his cavern tomb all carved in secret hieroglyphs and symbols of the ancient Lore, Azathoth woke the one who waiting lay, and from among the dead in majesty and silence came the Messenger to go among the fearing men.

In tattered garments hued like a vintage made of serpent's blood, he spread the awful word, and man and beast made homage. None dared fear or question him; though they were stricken dumb when he had passed . . .

*September 1934*

## The Inhospitable Tavern

Quorlan smiled cryptically at his servant when the knocking came upon the door. His beefy face slid into a mechanical and false smile as he rubbed his pudgy hands together. "Go, fool!" he exclaimed, angered at the mute's fearful gaze. The servant Varrak nodded and vanished into the shadows to comply. Quorlan peered with interest into the gloom to see who it was arriving at that late hour, for the tavern was foreboding enough in the day light.

A tall figure in a long cloak yet damp from the evening mist strode quickly in, with muttered oaths. He glanced about hastily and espied the paunchy innkeeper by the fireside. Brusquely he demanded lodging for the night. Quorlan, making what might have been almost frightened obeisance, scuttled up the stairs and flung open a massive ornately-carven door on the left of the little hall-way. The bearded stranger, who had removed his hat, and was seen to be not unhandsome in his foreign way, followed.

"This will do," he said imperiously, and as an afterthought, "Get out."

"But Sire, the rates?" inquired Quorlan, his three fatty chins bulging as he drew back to inspect his lodger.

"Get out, I said!" commanded the bearded man again, and followed the remark with a boot flung in the direction of the door. Master and menial, closely following, descended the stairway hurriedly.

At the bottom, shutting the door with quiet carefulness, Quorlan nodded his head toward the cellar, and Varrak the servant at once accompanied him there. Drawing a pen from his belt, Quorlan dipped it into an oddly shaped bottle upon the table, and hastily wrote "You saw his gold?" Varrak nodded. "Go through the passage and watch. Let me know when he is asleep. He must not escape as did the last one," was scribbled.

Varrak disappeared behind a barrel and crept through a low opening concealed there. Stealthily he followed the cramped passage between the thick walls of the tavern, and lifted himself by a series of pegs to the second floor, panting and leering in the dark. The spiders drew back in their web to let him pass, for here they recognized one of their own nature. When he reached the end he paused, and quietly removed the sliding cover from a peephole to which he applied his eye.

A dim shape was in the bed, and with a smile Varrak ran his hand over a long thin blade caressingly. Then he turned, and noiselessly began his descent, lowering himself slowly by his powerful cruel hands. But he did not complete it, for another hand, that of the stranger, laid upon his, and with quiet force drew him strugglingly up.

There was terror in the eyes of the gaunt misshapen Varrak, and he opened his mouth horribly, striving to scream, but it only gaped ridiculously and no sound came forth. Then merciless hands bent him backwards imprisoning him while his own knife was drawn from its sheath and driven into his body. The twisted brain of the mute ceased its turmoil of horror, and he slid to the floor, sprawling grotesquely with a peculiar look in his eyes. The traveler rose, half-spurned him with his foot, and went through the sliding panel, closing it behind him, his unwholesome task completed.

For he had not been at all surprised, like those who had preceded him, and he had planned this before his arrival.

Exploring the way carefully, to watch for pitfalls, he made his way cautiously to the cellar. Peering over the opening he saw the bulging figure of the proprietor lying drunkenly in a chair. With a sardonic humor the bearded man removed the top of a wine cask, and seizing him bodily, precipitated him into it head-first. A spasmodic kicking was all that marked his death. Then the bearded man overturned the candle and waited until the little flame ate its way across the room and into the woodwork. Then he left that place of horror for the clear, damp night.

## The Misfortunes of Butter-Churning

Within the lovely glade was a comely faun of perhaps twenty-two, for immortal though they be, these creatures are not always young and unwrinkled. His clear, brown skin merged naturally into his shaggy hair, and two tiny horns emerged from his short golden-brown locks that tossed as he capered through the blossoming vegetation. The flowers were not wholly in bloom, and their half-open buds held promise of unnatural loveliness. The faun moved with the fresh ardor of youth, and his glinting fur, in the sunlight, appeared almost yellow, with undertones of brown.

This did the demon Garoth observe, as he stood, cynically resting, in the midst of a thicket of brilliant green foliage.

The faun made his way across the clearing, pausing now to pluck a flower whose beauty he could not appreciate, only to bruise it with his strong fingers; now to taste of a cluster of crimson berries. It was clear he had a definite goal, and, although he was unhurried, the creature ultimately emerged into an adjoining glade bordered with reed-like grasses and twisted little bushes. In this lay a gossamer-clad girl of exceeding beauty, who had come from a nearby peasant hut, even without finishing the churning, to meet her forest lover. She arose from her mossy couch, and smiled upon him, with tender purple eyes searching his face enquiringly. He put his unclothed arm about her slimness, and they went together in search of forest depths where they might be unmolested.

This the demon Garoth saw, and he smiled, for he saw not only them. Another of the men of the woods roved nearby, in rather disgusting erotic fervor, and this other espied the pair intent upon their interests.

The second faun, uncouth and black-furred with a hide nowhere entirely free from coarse down, emitted an incoherent sound of rage, and charged upon the two. The girl screamed in fright, and plunged into the brush, where she watched with horror from her concealment. The two males began at once their struggle, and strained back and forth, now erect, their muscles bulging with the combat, now prone upon the disturbed soil they tore with their hooves. For a time the fight was indecisive in its outcome, but only too soon was the brown one twisted upon the sod, his life blood marring the smoothness of his tawny throat, while the coarse black thing twisted his worm-like lips in laughter, and barbarously mangled the yet-living body.

Garoth saw this, and he saw, also, the flight of the girl through the woods unto her hut, behind which her mother was doing the washing, and where she had not been missed. And he saw the tears falling into her churn, as she hurried with the butter.

Then the demon considered whatever may have been the moral of the affair, and again spread his wings in flight . . .

## "Till A' the Seas"

*With H. P. Lovecraft*

### I.

Upon an eroded cliff-top rested the man, gazing far across the valley. Lying thus, he could see a great distance, but in all the sere expanse there was no visible motion. Nothing stirred the dusty plain, the disintegrated sand of long-dry river-beds, where once coursed the gushing streams of earth's youth. There was little greenery in this ultimate world, this final stage of mankind's prolonged presence upon the planet. For unnumbered aeons the drought and sandstorms had ravaged all the lands. The trees and bushes had given way to small, twisted shrubs that persisted long through their sturdiness; but these, in turn, perished before the onslaught of coarse grasses and stringy, tough vegetation of strange evolution.

The ever-present heat, as earth drew nearer to the sun, withered and killed with pitiless rays. It had not come at once; long aeons had gone before any could feel the change. And all through those first ages man's adaptable form had followed the slow mutation and modelled itself to fit the more and more torrid air. Then the day had come when men could bear their hot cities but ill, and a gradual recession began, slow yet deliberate. Those towns and settlements closest to the equator had been first, of course, but later there were others. Man, softened and exhausted, could cope no longer with the ruthlessly mounting heat. It seared him as he was, and evolution was too slow to mould new resistances in him.

Yet not at first were the great cities of the equator left to the spider and the scorpion. In the early years there were many who stayed on, devising curious shields and armours against the heat and the deadly dryness. These fearless souls, screening certain buildings against the encroaching sun, made miniature worlds of refuge wherein no protecting armour was needed. They contrived marvellously ingenious things, so that for a while men persisted in the rusting towers, hoping thereby to cling to old lands till the searing should be over. For many would not believe what the astronomers said, and looked for a coming of the mild olden world again. But one day the men of Dath, from the new city of Niyara, made signals to Yuanario, their immemorially ancient capital, and gained no answer from the few who remained therein. And when explorers reached that millennial city of bridge-linked towers they found only silence. There was not even the horror of corruption, for the scavenger lizards had been swift.

Only then did the people fully realise that these cities were lost to them; know that they must for ever abandon them to Nature. The other colonists in the hot lands fled from their brave posts, and total silence reigned within the high basalt walls of a thousand empty towns. Of the dense throngs and multitudinous activities of the past, nothing finally remained. There now loomed against the rainless deserts only the blistered towers of vacant houses, factories, and structures of every sort, reflecting the sun's dazzling radiance and parching in the more and more intolerable heat.

Many lands, however, had still escaped the scorching blight, so that the refugees were soon absorbed in the life of a newer world. During strangely prosperous centuries the hoary deserted cities of the equator grew half-forgotten and entwined with fantastic fables. Few thought of those spectral, rotting towers . . . those huddles of shabby walls and cactus-choked streets, darkly silent and abandoned. . . .

Wars came, sinful and prolonged, but the times of peace were greater. Yet always the swollen sun increased its radiance as earth drew closer to its fiery parent. It was as if the planet meant to return to that source whence it was snatched, aeons ago, through the accidents of cosmic growth.

After a time the blight crept outward from the central belt. Southern Yarat burned as a tenantless desert—and then the north. In Perath and Baling, those ancient cities where brooding centuries dwelt, there moved only the scaly shapes of the serpent and the salamander, and at last Loton echoed only to the fitful falling of tottering spires and crumbling domes.

Steady, universal, and inexorable was the great eviction of man from the realms he had always known. No land within the widening stricken belt was spared; no people left unrouted. It was an epic, a titan tragedy whose plot was unrevealed to the actors—this wholesale desertion of the cities of men. It took not years or even centuries, but millennia of ruthless change. And still it kept on—sullen, inevitable, savagely devastating.

Agriculture was at a standstill, the world fast became too arid for crops. This was remedied by artificial substitutes, soon universally used. And as the old places that had known the great things of mortals were left, the loot salvaged by the fugitives grew smaller and smaller. Things of the greatest value and importance were left in dead museums—lost amidst the centuries—and in the end the heritage of the immemorial past was abandoned. A degeneracy both physical and cultural set in with the insidious heat. For man had so long dwelt in comfort and security that this exodus from past scenes was difficult. Nor were these events received phlegmatically; their very slowness was terrifying. Degradation and debauchery were soon common; government was disorganised, and the civilisations aimlessly slid back toward barbarism.

When, forty-nine centuries after the flight from the equatorial belt, the whole western hemisphere was left unpeopled, chaos was complete. There was no trace of order or decency in the last scenes of this titanic, wildly impressive migration. Madness and frenzy stalked through them, and fanatics screamed of an Armageddon close at hand.

Mankind was now a pitiful remnant of the elder races, a fugitive not only from the prevailing conditions, but from his own degeneracy. Into the northland and the antarctic went those who could; the rest lingered for years in an incredible saturnalia, vaguely doubting the forthcoming disasters. In the city of Borligo a wholesale execution of the new prophets took place, after months of unfulfilled expectations. They thought the flight to the northland unnecessary, and looked no longer for the threatened ending.

How they perished must have been terrible indeed—those vain, foolish creatures who thought to defy the universe. But the blackened, scorching towns are mute. . . .

These events, however, must not be chronicled—for there are larger things to consider than this complex and unhastening downfall of a lost civilisation. During a long period morale was at lowest ebb among the courageous few who settled upon the alien arctic and antarctic shores, now mild as were those of southern Yarat in the long-dead past. But here there was respite. The soil was fertile, and forgotten pastoral arts were called into use anew. There was, for a long time, a contented little epitome of the lost lands; though here were no vast throngs or great buildings. Only a sparse remnant of humanity survived the aeons of change and peopled those scattered villages of the later world.

How many millennia this continued is not known. The sun was slow in invading this last retreat; and as the eras passed there developed a sound, sturdy race, bearing no memories or legends of the old, lost lands. Little navigation was practiced by this new people, and the flying machine was wholly forgotten. Their devices were of the simplest type, and their culture was simple and primitive. Yet they were contented, and accepted the warm climate as something natural and accustomed.

But unknown to these simple peasant-folk, still further rigours of Nature were slowly preparing themselves. As the generations passed, the waters of the vast and unplumbed ocean wasted slowly away; enriching the air and the desiccated soil, but sinking lower and lower each century. The splashing surf still glistened bright, and the swirling eddies were still there, but a doom of dryness hung over the whole watery expanse. However, the shrinkage could not have been detected save by instruments more delicate than any then known to the race. Even had the people realised the ocean's con-traction, it is not likely that any vast alarm or great disturbance would have resulted, for the losses were so slight, and the seas so great. . . . Only a few inches during many centuries—but in many centuries; increasing—

* * *

So at last the oceans went, and water became a rarity on a globe of sun-baked drought. Man had slowly spread over all the arctic and antarctic lands; the equatorial cities, and many of later habitation, were forgotten even to legend.

And now again the peace was disturbed, for water was scarce, and found only in deep caverns. There was little enough, even of this; and men died of thirst wandering in far places. Yet so slow were these deadly changes, that each new generation of man was loath to believe what it heard from its parents. None would admit that the heat had been less or the water more plentiful in the old days, or take warning that days of bitterer burning and drought were to come. Thus it was even at the end, when only a few hun-dred human creatures panted for breath beneath the cruel sun; a piteous huddled handful out of all the unnumbered millions who had once dwelt on the doomed planet.

And the hundreds became small, till man was to be reckoned only in tens. These tens clung to the shrinking dampness of caves, and knew at last that the end was near. So slight was their range that none had ever seen the tiny, fabled spots of ice left close to the planet's poles—if such indeed remained. Even had they existed and been known to man, none could have reached them across the trackless and formidable deserts. And so the last pathetic few dwin-dled. . . .

It cannot be described, this awesome chain of events that depopulated the whole earth; the range is too tremendous for any to picture or encompass. Of the people of earth's fortunate ages, billions of years before, only a few prophets and madmen could have conceived that which was to come—could have grasped visions of the still, dead lands, and long-empty sea-beds. The rest would have doubted . . . doubted alike the shadow of change upon the planet and the shadow of doom upon the race. For man has always thought himself the immortal master of natural things. . . .

## II.

When he had eased the dying pangs of the old woman, Ull wandered in a fearful daze out into the dazzling sands. She had been a fearsome thing, shrivelled and so dry; like withered leaves. Her face had been the colour of the sickly yellow grasses that rustled in the hot wind, and she was loathsomely old.

But she had been a companion; someone to stammer out vague fears to, to talk to about this incredible thing; a comrade to share one's hopes for succour from those silent other colonies beyond the mountains. He could not believe none lived elsewhere, for Ull was young, and not certain as are the old.

For many years he had known none but the old woman—her name was Mladdna. She had come that day in his eleventh year, when all the hunters went to seek food, and did not return. Ull had no mother that he could remember, and there were few women in the tiny group. When the men vanished, those three women, the young one and the two old, had screamed fearfully, and moaned long. Then the young one had gone mad, and killed herself with a sharp stick. The old ones buried her in a shallow hole dug with their nails, so Ull had been alone when this still older Mladdna came.

She walked with the aid of a knotty pole, a priceless relique of the old forests, hard and shiny with years of use. She did not say whence she came, but stumbled into the cabin while the young suicide was being buried. There she waited till the two returned, and they accepted her incuriously.

That was the way it had been for many weeks, until the two fell sick, and Mladdna could not cure them. Strange that those younger two should have been stricken, while she, infirm and ancient, lived on. Mladdna had cared for them many days, and at length they died, so that Ull was left with only the stranger. He screamed all the night, so she became at length out of patience, and threatened to die too. Then, hearkening, he became quiet at once; for he was not desirous of complete solitude. After that he lived with Mladdna and they gathered roots to eat.

Mladdna's rotten teeth were ill suited to the food they gathered, but they contrived to chop it up till she could manage it. This weary routine of seeking and eating was Ull's childhood.

Now he was strong, and firm, in his nineteenth year, and the old woman was dead. There was naught to stay for, so he determined at once to seek out those fabled huts beyond the mountains, and live with the people there. There was nothing to take on the journey. Ull closed the door of his cabin—why, he could not have told, for no animals had been there for many years—and left the dead woman within. Half-dazed, and fearful at his own audacity, he walked long hours in the dry grasses, and at length reached the first of the foothills. The afternoon came, and he climbed until he was weary, and lay down on the grasses. Sprawled there, he thought of many things. He wondered at the strange life, passionately anxious to seek out the lost colony beyond the mountains; but at last he slept.

When he awoke there was starlight on his face, and he felt refreshed. Now that the sun was gone for a time, he travelled more quickly, eating little, and determining to hasten before the lack of water became difficult to bear. He had brought none; for the last people, dwelling in one place and never having occasion to bear their precious water away, made no vessels of any kind. Ull hoped to reach his goal within a day, and thus escape thirst; so he hurried on beneath the bright stars, running at times in the warm air, and at other times lapsing into a dogtrot.

So he continued until the sun arose, yet still he was within the small hills, with three great peaks looming ahead. In their shade he rested again. Then he climbed all the morning, and at mid-day surmounted the first peak, where he lay for a time, surveying the space before the next range.

Upon an eroded cliff-top rested the man, gazing far across the valley. Lying thus he could see a great distance, but in all the sere expanse there was no visible motion. . . .

\* \* \*

The second night came, and found Ull amidst the rough peaks, the valley, and the place where he had rested far behind. He was nearly out of the second range now, and hurrying still. Thirst had come upon him that day, and he regretted his folly. Yet he could not have stayed there with the corpse, alone in the grasslands. He sought to convince himself thus, and hastened ever on, tiredly straining.

\* \* \*

And now there were only a few steps before the cliff wall would part and allow a view of the land beyond. Ull stumbled wearily down the stony way, tumbling and bruising himself even more. It was nearly before him, this land where men were rumoured to have dwelt; this land of which he had heard tales in his youth. The way was long, but the goal was great. A boulder of giant circumference cut off his view; upon this he scrambled anxiously. Now at last he could behold by the sinking orb his long-sought destination, and his thirst and aching muscles were forgotten as he saw joyfully that a small huddle of buildings clung to the base of the farther cliff.

\* \* \*

Ull rested not; but, spurred on by what he saw, ran and staggered and crawled the half-mile remaining. He fancied that he could detect forms among the rude cabins. The sun was nearly gone; the hateful, devastating sun that had slain humanity. He could not be sure of details, but soon the cabins were near.

They were very old, for clay blocks lasted long in the still dryness of the dying world. Little, indeed, changed but the living things—the grasses and these last men.

Before him an open door swung upon rude pegs. In the fading light Ull entered, weary unto death, seeking painfully the expected faces.

Then he fell upon the floor and wept, for at the table was propped a dry and ancient skeleton.

* * *

He rose at last, crazed by thirst, aching unbearably, and suffering the greatest disappointment any mortal could know. He was, then, the last living thing upon the globe. His the heritage of the earth . . . all the lands, and all to him equally useless. He staggered up, not looking at the dim white form in the reflected moonlight, and went through the door. About the empty village he wandered, searching for water and sadly inspecting this long-empty place so spectrally preserved by the changeless air. Here there was a dwelling, there a rude place where things had been made—clay vessels holding only dust, and nowhere any liquid to quench his burning thirst.

Then, in the centre of the little town, Ull saw a well-curb. He knew what it was, for he had heard tales of such things from Mladdna. With pitiful joy, he reeled forward and leaned upon the edge. There, at last, was the end of his search. Water—slimy, stagnant, and shallow, but water—before his sight.

Ull cried out in the voice of a tortured animal, groping for the chain and bucket. His hand slipped on the slimy edge; and he fell upon his chest across the brink. For a moment he tottered there— then soundlessly his body was precipitated down the black shaft.

There was a slight splash in the murky shallowness as he struck some long-sunken stone, dislodged aeons ago from the massive coping. The disturbed water subsided into quietness.

And now at last the earth was dead. The final, pitiful survivor had perished. All the teeming billions; the slow aeons; the empires and civilisations of mankind were summed up in this poor twisted form—and how titanically meaningless it all had been! Now indeed had come an end and climax to all the efforts of humanity—how monstrous and incredible a climax in the eyes of those poor complacent fools of the prosperous days! Not ever again would the planet know the thunderous tramping of human millions—or even the crawling of lizards and the buzz of insects, for they, too, had gone. Now was come the reign of sapless branches and endless fields of tough grasses. Earth, like its cold, imperturbable moon, was given over to silence and blackness for ever.

The stars whirred on; the whole careless plan would continue for infinities unknown. This trivial end of a negligible episode mattered not to distant nebulae or to suns new-born, flourishing, and dying. The race of man, too puny and momentary to have a real function or purpose, was as if it had never existed. To such a conclusion the aeons of its farcically toilsome evolution had led.

\* \* \*

But when the deadly sun's first rays darted across the valley, a light found its way to the weary face of a broken figure that lay in the slime.

## The Temple

*Introductory note:* "When the planet he had so long frequented was destroyed by cosmic fire, the fourteen-thousand-year-old demon named Garoth was at loss for occupation." Thus begins the *Book of Garoth,* an incomplete and wholly unmotivated narrative upon which R. H. Barlow spasmodically writes. Bear in mind throughout these laborious episodes that the hero is no mortal whatever avatar he may assume, but a member of the old race that guideth man. Bear with him patiently. We here present Chapters 3 and 4 from the Book of Garoth.—*The Perspective Review*

### [Chapter 3]

It may have been he dozed, for there was a great silence surrounding the bizarre temple, and the moonless night radiated only a pale green glow over all the city. Garoth lay waiting for a long time, expectant of what he knew not. He was startled to hear suddenly a vast rattling and creaking. He drew back, for he thought he had been discovered, but it was only a cart with two peasants. Their monster-steed breathed heavily, and made a ceaseless squeaking noise as the whole affair passed by without noticing the hidden watcher. And then there was quiet again.

But after a time, when the lustre of the moonless sky was most brilliant, the demon Garoth saw a strange and terrible sight. Within the courtyard of the curious temple stood four carven statues. What they represented Garoth knew not, for they were at best indistinct. But now the priests came out of the temple chanting a thin wailing tune that at times died away entirely, though he felt it to be yet there. And they were clad in resplendent robes, embroidered in crimson and gold, with rare dyes. The designs were wondrously wrought, so that they gave the impression of bright flame, and the lurid glare from their torches made the accouterment of the aged ones shine like sunlight. These men, eight in all, walked with stately tread, and taking their places before and between the grey statues that faced upon the paving, dragged forth from the building a lovely young girl, strangely clad, and each bewitched her with a malignant curse.

And the first caused her to become a living torch as if a thousand little painful fires had blazed within her, and these fires shot forth and vanished, and she shrieked and fell to the ground.

Then the second summoned a hideous fiend in the form of an evil green thing with soft scales and puffy limbs ending in cruel claws. This abhorrence of perverted sorcery leered at her, and made great scratches on her smooth flesh; and then clutched her, with ease tearing off her head, though it bled not, and Garoth knew this was magic. It cast the corpse and head aside and vanished at its master's command.

The third priest bewitched her decapitated body, and she writhed in terror. The head rolled most horribly back to its original position, and she was again living. The girl moaned fearfully at the thing that was being done to her. Her limbs and body withered, shrivelled as if a hundred years of desiccation had become compressed into a moment; and she became an ancient and repulsive beldame.

Many were the spells that were worked upon her, and each was more terrible than the last. Garoth saw feats of magic stranger than even those of the evil-folk, whose wisdom is greater than the gods, for do they not hold greater power?

When the last of the ordeals was over and the girl lay twisted on the flagging between the curious statues, the priests summoned up a fiend of green flame that gleefully carried his victim to some unseen Draalstrand.

And the eight saturnine men that were so old sedately entered the temple and were seen no more.

"Truly," thought Garoth, "my quest for diversion is most gratifyingly unique thus far. Yet I am not wholly satisfied with these recent events, for I think they require explanation. So I shall endeavor to find her captor and ask the gentleman what has been the girl's crime to justify so unfortunate a demise."

Thus speaking, Garoth winged himself past a particularly lurid planet, and flew directly for a far part of infinity that he knew to be frequented by unpleasant beings.

And directly he had first seen his destination the demon found himself there, for such is the speed of man's masters.

## Chapter 4
### A Moral Explanation

He found the genie amusing himself by a black pool, quite alone. All about were jagged peaks of surpassing height, and within the pool were several corpses. Then did Garoth hold converse with the evil creature, and it replied in amusement. "Come," said the thing, "I should be pleased to assist so great a hunger for learning." And he took the wing of Garoth in his scaly claw, and the two plunged into the foul water of the pool.

They progressed through the subterranean river for some distance, and Garoth saw the water become erubescent as they neared the source. Progress was in a measure difficult because of the inordinate number of corpses cluttering the stream; and Garoth thought it indeed untidy compared with the manner of interment practiced among the Janou-birds who turn a burial into a restrained and decorous orgy and devour the body. But they had reached the end of the passage and shot upwards into an intolerable red light.

Garoth did not recount to his guide the sentiments which had been his on first sight, for he felt it would be both rude and indiscreet. The genie, he found upon a critical inspection, was neither terrible nor hideous as he had first thought. But his reflections were cut short as his companion concluded, "You will notice the murals of which we are justly proud," he was saying.

Garoth gazed about the walls of the vast flame-lit cavern. It had seemed odd at first glance, as he saw it now indeed to be, for the cave appeared to be composed of interwoven snakes, all of gay hue. They were actively twisting, so that their arrangement was eternally changed. The floor of the place was obscured by pillaring flames that leaped and stretched ceaselessly and a few demons were engaged in torturing people in the midst of them. About the base of the fires unnaturally flowed the river in which they had travelled, and when the devils were through they tossed their victims into the current.

Garoth watched their occupations for a moment; and then spoke in high praise of this arrangement, although he did not think it at all nice in reality. The place impressed him as abominably ill-managed and totally unlike a well-constructed Hell.

"But you were interested in my latest acquisition," said the genie, waving a scaly hand. "She is over in that flame right now, so I'm afraid she would be of little help personally. I can show you, though . . ."

And the being caused a certain large flame to become transparent, so that a picture appeared, with indistinct outlines merging into the fire.

Garoth saw the young lady just as she had looked before the priests began.

She was lying voluptuously on the moss-covered bank of a silent river, and all about her grew rich and gaudy blossoms. Some were spotted with a purple like that of bruised flesh, while yet others were the ruddy shade of newly-congealed blood. No ordinary mirage was this, for the colors of the blooms and the cloyingly sweet fragrance of the curious plants were as reality. The girl lay half-turned, and her nearly closed eyelids held a musing speculation. She toyed with the border of her thin silken garment and seemed not wholly aware of her surroundings.

The ceaseless flow of the glinting water possessed an hypnotic quality; Garoth regarded it for a long period before he was distracted by a dark figure moving cautiously along the edge, through a thicket of the clustered flowers. He could not clearly distinguish its aspect, but it held a semblance to a giant spider-thing with pulpy tentacles that were covered with thick fur. It progressed with extreme care, as if stalking some prey. The shocking truth came to Garoth that its prospective victim was the girl who lay oblivious. He strove frantically to warn her and at the same time was conscious of the futility. He could do naught but watch. The slow approach of the monstrosity was infinitely ter0rible to the taut watcher. Garoth hoped helplessly that some intuitive sense would prompt the girl to turn and see the thing now close upon her. Yet she lay still unmoving as the thing rushed forward with its awful limbs extended menacingly. She sprang to her feet, and whirling about showed for the first time her whole face. And it was such that even the demon shuddered and was afraid, for the girl was not wholly human. Her lips were too small and roundly vermilion, and behind them lay a split tongue like that of the serpent; she possessed many little teeth of surpassing sharpness. Moreover, her slim arms were like twin flexible rods of steel that clutched her adversary and held the thing while her tiny teeth sank into the fur of the throat. A wound was made, and with evident satisfaction the girl applied her mouth to it, drawing foul nurture from the weakening creature.

And Garoth knew the girl for what she was, and he would have fled shrieking but for the lethargic trance that forced him to witness both this and other equally hideous obscenities.

## From the Book of Garoth

### Chapter 10
### The Castle in the Desert

The desert was like an artist's unfinished canvas with great daubs of yellow and orange smeared about. From the vaporless deep green sky to the barren land that stretched to a far off mountain range, the entire scene was uniquely odd. The coarse brown sand grated harshly under foot as Garoth made his way past littered boulders that were colored like dead cinders. There appeared to be no sentient life, although queer lichens writhed against the rocks, their redness causing it to appear as if flames were springing from the pitted surfaces.

As he walked along, the demon speculated as to the probable nature of his next adventure. This matter occupied his attention entirely, and he did not see the creature before him until it spoke.

"Greetings, stranger," said the thing, and its voice rasped strangely.

Garoth directed his gaze to the source of the words, and saw that an androcephalous-being was before him. Its body was like that of a bear, but curiously pied with spots of greenish yellow; the hairless face was ugly in the extreme. There was a suggestion of hands in the paws it awkwardly walked upon; and though the shaggy creature was tailless, it bore a spiked knob in *loco caudae*.

The demon stared in surprise for he had known no such animal upon the world he once ruled, but he was determined to be polite. Consequently he returned the salutation and inquired his way.

"O curious being from another world, for that I know you to be, if diversion you seek, you will find ahead the castle called Alair whose rocky vaults contain strangely guarded treasures. There is, I believe, a maiden who desires to be rescued from her captors; in short, all things essential to romance, adventure, and similar foolishness await you. Go then to this castle, if you desire to become a hero, and seek out the maiden named Sasta." Thus finishing, the androcephalous creature looked at Garoth with a curious appearance of amusement.

For a moment the devil considered the suggestion and then gave assent. Thereupon certain secrets were imparted to him, and in particular was he warned not to touch the bell-rope, but to enter into the castle through some other means.

Garoth thanked the other civilly enough and left it standing with watchful gaze as he made his way rapidly across the wasteland to the ragged patches of shadow where the castle rose evilly in the mountain's shadow.

The walls beyond the gate were very high, and they rose unbroken by any window. Garoth thought this odd, nor did he change his opinion as he perceived that several piles of bone were stacked before the dismal portal. A green wyvern-thing rose hissing, and fled beyond the turrets where it lit and regarded the intruder with calculating sullenness.

Garoth hesitated before the strangely wrought gate and peered at the bell-rope speculatively. True, the man-bear warned him against touching it, but then there was a suspicious appearance about this great desire of the creature to assist. It might be—

Garoth pulled the rope, and a far bell sounded brazenly.

But no one came.

He waited.

There was no sign of life within, and the slowly crumbling paving stones seemed forlorn in their agedness. Through the great rusty gate might be seen a garden long overgrown with wild vines, matted and intermeshed till they formed an almost impassable barrier.

He rattled impatiently at the gate; receiving no reply, he drew his sword and set to work breaking the lock. He bent to the task with a will and had partly succeeded when a voice interrupted him. "What do you do here, destroying the property of an honest man?"

The demon-man glanced up with surprise and interest. The speaker was a fat and bloated old man, garbed in a worn black robe. His eyes were bleary, and huge masses of revoltingly puffy flesh formed deep folds upon his face. Venomous eyes of greenish hue shot with tiny streaks of blood peered from sockets almost obscured by rings of unhealthily swollen flesh. His mouth was effeminately small and of a livid purple, but his features were unimpressive save for the calculating stare. A thin wisp of hair fell scantily from beneath the skull-cap that covered his nearly bald head. He spoke again, and Garoth could see vast ripples shake over his paunch when the wheezing tones came forth.

"Who be you, and what do you here?" he inquired with arch primness.

It was not the custom of the young demon-lord to shilly shally. He replied with promptness, and stated his purpose succinctly.

"I am told that the maiden Sasta lies imprisoned in this castle and awaits her rescue."

The man started, then regarded Garoth with tiny eyes. "And what concern is this of yours?" he inquired.

The man-demon explained with a suitable lie, congratulating himself on the slyness of the ruse. No doubt he should shortly be within the castle himself!! A piece of fine fortune indeed! How well he was putting it over on this slow-witted rascal. . . . Thus thought Garoth.

The man considered a moment, and then he abruptly unlocked the gate with an enormous key, admitting Garoth. He relocked it at once, and bidding the other to follow, led the way along a weed-clogged path. They crossed the garden, or what had once been a garden, and entered a low round door overhung with a massive carving depicting numerous unpleasant subjects.

Inside, although there were no windows or sources of light apparent, the passageway was illuminated with a yellow glow. Garoth looked interestedly about him, and perceived that there was no furniture or ornamentation of any kind. The black stone walls and the low arched roof were bleakly devoid of decoration. And there was another odd element present in the fact that the roof grew continuously lower as they progressed, until the demon was unable to stand erect. When they had walked a distance down this corridor, his companion stopped and looked at Garoth peculiarly. They faced a small door.

"I shall go no farther," said the fat one, "but if you care to proceed, please close the door behind you. I don't wish any drafts."

Thus saying, he pushed Garoth through the opening. So taken by surprise was the demon that he was unprepared to resist, and he fell awkwardly through the gloomy opening. He sprawled on a floor lower than that of the passage, and caught only a glimpse of the evil laughing face in the yellow glow. Then the door slammed behind him, and he heard a key turn.

Chapter 11
The Erring Knight

It would have gone ill with Garoth had his eyes not been more than those of men. As it was, the series of dungeons were clear to his vision, and he readily perceived the trap which lay before him. Between the bolted door and the opposite wall, bordered only by a narrow ledge, was gaping nothingness. He peered over the edge; he did not see any bottom, although somewhere there was a sound of lapping water.

This prison was constructed of curious blue-black stone, and there were strange patterns of fossilized vegetation in the blocks composing the wall. The roof was low, and the slimy growths adhered to its damp clamminess. The uncirculating air was stale, and a vast oppression filled the gloom. Garoth wondered mildly at the constitution of the captive maiden, which must be indeed strong to survive this dismal fate.

This consideration brought his thoughts to the highly chivalrous purpose of his mission. Where he might find the captive, Garoth was uncertain; but she must be imprisoned somewhere near, he felt. So he began a systematic exploration.

As he edged precariously along the rim of the pit, he likened his activities to those of a rat upon a well-top. By clutching the slippery wall-stones he managed to evade the overwhelming abyss, and he was shortly on the other side, where little better foothold was afforded. But here there was the opening of a tunnel, and he followed the winding passage cautiously.

This was fully as dark as the circular chamber of the pit, but Garoth had little difficulty in avoiding certain judiciously placed traps; before long he had reached the threshold of a large room. There was a faint blue light here; he saw it came from a most peculiar source, nothing less than the fiery breath of a large monster that lay sleeping directly in his path. The man-devil drew back, but the thing was unaware of his presence. Presently, as it did not move, Garoth cautiously stepped over the slightly-writhing tentacles, and found himself in the room.

This room was very long and narrow, and strange iron doors were ranged down either wall. These tightly-bolted portals had small eye-holes with sliding covers, and from under one came a thin stream of green liquid.

But Garoth unwisely delayed in his escape. Still hoping to find the captive maiden, he applied his eye to the nearest door, gazing within.

He drew back with a start, for beyond that barrier there was a strange inhabitant which had obviously been once a man. It moaned and came over to the wall, scratching upon the iron with strange talons as if expecting food. Since its diet appeared to be mainly dismembered portions of the human body, Garoth did not supply it; hastily closing the peep-hole, he proceeded to the next.

The second chamber, somewhat to his relief, was vacant; and he continued down the corridor, finding at one place a room filled with damp grey mist from which came dismal groans and clankings of iron. Another was not a cell at all, but opened upon a lurid hell-lit world where innumerable obscenities were a-work fashioning objects from a white-hot forge that spurted molten silver. This peep-hole he promptly shut, transferring his gaze to yet another cell.

The next door, however, revealed a surprising occupant, in the form of a tremendous monster-woman, whose pulpy green expanse filled the entire chamber. Her form was obese, and her sleeping was accompanied by odd roaring sounds not pleasing to the ear. This woman-thing had numerous unclassifiable limbs of extremely plump size, and her face was distinguished by the fact that in its horned scaliness no nose was apparent.

Her mouth was of a flabby vastness, and her hairless pate glistened in the light admitted by the peep-hole. Garoth was about to close the opening when the creature blinked and opened her four large eyes, staring through the light directly at the demon. He waited uncomfortably, feeling it would be impolite to close the door in the face of even so peculiar a lady. So he stood there, shuffling uneasily as she regarded him. He was first to speak.

"I beg your pardon. I didn't intend to spy," Garoth ventured.

"It's been ever so long since I've seen anyone. Will you converse with me a while?" She rolled her eyes oddly.

"I've really not the time, but to refuse a lady's request would be unchivalrous in the extreme," he said, "although I'm doubtful as to the topic we might select."

She moved her broad head very near the grating and smirked as she replied, "Suppose you tell me what you are doing here?" He noticed her teeth were very long and sharp.

"Would it be impolite to return the query?" he inquired. "I confess I can not comprehend why you reside in so bleak a bed-chamber."

"I am one of the prisoners," she confided sadly. "There are many of us, all bound by sorceries till some brave one will break the spell and set us free." Her vast visage brightened, and she added the afterthought, "Perhaps you would be so kind as to release me!"

Garoth was upset. Nevertheless his reply was tactful. "I should like very much to accommodate you, but I regret to say that I am already upon a quest of much the same nature . . . the best sort of makeshift excuse for my vacation I could muster. To be forced to save *two* ladies, who would undoubtedly dislike one another and squabble for my favors, would be indeed an involved situation. I seek a certain prisoner, the captive maiden called Sasta."

In pandemonium she leaped against the stout door joyfully proclaiming her identity.

"I am the maiden Sasta!"

## Chapter 12
### Below the Sub-dungeon

Down long reaches of the corridor he fled, and always behind him came the cries of Sasta. He fervently hoped that the hideous maiden would not escape and pursue him, as was her apparent intention. From the cell echoed shrieks of both delight and dismay, and with them the sound of a rattled and yielding lock. To the horrified ears of Garoth came the creak of a door and a following slither as Sasta came down the passage. It was evident that there was no time to be wasted. Garoth heard her close behind him as he neared the bottomless well-abyss. With a shudder he dived from the rim . . .

Breathtaking was the fall, and rushingly quick the plunge. On all sides the walls towered in mad senselessness away from him; in a brief flash of perception Garoth saw that the sides were walled with artificial shapen blocks, neatly fitted together. Then he struck the water and knew no more.

---

It was cold and moist when he recovered consciousness. Had it not been that he was more than mortal, then surely would he have perished. Such was the blending of natural and supernatural powers that while a man in every aspect Garoth could yet survive all manner of vicissitude unharmed. This was at once apparent in the fact that while totally submerged in deep water, he was not at all inconvenienced, nor was breath any more difficult than if he had been on land. He considered his present surroundings, and was thankfully observant of the fact that Sasta had not emulated his surprising mode of exit from the dungeons. The deep pit, it was clear, ended in some obscure connection with an underground river in which he lay even now.

Soon recovered, Garoth swam unconcernedly along the eroded channel.

## Chapter 14
### A Conversation in the Forest

He came one day—or what would have elsewhere been a day, though it was but a murky gloom—into the Doubtful Zone, where shadow rocks are heaped into Titan rubble-piles, and where dim, threatening clouds are always present. Hiding behind a rock, he heard a snuffling sound, and the monster Groonta emerged from its burrow, a shadow among shadows. Many protuberances like huge misplaced fingers were upon its back, and the thin tapering snout was strangely fitted to the heavy lumbering body. He remained unseen as it looked about with a half-smirk and went upon its devious business, and then the demon fled.

Yet he must have lost his way, for then did Garoth pass through a place of utter night, where in the blackness shone delicate shapes of lacy crystal, formed in various fragile outlines. They were of a surpassing beauty, and each luminous form seemed possessed of sentient life in its graceful floating motions. In Garoth's senses all directions became one, and were lost to him as he strove to escape this sudden night.

Out of the dark floated the shimmeringly etched shape of a woman's head with streaming hair like spun glass. And her eyes were closed, nor did she open them, though from her pale lips came an unending stream of hideous blasphemies . . .

And again, he came to a curious wood where all the vegetation seemed animated with unholy motions and through which ran a wall without beginning or end, but bearing many evil eyes.

As he stood regarding this odd phenomenon, a crash came from the forest depths. The fat crimson leaves parted, and through them came a tall, slender creature thrice the height of a man. This eccentric individual was of a pale green hue, and wore nothing whatsoever. Its eyeless face bore a long proboscis that waved searchingly about, and the pumpkin-like head seemed repellently soft.

In his surprise Garoth stood too long amid the prismatic vegetation, and found to his dismay that many little creepers had twined about his feet, binding him fast at the mercy of this creature. He called out in the tongue of the demon folk, and the thing replied with sibilant accents, asking what he might be doing there within the wood. The creeper was by this time aspiring to Garoth's thighs, so that he explained very quickly his plight. Then the thing released him by tearing away the vines, and quite rudely ordered Garoth to keep out of the vegetable patch henceforth. Thankful for his release, the demon was departing when a thought troubled him. Addressing the creature he asked if it knew aught of his desired quest, but it did not reply, and Garoth walked slowly off, rubbing his numbed ankles.

As he limped along there came a great whirring of wings that beat upon the air, and over the treetops, against the crimson moon, poured a monster-horde astride strange mounts. Some were vaguely human, yet in many cases the mounts were more so than their riders. There were creatures with small flat heads and pulpy horn-like antennae, while others were round and crimson and bulgingly distasteful to the eye. These and countless other malformations poured on in a rushing tumult, and the main body had gone by overhead and out of sight into the gaudy sky, when one small bloated thing of grimy white stopped and reined its mount upon the sward.

Garoth surveyed the creature for a moment, and they confronted one another without words. Then the small thing observed:

"'Tis a strange place and a strange time for mortals to be about."

Garoth replied in civility, and tried to explain. "I am no mortal," he began. But the thing glared at him with its many small red eyes and said indignantly, "Think you I am mistaken? Nay—it is obvious that you are the one in error."

Garoth did not finish, but asked it where all its brethren were going.

"Do you not know?" asked the thing incredulously. "It is for a festival that we hold each year. Our pilgrimage takes us to the Black Mountain, where we worship and do honour to the Relic."

"And this relic of which you speak," enquired Garoth. "Is it something very holy?"

"Oh, yes," the thing assured him. "It is a nail-paring of our most venerated patron, Great Yeb."

Garoth would have spoken further upon the matter of this singular fetish, but the thing had climbed back upon its mount, and was leaving very ungraciously.

"Hold on," he exclaimed. "I wish to ask you something. I am, to phrase it paradoxically, in quest of a quest . . ."

But the thing had flown away, tenaciously perched upon its many-dimensioned steed.

"Heigh-ho," said Garoth, and walked on.

The land was more broken up, here, and the rich black earth had given way to many boulders. The bulk of the Black Mountain rose before him as he toiled upward, thinking of the festival of

which he had been told. "Right well would I like to view this celebration," he thought, "for magickers could surely find my quest for
me." But he had neglected to ask where among the many peaks and
caverns it was to be held, and so he thought no more about the
matter.

Sparse vegetation covered the glossy slopes of the rounded
rocks, and the sun became very hot. Garoth thought of resting, but
there was no shade large enough to shelter him, so he continued his
climb.

Presently, as he toiled along, he heard odd sounds ahead; clanging, and muted groans. This was very singular in the deserted landscape, so he hastened his step, and rounding a boulder, saw the
origin of the racket. And a very strange sight it was. Upon the barren hard-packed soil, amid a field of many pebbles, stood two
bright and intricate machines. Through silver webs and spokes the
porcelain heavens shone, but Garoth caught only a confused impression of the puzzling machines. They rose above his height on
the desolate and rock-strewn ground, and seemed not quite complete, as if they formed but a scaffolding for some other purpose.
Yet it was not the machines, but their occupants who attracted his
notice.

For, in the heart of each contrivance, bound by many wires and
pedalling furiously with straining limbs, was a being of remotely
human appearance. The nearer device contained a being of greenish
cast, while the more distant one held a creature dark and carrot-
hued. Apparently each man-thing worked a curious sort of tread-
mill, and sweat bespeckled the leathern hides of the toilers and they
trod in ceaseless labour. Some cunning form of torture had
stretched each head to grotesque extremes of elongation, and sweating bodies showed the marks of monstrous alteration. Their lips
were moving horribly, but there was no sound in that desolate
place but the breath of the demon. What their strange task might
be, Garoth did not know, and they were heedless of his surprised
regard. But as he gazed in shocked wonder, the cage of the green

man revolved slowly upon a hidden base, and the thing that ped-
alled faced him; its lips opening and closing endlessly. . . .

Garoth fled, the sounds echoing terribly in his ears.

When he was far from the things that worked the squirrel-
cages, and the hateful sound was lost in the distance, Garoth sat
confusedly upon a lichened rock. He could only guess what sacrilege these beings had committed to make them spouses of the knife
and rack. The blackened crypts where they had known the inquisi-
tor's touch, the spidery metal webs they trod—these things and the
marks thereof bespoke the punishment of horrid and unknown
deeds.

Walking thus, and reflecting upon the diversity of the events
which had befallen him, Garoth was unaware that he was accompanied by a most singular phenomenon. It was some time before he
noticed the dimly unpleasant shadow that walked erect beside him;
but when he turned and looked at the rearward path as through a
black mist, he knew at once what thing had come. Hoping to be-
fool the familiar, he turned abruptly around a rock and embarked
upon a new path, more difficult than the one which he had been
traversing and strewn with red boulders and outcroppings of yellow
clay. He peered over his shoulder and, no longer seeing the thing,
concluded that it had been sidetracked. But as he chuckled, it came
to Garoth that the thing was now in front of him, gauging its pace
to his, and maintaining an even distance. Garoth tried many ruses,
but always the thing continued to dog his way, though it remained
in silence. Finally the young demon stopped short, and demanded:
"Why do you follow me?"

The thing did not reply, so after a moment Garoth spoke again.
"Can you tell me the name of this land?" he asked, "and where I may
find the celebration of which I was told? I would join in the worship
of this exotic relic."

Then he received a reply; the first sound that the shadow had
made since it began these pestiferous attentions. "What celebration?" it enquired in dismal tones.

Garoth sighed and explained. The shadow assumed a dubious expression, although its features, being indistinctly formed, were even more dubious. And then, after a hesitating moment, the thing observed, "I *could* take you there . . . but why should I bother?"

"Surely," said the demon, "it is the duty of those who are acquainted with their lands—even such peculiar lands as this—to display their sights to travellers. It is but civility."

"Since you put it thus, I suppose that I must take you to the Festival," replied the shadow. "But you must do in all things as I do, for guests are not permitted to witness our holy rites." Thus it turned its back upon the demon and walked quickly away. Now was Garoth free of his companion, but what it had said appealed to him, so he hurried after it.

The thing strode rapidly and Garoth was hard put to follow, but with effort he managed this, and he tried to question his guide as they hastened up the barren slopes. Apparently, their destination lay somewhere near the large cave he now perceived within the hillside.

"I esteem your kindness," he began, "but I should like to plague you upon one thing more. Since you appear to be acquainted with this terrain, could you tell me . . ." and he explained about the two machine-beings.

The thing meditated a moment, and then replied, "They are placed there for a punishment. The sin they have committed is beyond human ken, for they attempted to rob a child."

Garoth would know who the child was, and the thing answered, "It is son's son to Azathoth. It is the Sublime Overlord—great Yeb!"

Now the demon had heard of this mighty one, and what he had heard was not inviting.

There was a confusion of sound as they neared the dark opening. Garoth regarded the place distastefully. "I should like to see mighty Yeb fully as much as the feast of the strange ones," he ventured. For a moment the shadow did not reply, and now they were well-nigh within the cavern. It yawned vast and gloomy, and as his guide stepped into it, he observed calmly, "Doubtless we shall. He is generally around when there is mischief afoot, and this night high revelry is projected. Last lunar-cycle the most amusing diversion was provided: we caught one of the peasants of the village beyond the mountain . . . he was walking alone, and squealed fearsomely." Then the thing described what had taken place.

For some small while Garoth was unable to speak, so graphically horrid was the description. After a cough he broached the subject of a change of plans; but the racket had by now grown so great that either his voice was lost with that of the hidden clamorous multitude, or his guide did not heed. The shadow had quickened its pace and the other followed with misgivings.

Dark and unlit was the cavern, and extending interminably as a downward incline. From the far reaches of endless dark came a great commotion. Some wildly enthusiastic noise was being made at the celebration.

Chapter 16
A Few Denouements

"What a deafening clamour," thought Garoth as the vast cavern was revealed by a sharp turn in the passage. The black stone that had comprised the confines of the tunnel-like slope gave way to a tremendous brightly lit place, where multitudes of creatures of many aspects were holding an involved and loose-moraled ceremony. Some were the things that had passed him in the wood, though the pulpy one to whom he had spoken was nowhere in sight, and a large number were of various devil-classes. A scattering of witches were concocting spells, and in the writhing, nigh-indistinguishable and inseparable mass Garoth saw one or two mortals being slain in peculiar ways. Their shrieks mingled with the noise of the saturnalia, and now and then one group of the horde would become embroiled in a fight usually ending in the rending of pieces of some monster-thing. Their behavior was both ill-mannered and not wholly decent, and Garoth saw that a strange manner of worship was that devoted to Yeb.

That brought his thoughts to another subject, as he and his shadowy guide stood there regarding from above the noisy multitude. Where was the Relic of which he had been told? The nail-paring of Great Yeb? Yeb, it seemed, was a prominent deity in these parts, for he seemed to be bumping into him at every corner . . . the things in their machines of torment, the unencouraging observation made by the shadow about Yeb's probable presence . . .

Garoth sighed. "At any rate," he thought, "I shall probably get a little excitement and perhaps some information upon this escapade!"

Now came a lull in the voices, for the pair had been spied upon their high balcony of rock. Some of those assembled whispered noisily, and a blue-spotted thing of tall lank hairiness made its way up to them, by a path which Garoth could not discern. Without any word of explanation the thing threw a coil of curious metal rope about the two, neatly trussing them up, so that they could not do else but follow him. Neither resisted, and Garoth was surprised to find the shadow tangible enough to be thus bound.

When they descended by the path . . . Garoth found it to be a narrow and precarious ledge at best . . . the two were led before an assembly of beldames and wizards that had gathered in a separate little group. Some of their familiars were there, and Garoth liked not one spidery one in particular. There was a withered but powerfully-built man with brilliant glassily blue eyes and heavy brows that stood taller than any of the other humans, and he seemed to be the leader of the group. Before him were the captives brought, and he quizzed them searchingly. It developed that it was thought they were two mortals spying upon the festival, and that, of course, would have never done. But after a time the man seemed half-satisfied of their identities and business, though he did not loose their bonds, and Garoth liked this ill.

His attention, however, was soon directed to certain remarkable proceedings that were taking place. These centered about a dais, made of some blue metal, that reared hugely in the central part of the vast cave. About it were clustered the throng of witches and many unidentifiable horrors that writhed and squirmed in such activity that they were never still at once. The clamour broke out anew as a swooning peasant girl was brought in; on her had been placed a black robe of simple pattern, with certain symbols woven into the cloth. Garoth soon perceived that he and his guide had arrived at the height of the festivities, and wished heartily they would be soon over, for Garoth was a demon of careful upbringing and liked not the indelicate occupations of some of the monster-things, nor the surprising amatory desires of one being who kept reaching at the girl, and was finally destroyed by the priest, who stepped forcibly upon its pulpy head.

Two small red things, swart with coarse hair, dragged the body out of the way and Garoth spied them later carefully removing the hide which they preserved. The body was dumped into a pot of boiling slime, where it fast dissolved. This episode did little to hearten Garoth, and his gaze returned to the involved ceremonial.

Upon the dais had been reared a structure not unlike a three-dimensional spider-web, and in this the unconscious girl was placed. the old wizard thrust her firmly into place in the net-like cage, and promptly ignored her for the rest of the chant which had begun. All were howling more loudly than ever now, and Garoth did not wonder that the center of a mountain was chosen for their rites, so appalling was the sound of their celebrating. The large wrinkled wizard with the staring blue eyes started intoning a chant in a deep voice, while a witch huddled at his feet in a crouching position. She was indistinctly doing something with a small bottle. It was preposterous that the crone should have so much hair—it resembled a pile of mildewed straw upon her withered pate. She started gabbling furiously in a high nagging voice. The cacophony reached a height and then unexpectedly all was still, for the shadow beside Garoth stepped forward and interrupted the procedure.

"Cease!" he shouted.

Everything grew ominously quiet. The old hag muttered and stood up, hugging her bottle tightly. The wizard ceased trying to adjust his newly-donned mask, and all gazed malignantly at the shadow.

"Why do you interfere with our ceremony?" asked the wizard in a harsh voice.

"Is it not the custom that the person of greatest importance be each year made chief necromancer and ruler of this horde?" asked the shadow.

"Yes," said the wizard sullenly. "I am highest."

"But you are not! Behold, you assembled demons! I lay claim to the seer's office and the honours thereof!"

"Who are you?" demanded a thin unseen voice.

"I am he who all witches know and dread! I am the one that leads all spells if they seek power! I am the Black One that guideth the faithful to Yuggoth and the farther places when you desire! I am mightier than any here!"

All fell back as the Black One, more solid now, stepped forward to direct the sacrifice. None attempted to interfere, but as he took the mask from the down-cast wizard, Garoth thought him this was an easy thing. If so readily his companion . . . a far lesser creature than himself . . . might rule the horde, then might he also supplant the shadow! With as austere a visage as he could present, Garoth in turn stepped up and shouted "Again cease your activities! If this law be true, then am I the mightiest here, and entitled to rulership!"

"Fool!" screamed the hag from the dais. "You simple mortal?"

"Yet that I am not," replied Garoth. "This is not my natural form. Behold, I cast it aside like an old sandal!" And thus speaking, the demon left the human guise he had so long assumed, and stood in awful majesty upon the platform.

The spawn of the evil powers drew again back, making way for their new ruler. The shadow gaped, and then with a resigned smile, left the arena in Garoth's place.

The much-interrupted ceremony was started anew, and Garoth saw the girl had come to herself, and lay with wide-eyed terror in the web. Garoth supposed he would have to sacrifice her . . . well, no matter. Here he was, a lord of vast number—something he had not looked for when first he knew of the feast.

But then the girl shrieked, and stared in fright at something high on the ledge whence the pair had descended. A monstrous and vaguely human shadow was cast over the multitude. At once he heard but a titan bellow.

"Do me honour, O my vassals! Thy master Yeb has come to you!"

## Chapter 18
### Sona Moskorum

Even more animatedly than he had evaded the amatory desires of Sasta did Garoth flee the cavern of the followers of Yeb. In the excitement of the arrival of the looming grey thing that called itself Yog-Sototh and the bitch-goddess Shub-Niggarauth, Garoth slid off the back of the dais, which was not so well-illuminated as the other side, and scurried along in the shadow between it and the wall that rose sheer and rocky at his right. No opening was there in which he might hide, no refuge or place of evasion. Mightily did Garoth fear the greatness of Yeb, and dared not even look a second time upon the gigantic, furry, puffy thing that he had seen. As his fears grew doubled by the renewed racket of the crowd, he was infinitely relieved to see a small dim passage-hole behind a tall coffer filled with magic herbs. From this place came a strange and stuffy reek, but he plunged into it without delay, and found himself shortly within a small room, filled, apparently, with the appliances of wizardry in every phase of its aspects. This he knew to be the storeroom of all the assembled wonder-mongers, and countless were the marvellous objects in that dark place. He would have fain inspected them further, but fearing Great Yeb, the fearful demon sought a still more inaccessible hiding-place.

This he found in the shape of a low door-way with a heavy carved lintel that hung ponderously, projecting from the wall. On this were some exceeding odd sculptures, but which he did not stop to investigate, but went through.

[...]

### [Unknown Chapter
### Untitled][1]

There are silent ruins that would bespeak themselves of the past if they had but tongue, there are crumbled vestiges of ancient fame. There are fallen, half-decayed piles of giant masonry that once reared supreme, but now are slid into bleak chaos.

Where great and mighty rulers once dwelt and held their courts; these now are the stronghold of the spider and the bat. The field-mouse has supplanted man in the banquet-room and the temple and the stable. Yet when the moon glows down upon them the cracks are not so naked or the walls so marred, for it is then that a breath of their ancient grandeur returns to the haughty towers and austere walls that succumbed to no enemy save Time. In this kind illumination they regain something that has never been wholly lost, but only hidden.

Far across a glistening plain he saw a ruined structure of great magnitude, that was alluring in its desolation. Toward it Garoth led his path, thinking not to find it inhabited, but thinking it of likely interest, when something interrupted contemplation of his goal. There lay half-buried in the clay a sizeable grey stone.

Now it seemed not right to Garoth that this stone should bear an eye, moreover, the eye stared him in an exceeding familiar way. Also did the stone possess a disembodied voice, for thus did it address him:

---

1. [The following text derives from a T.Ms. (JHL), where it is identified as page 2 of "Conversation in a Forest." But it does not appear to be a continuation of that story.—Ed.]

"It is high time I prophesy. You have come far upon your un-questing journey, and this I shall say:"

"I do not care for such foolishness," interrupted Garoth. "And you are likewise mistaken. I have indeed a quest, for I search a plausible excuse for my wanderings. There is an excellent opportunity for a pun there."

"That matters little," observed the object rudely, and began without waiting. "I dreamed last night, and there was a poem. Only these lines remain, and they are [. . .]

## The Experiment

From the outside it was an unassuming new brick building; perhaps even a bit small, considering the city; with a neat brass nameplate on the door spelling MARCUS EDWARDS, M.D. But those who strove for appointments with the doctor were invariably surprised at his unconventional methods of treatment, which had quickly earned him a reputation for insanity. He was repudiated by the medical societies, despite the fact some of his discoveries surpassed those made in the preceding four centuries. He had come to be known, by certain esoteric groups, as an independent experimenter in the lore of obscure mental diseases and processes, which, strangely, he based upon ancient runes and savage magic practises.

If one entered, he would at once perceive that although the room was large, it was devoid of unnecessary ornamentation and furniture. Neatly polished glass cases stood along the white walls, with book cases incongruously in between. The bindings of the volumes were old—far older than one might expect outside of a library of incunabula. And the Latin titles were unusual for a private sanitorium. Here were no medical works, but instead the most outlandish and fantastic treatises on witchcraft and necromancy, interspersed with works on hypnotism and related subjects. This seemingly heterogeneous lot was carefully arranged and labeled, and all bore evidence of frequent reference.

The cases likewise were filled with things other than surgical instruments. True, the former were present, but amid them one might discover totally out of place some savage device for exorcising evil spirits, or a peculiarly inscribed clay cylinder of antiquity beyond belief.

But the gaze would be at once directed toward the central object—a flat table not unlike those used in operating rooms. On it was the reposing form of a man—young Edwin Coswell, likewise a student, of independent means because of his meritorious work. He had encountered Edwards some time previously, after they had frequently crossed one another's trails. Finding that their researches overlapped needlessly, they had joined forces.

Beside the table stood a tall bearded man—Edwards—engaged in making an odd concoction which he fed into a flaming brazier.

All was silent; the lights glared upon the strange helmet upon Coswell's head. Coswell lay motionlessly thinking perhaps of the experiment—the climax of their studies.

Abruptly finishing preparations, Edwards spoke. His voice was guttural.

"You are fully prepared?"

The man on the operating table nodded. "Yes."

"Then close your eyes and relax."

He did so. The smoke from the brazier lifted steadily into the air.

"Make your mind a blank. Think of nothing. You are sleeping . . . sleeping . . . sleeping . . ."

Despite his willingness, Coswell's mind rebelled. His thoughts kept asserting themselves, protesting, struggling with those of the Doctor. Perspiration broke out upon Edwards, and he passed his hand tiredly over his forehead. Then he leaned forward and concentrated intently upon his telepathic effort.

Coswell's body suddenly went limp. For a moment Edwards stood beside him, swaying slightly from the great mental effort. Then he said: "You hear me?"

"Yes—I hear you," came the low reply.

"Are you awake?"

There was a brief hesitancy. "No."

The smoke twisted into fantastic shapes, although the air was still.

"But you are conscious?"

There was no reply. He repeated the question.

"I am conscious only in that you may command me," was the answer.

Edwards smiled.

"You are still asleep; but your ego will leave its body. You are to keep in communication with me. Do you understand?'

"I understand."

For a long moment there was no change apparent in the figure on the table. Then gradually all colour faded from it. Edwards leaned over and watched the faint respiration with satisfaction. The heart was beating slowly and quietly.

During the period in which Coswell's soul left its habitat, a perceptible change of lustre was evident in the odd headgear. At first dull and frosty, it quickly brightened until it was a living pulsating gold.

"You are out of your body?"

An inaudible murmur came from the lips.

"Speak!" The Doctor's face was strained.

"Yes!"

"You are conscious now?" The smoke hung in heavily narcotic clouds.

"Yes!"

"Where are you?"

"In a grey whirling void."

"What is it like—out there?"

"I am alone. A vast buzzing sound fills the universe. . . . I can see all my past and my future. And the past and future of the whole scheme of things."

"Is there any . . . *reason* . . . in this illogical arrangement?" asked the Doctor curiously.

"Yes, far in the future. It is dim. But there is a radiance."

"Try to penetrate it."

"I cannot."

"What prevents you?"

"I do not know. I seem to stop at a certain point—aeons ahead."

"Can you see into the past?"

"Yes. Clearly."

"What is there?"

"A maelstrom of lurid flame. . . . That is the vast sun from which Earth was spat."

"Before that?"

"Emptiness."

"Come nearer our time."

"I seem to be walking down a street paved with worn stones. I am in Oriental garb . . .

"The scene changes . . . I am in a jungle of unbelievable beauty. . . . My form is not yet human . . .

"A Christian slave, under Nero . . .

"A druid-priest in ancient Briton. Some ceremony is taking place. I must not describe it.

"The scenes are ever changing; more quickly, now.

"A monk in a dreary cell . . .

"An African savage . . .

*"The grey stone walls of a feudal castle!"*

The last words were said with strained intentness. Then he was quiet, although his hands writhed.

Edwards' face was twisted agonizingly.

"Quickly! Speak! What do you see?"

Coswell was silent. Again came the command.

An inarticulate sound escaped him. Then with an obvious effort, he broke into speech, only to mumble a few words in a strange tongue. Again he was silent, although his lips moved.

Then, quietly, came the words:

". . . moat. There are many dressed as I, and all are armed with crossbows. A few have armor. We are up on the ramparts, and from the tower I can see far into the forest. It is spring, and the tops of the branches are swaying as if by a breeze. We await the attack nervously. The man who brought us the news this morning is below; dying, perhaps. It were better. Battle with human foes would be playfulness compared to the monstrosities we must combat. What foul creatures they are! Like jellyfish emulating humanity—a gross travesty of natural laws. Their tentacles are writhing things of horror. We are many, but I fear . . .

"The sun is yet high. I would that we have battle before nightfall, for my courage would falter at encounter after dusk."

The Doctor interrupted. "What year is it? What country?" he asked eagerly.

"Long ago—or perhaps—no; I do not know. It may be the future, the Armageddon of mankind. The country is Illoe. I am . . ."

His face contorted, and his natural voice broke torturedly through the lifeless monotone. "Wake me, Edwards! For God's sake wake me!" Then the dull speech continued as Edwards made futile efforts to arouse his friend. He smothered the brazier, shook him violently, hastily adjusted a small dial upon the helmet, but the dead voice went on inexorably.

"We can see them quite plainly now. I am afraid, deathly so. They are as we had expected; but none of us can overcome our nausea. They are swarming across the plain before the forest. If only we might have fled! But where? When all the world is overrun? How useless. Here is the last outpost of our kind, and we are defenseless. Must our race be wiped out? If our forefathers had but destroyed the first of them! Or if we had the old death-machines . . . but they are fallen into disintegration, like the race.

"A far off tumult is audible. The seething wall is approaching. The sun is low; livid. There are thousands of them—nearer now. As we had feared our arrows take little effect.

"Our men are killing one another. That is merciful. They cross the moat! Fill it with their bodies while others *ooze* over then.

*"They are mounting the walls!"*

A single shriek of unbearable terror was torn from him. Then he was still, as the metal helmet swiftly faded to a dull tone.

There were peculiar marks about him, and the expression was most shocking.

## The Herbivorous God

The serpent of darkness settled her coils about the houses of Babylon. She lapped up their whiteness swiftly, nuzzling about the garbage-littered alleys and venturing at last into the principal road, where, a little north of the Ishtar Gate, she encountered a tiny group of worshippers. They were going rather guiltily toward the distant temple, now a little disreputable because of the ascetic tendencies of its priest, called [        ], and dedicated to the goddess Ishtar, to complain about the king. Complaining about the king was a pleasure best experienced with a friend over a consolatory cup of wine, or in the relative snugness of matrimony, with one's very favorite wives, but this was a very difficult thing, those days. Only the gods could be wheedled into checking the monarch's high-handed actions. What was he doing, asked the traders come from the questionable lands beyond the desert, those with the sneaky ways ever so anxious to get the better of one in swapping trinkets. What was he doing! The man was mad! The hot sun of Uruk had got him. He was draining the coffers of the municipal government and squeezing the church for money to build a silly foolish mud wall all around the city. Make the city hotter than ever, it would, waste the good citizenry's time, and all because of some idea of national defense. Anu be pacified! Nobody was going to come and attack great Uruk, which had been ruler of everything that mattered as long as the present universe had existed. What preceded it was not divinable through its celebrated disorder under the goddess of Chaos. He was keeping the son from the father and the lover from the maiden, besides spending a great deal of money! Outlanders loved to bring the topic up, for the Urukites became so upset that they often lost count of whatever they were buying or selling.

One was likely in those days to surprise his friends, industriously praising Ishtar or the spider-headed god whose name was not spoken or some other god regarded as influential with Anu, in the hope that a distraction be sent Gilgamesh the king before he'd spent all the money and the hands for the bean-crop were all carried away to work on his foolish project. Hence the devout party of three suitably laden oldsters by the Ishtar gate. They turned north by the Prolongation of Paradise wine-shop, where one could get very tolerable beer, and pushed with reverence in between the priestesses who were soliciting indolently in the warm evening before the temple gates. Most of them had been presented to the temple by proud parents, complete with dowry, to alleviate the monotony of divine life for the gods and their chief representatives. Most of the gods lived in the temples, where the boarding was not at all bad, what with the large squashy figs, the brittle and virile cucumbers, the chickens, ducks, oil, cakes and what-all left by the whole parish to hold their attention. The gods came like flies, it was told, to smell the offering Utnapishtim had burnt on the mountain after the Flood. The fact that the priests were also the local government may have influenced the exceeding prosperity of such wards as also boasted jails.

Inside the temple it was dark enough to encourage the rental of oil lamps, each of which bore the name of the temple stamped deeply in its clay bottom, so the old man was forced to shell out most of the profit he had so enjoyed making off that foolish melon-buyer in the morning. He rented one lamp for the three of them— his two sons and himself, and they proceeded with it to a small dark shrine decorated with some drooping flowers.

The two sons, who were fourteen and sixteen, stared at the lush figurine of the goddess with a mixture of awe and desire, and began stumblingly to intone the Pluck thy little Squash-Blossom song in order to collect themselves. Ninigi, the younger, hoped the goddess didn't suspect his flash of impious thoughts, while Kigub, the elder, though it was a pity the goddess wasn't present for him to convince, in his rough but thoroughgoing way, of the desirability of answering their prayers.

"Show thyself to us, O frog of the midnight skies," droned the man. "Cometh alight upon my brow," added the little boy. "Let us gather the harvest of the overripe kisses," Kigub improvised. There was no one else in the temple. Even the shaven-headed priest had disappeared after assuring himself of the familiarity of the faces.

If it hadn't been for the acoustics of paradise, and for the rather charming black curls inclined before her shrine, Ishtar might have been annoyed at the prayers which kept blaring out in the middle of important conversations she was rehearsing while taking her twelfth foam-bath in a handy spot where one of the younger and more or less identifiably male gods might chance by. As it was, she laid on one bank the broiled pigeon she had been toying with, twisted a few bangles into her hair, and appeared to the worshippers; that is, to the tall and rather brawny youth called Kigub, whose long wielding of clay sickles had given his braceleted arm such an astonishing development. She appeared to him alone, by way of a trick she knew, just as he cried out, for he was by now very excited, and the incense was slightly intoxicating. "O sharer of the mat of Anu, make thyself one with the worshipped."

"Did you say something?" she asked, leaning suddenly against a pillar, purely for effect, since she could have walked right through it. He turned to look at her, and decided at once that she was the most agreeable temple prostitute he had yet seen. "I was praying," he said. "Why?" "Because father told me to." "Perhaps I could help you," suggested the goddess, modestly. He put his head on one side and appraised her. "As soon as the praying's done," he answered. Here his brother pinched him and demanded, "What's the matter with you?" "Oh, basket of the Harvest," Kigub began hurriedly, "show thyself to me."

Here Ishtar smirked. "I think we'd better go into the court-yard," she said. He stared at her, and seeing the faint light from her perfumed half-flesh, knew.

Later he explained to the goddess that it was his father's pious complaints were about.

"What do they expect me to do about it?" she queried idly.

"Well, they seem to think you could keep him busy some other way."

"Oh, he's always bragging about the Nippurites he's going to kill in the next war, or the Lagashites he ambushed in that sneaky way of his last spring. Besides, I don't mind warts if they're reasonably situated. . . ."

"No, I didn't mean that," said the youth. "They want you to create somebody to row with him. You know how quarrelsome he is."

"A new concubine?"

"A warrior would be better. Somebody handy with a battle-axe."

Ishtar thought a while, then gathered up a little of dust that the head priestess had swept behind a pillar of the arcade. "It will be arranged," she said, stepping into the moonless murk, where, searching for her presently, the youth Kigub found nothing.

The youth Kigub on the following day was engaged in whacking down some wheat in the northern acre, when he discovered that his water-bottle was cracked. It would be necessary to fill it at a creek some fifteen minutes' walk distant, which walk he undertook less from thirst than boredom. As he proceeded he wondered at the delectable but insubstantial creature of the previous night—what she had intended to arrange in answer to his prayers, and why she had gone away without arranging it. His gaze upon the stubble beneath him, Kigub did not see the fellow until he heard the snorting.

Belly-deep in the rushes of the north side of the ambling little creek stood a massive individual entirely dressed in sheepskin, according to his first impression, though on drawing nearer the boy was not sure at all. It seemed rather to be all the product of the strange being's virility—it was his own fur, apparently, which sprouted from him like grain. The hair of his head was like a woman's, and he was munching a drippy thing much like a water-lily.

Kigub drew back, considered a moment, and decided he wasn't thirsty. Retiring some distance with the speed of a crawfish, he turned his course homewards, where he frightened his father and thereby increased his own fright by telling what he had seen.

The old man reflected. "It was probably a demon," he ventured. "Better leave it alone. Work in the south field this afternoon, I don't want it following you in the house."

Had he not received the prohibition, Kigub would never have thought of returning. As it was, the following day, he walked away from his companion reapers, for here he was not alone, ostentatiously toward the bushes he might normally consult, and once in them,, scuttled out of sight. As he trotted through to the northern [field] which used to belong to a cousin of his father's lacking in the latter's business ability he saw the demon or hill-fellow or whatever he was drinking with a somewhat underfed gazelle in complete comradeship. The gazelle, however, finished his drinking by scratching a flea behind its ear with a delicate hind-hoof, a thing the man-creature essayed to do without much success. In doing so it looked up, and saw Kigub.

"Praised be our mutual gods," said the youth a little tremulously.

The being shut its eyes for a full minute, as if waiting for this apparition to go away, then opened only one.

"The market is tomorrow," went on Kigub. "Have you come to buy or sell?" He was thinking the being had better buy some kind of loincloth.

Abruptly the heavy body turned and lumbered away.

There were several bird-traps by the edge of the creek, Kigub's

personal devising. He was annoyed to find that they had been destroyed, and blamed it at once on the wordless hill-billy. He took so
much time repairing them that his absence had been noticed by his
father on returning to the south field, so he told where he had been.

His father opened his mouth, shocked at the interference with
the traps, and said he'd ask the king for an audience.

Now a robbed bird-trap was by no means too humble a matter
for consulting one of these city-kings, whose title of Herdsman of
the People denoted their position. Gilgamesh, as a matter of fact,
was stretching his great muscles carrying mud-bricks for the wall he
was so persistently building, and the father [was] sent there from
the palace, where nobody was awake except an old woman who
spoke some heathen language and was picking fleas off a cat, both
staring inquisitively at the visitor.

"Well," suggested Gilgamesh, wiping the sweat off his face with
a hairy forearm, "if I had time, I'd come and kill him for you, but as
it is, you'd better go ask for a priestess."

"But it's a big thing, kind of like a bull, my son says."

"Probably only a demi-god, something that feels it has to protect wild life. If it's human we'll soon find out. Ask 'em to send a
priestess from the Ishtar temple. Tell her to paint up and take a
bowl of oats."

She teetered complainingly along the stony path behind the
youth Kigub, this soft-faced harlot, and said she hoped it wasn't
another of those things that strayed in from the desert during the
dry season. Her sandals were made for courtyards and not for stubble of cropped wheat, and as for the mantle she had chosen from
the large clay jar serving as closet, it gave as much protection as a
hummingbird's shadow from the exuberant rays of Shamash the
sun-god.

Coming to the creek, where it widened out into a dispiriting
marsh made by the river's overflow, they saw footprints like those
of a heavy man overlying the little geometrical scratches of birds,

and Kigub knew that the stranger had been there. This was made certain by the first of his bird snares, which had been sprung without holding anything. This devotion to the welfare of the birds was too much for the outraged youth, and he bounded back complaining to the uneasy harlot whom he had left in the path. "He's been here again! Now we'll have to eat mush again for dinner."

"Maybe something ate it," she suggested, hoping that the something didn't have other appetites.

"No, there weren't any bones. He let it loose if there was anything. You've got to figure it out, Miss. I'll leave you here by this palm; I hope you brought some lunch; and go on down to the south field for a while. Since you have Anu for a protector I'm sure you won't mind. Just be sure when you destroy him not to let anything get away to come bumping around our house in the night." And he left her, with that confidence in the gods held only by one never closely associated with them.

Nin-Karsag sat down gingerly in the weeds and waited, fingering the charm the priest had given her, but more confident in the charms of her person, which was concealed only as the Euphrates was concealed under the capricious mists of early day. A pigeon gave her a considerable fright once, struggling with a young eel, and the bugs soon discovered her. Shamash climbed, the water seemed visibly to ferment, and everything which had disappeared upon their arrival renewed its business after Kigub went.

Then she heard the footsteps. Something the size of a bull was plowing through the mud energetically. She heard it snuff, after a moment, a little way downstream from her, and peeping amazedly through the shoulder-high reeds, saw the creature.

If he were a man, and in certain aspects he seemed clearly enough to be, he certainly belonged to one of the messy little tribes living in the murk east of the valley and civilization. If he were a demon, he seemed to be pretty harmless, since all he had done so far was set some birds loose and run away. If he were a god, well, she was a priestess, and her profession was to make bearable such negotiations with mortals as were necessary to obtain the proper sacrifices and offerings. She thought she'd venture forth, doing her hair unconcernedly, as if she were one of those bulgy women who lived in the huts and used the creek as a mirror to their limited charms. "I don't see why they bother," she thought, plucking the golden flowers and onyx pins from her dark stream of hair, which resembled the creek at midnight with torches of frog-spearers upon it.

The creature was down on its elbows sucking up the scummy water with a look of infinite bliss. Its sides were heaving. It had trotted a long way, probably from the mountains. The amount of its hair was amazing, and very much in need of combing.

She stepped on a stick to break it purposely. At the sound her animal-man leaped up (she already considered him hers) and stared at her. "Good-morning," she chirped, and let it go at that, meanwhile doing up the hair she had just let down.

He eyed her.

"You're not very agreeable," she said, after a moment. "Can't you talk?"

"I never tried," came the words harshly. Their utterer seemed as surprised as she was by the remark.

"Oh, I suppose you were just born yesterday," answered Nin-Karsag.

He nodded. "Sort of. I was created, I think. What kind of animal are you?"

"That," she gasped, "is something you might try to find out if you have the time." And smiling unabashed, she let her robe swing open for a moment that he thought was accidental.

"I'd better go now. My friends are expecting me."

"Who are your friends?"

"Some gazelles I met yesterday," he said. "I like them better than turtles, don't you?"

She stepped suddenly in his way as he began to retreat.

"I adore them both," she remarked, "but I hate brambles. Look, one of the nasty things scratched me." And she took occasion to show him her leg, which, it appeared, he appreciated of a sudden.

Well, he was awfully hairy, but that made it kind of exciting, and what great logs of muscles he had!

"Are there many things like this?" he asked after a while. "I guess this is better than gazelles, even."

"Well, not exactly, but there are lots of preparations—gowns and shiny things to put on, and ways to make your eyes big. You ought to get yourself a sheep-skin or something," she reflected, "although I like you best this way. Come into Uruk and we'll see a weaver."

"What is Uruk?" he asked.

"It's down there," indicating the lower river.

"Is it those lights I saw the night I was created? I didn't dare go near when I found it wasn't flowers. The owls said it wasn't ready yet, for us people of the steppe. They said, 'En-Gidu, you are partly divine. Wait until they have had a war, then we shall all live there.'"

"Yes," she said, "probably it wouldn't be safe, anyhow. Our king Gilgamesh is more powerful than anyone in the world."

"More powerful than me? Hm," came the reflective bellow.

"He probably wouldn't let you in."

He sat up suddenly, and she was some time calming him.

That night they stopped with some shepherds, in order to get him used to other people. He was not sure what other sort of behavior was proper, but after pawing the excited grandmother perfunctorily, as she limped by with cheese for the table, he decided there were some females one only looked at. Grandmother picked up the cheese snappishly, the young shepherds stared at the great hairy man clad in a frail robe the harlot had loaned him from her scant store, and they gathered together around the dinner-mat.

They were three brothers, in their twenties, reared by the old lady after their parents had made the mistake of selling decayed mutton to the previous king. To the eldest Nin-Kirsag said, after nibbling a crumb of cheese, "How lonely it must be here in the country all the time! No music!"

"What," demanded the eldest, "do you want music for? Scare all the sheep."

"Oh, but to dance to! I adore dancing, don't you?"

"Don't know. Never tried it. Never cared to," he added.

Grandma squatted down beside them and thrust the leaf at Engidu. "Here," she said, "though it doesn't look like you'll need much feeding." And she tittered.

Engidu took it and looked helpless. Nin-Karsag said, "You break a piece off and chew it."

"They didn't catch it in a trap?" he asked anxiously.

The eldest brother laughed to himself. "Have some wine," he said.

Engidu accepted the cup of muddy red fluid doubtfully, then drank it at a gulp. Strangling a moment, he coughed vigorously, and looked surprised. "That is better than pond-water," he said, offering his cup for another filling.

Nin-Kirsag had become occupied in a low conversation with the youngest shepherd, who was chubby and amiable and chuckled his words. It appeared after a brief while that he had to examine one of the sheep who had hurt itself, and it also appeared that Nin-Kirsag had great interest in veterinary activities, so they went out together. The middle brother looked annoyed, and the eldest mumbled through a mouthful of bread, "There was a lion around again last night. Hope it doesn't catch them."

Engidu sat up. Here was the only topic he knew. Animals!

"Nice creatures, the lions," he said. "I can't understand why they have those tempers, though. I was helping one carry a sheep . . ." and he stopped abruptly. The brothers, however, had not been listening.

"Have some more wine," said the eldest brother.

And Engidu did.

There was a distant howl.

"Hear that?" asked the eldest rhetorically. "Come and steal our sheep. Probably going to bite your woman, too, unless she hurries up."

Engidu stood up before he had really decided to, and stood amazed by the pace of his blood.

"Can you handle lions?" they asked him. He nodded his head vigorously. So they searched for the club with the broken off branches which was their chief weapon, but while they were searching he strode out.

Nin-Kirsag came back a moment later, and seeing her protégé gone, counted the brothers hastily. She didn't want him to go off with one of the brothers because he looked kind of like a sheep himself.

"Nasty scratch that sheep has," she improvised. "Where's Engidu?"

"Went off to get that lion, I suppose. But he hasn't got anything to kill it with."

She burst into tears. They all regarded her with discomfort. Then Grandma came over to the weeping harlot. "Here, honey, have a piece of cheese."

"I don't want to. I don't want to eat anything any more. Just think, something may be eating him right this moment."

When they went out in the morning, however, they came upon Engidu not far from the well, asleep in a very complicated fashion with a sad faced young lion. Both snored thunderously.

## The Bright Valley

Because old tales spoke of a land amid those dark enormous cliffs rising to the east of his village, Cern set out to find it. There, in a fertile valley region shielded from the beast, his people might find sanctuary.

It was said, among those who spoke of old things, that a time had been when the rich concealed land was visited by men, and that in other years rich gain had come of it, in fruits and animals. In those times hunters returned from the bright valley laden with fowl whose sweet flesh bled newly from the arrow. But afterward, ancient tales narrated, glittering rocks had fallen upon the earth; and those rocks were of the fires burning over men in the night. Their falling was for minutes like thunder upon the plains and crags, or like the hurtling of tremendous hooves. These rocks were chilled from the darkness whence they came, and fell most thickly over the valley set like a gem amidst the mountains. And afterward men did not camp there, fearing things that come from the sky; and the hunters drew no bow in the bright valley, though there were few birds upon the plain.

It was this land Cern sought, in a later time, when the old tales were not much believed. For three days he walked, and still before him were leagues of desolation. By night and by the burning cobalt of day he had made his path through a plateau grassed with corpse's hair. Dagger-like reeds were set against him, and mocking crumbs were all that he possessed as food. Now a cloud flecked the heavens with white dappling, but nothing stirred beneath the bloody and unwinking sun, save the orange facets of a serpent that slid away flickering her tongue. Upon what flesh she were fed, Cern did not know, until white, brittle skeletons of toads crunched under his foot.

This land was silent, as if all life had fled before some fast-approaching doom. There was no road to the goal Cern sought, nor anything to guide him save the dark, jagged and unknown cliffs, hung between sky and the earth. Since beyond them rumour placed his goal, he strode on beneath the declining orb, and did not take his gaze or thoughts from the place ahead.

A golden softness lay upon the plain, for the sun was now upon the low steps of his throne; and ravelled clouds had coursed into the sky diffusing his rays. Soon there spread before Cern in the amber light a meadow running to the edge of the sombre cliff, but there was no longer any light upon the cliff itself. Like some dread fortress, or like a menacing galley prow, it towered now above him—a rugged and awesome precipice whereon the late sun was hesitant to glow. The surface was oddly smooth, as if poured from molten glass; and where caverns had anciently formed, they were like misshapen bubbles.

The barrier was difficult to scale, for it seemed to fall endlessly into the sky; but on reaching the fragrant place beyond, he might rest and refresh himself with fruit; for all these things were told of in the outer land. Within the valley Cern might dwell through all the day on idle banks where there was no plain-grass, but only flowered loveliness.

As he climbed among the briars strewn over the undulant cliff and made his ascendant way among old boulders, he wondered that men had abandoned the place beyond on account of a few fallen stars, and why so reputedly bountiful a land was not cultivated for its grains and trees of fruited bloom, and other things that root in the dark soil, but do not grow well upon grasslands. And he cursed his fathers because they had chosen the barren plain rather than this enchanted beauty.

For suddenly he could see all the valley from a bouldered eminence, and it was like a figured tapestry wrought with exquisite happenings. The trees were leafy ferns, and the meadows a bright scarf with tiny lakes as brooches.

A little while he stood there, resting against a boulder as weathered as an earth-embedded skull. This place was a fortress holding fair gardens! Beneath him fluttered the plumage of radiant fowls, while as he saw this there came to his ears a faint musical confusion. It was made by parrots and cockatoos and pheasants as they bade the golden day farewell. In that sound-filled sunset, while the clicking of insects and the droning croak of frantic toads filled the earth, a chalky purple overspread the sky, and during slow moments nightfall deepened into a cold and shadowed blue. Faint hues of pink were blossoming in the sky as the spotted trees grew dark and flatly printed on the cool heavens. A subtle change set in with day's passing; and new, strident cricket-voices shrilled from dim boughs. It seemed as if their advent marked the certainty of night, for all the glowing colour drained away beyond the ranks of tangled pines, and left the paleness of a young night. Softly tossing trees subsided into dimness, and the small voices fluttered less stridently among them as the clamorous sunset hues declined.

And now the night had spread a jewelled mantle overhead. Beneath looping constellations Cern set upon that brief descent. Here was no longer any rock to bruise his flesh, and no sharp pebbles underfoot. The wearisome stretch of reeds and crisp grass was gone, and he felt beneath his tread a sward green as the wing of a moth.

As Cern went beneath the fragrant boughs, with the scented wind gentle against his face, he sensed a malignancy about him, and shrank against the trunk of a thick pine. Fear comes to man in subtle ways. Her servant is less the blood-hungry animal, which he may combat, than the elusive spirit of an unknown sight or an unforeseen noise. But the greatest terror is in the abrupt facing of a thing which he cannot comprehend—like that fear induced by the fragments of a sea creature found upon a silent beach, or by the darkness which seems to move in the night before him.

Far away, in the heart of the valley, danced curious shimmerings that waxed in brilliancy. Pallid veils of light, borne by no creature. These webs wove a phosphorescent tapestry, and shifted as no lights should. They were phantasms: forms more pale than the stars, and hung upon the breeze as if they had no weight or substance. They swung and soared before the man, and dropped like dying torches everywhere within the valley.

From where he crouched in new, unfathoming terror, the whole valley was visible beyond a pine bough. Everywhere the glow was teeming and bubbling like an obscene brew, and the man felt the emotions of one who sees an enemy camped before homeward gates, knowing what the alien fires mean. That place which Cern had thought beautiful became to him accursed, for it was fouled with this evilness.

The things had come out to feed, and they swirled and netted and spread apart, roving and searching among old trees and drifting across small lakes. The whole expanse of the valley was alight with their cold, deliberate forms, a misty glimmer beneath the stars. They swarmed over little hills and thronged on gentle upward slopes to the edge of that accursedly beautiful valley. Cern saw the procession of goblin-torches blotted out for a moment as they drifted through a little wood. In dull fear he watched them waver brightly again, inevitably towards him, and yet he made no effort to escape. If he fled but a little way, he might gain the black summit of the embracing cliffs, but the light was strange and glorious. It poured upon him with the freshness of a mountain spring. The air about him tingled as he watched with dim, uncomprehending eyes. Sparkling, exhilarating, like the bleak wind that slithers upon a day of perishing winter, it merged into his very body, as if he were but a phantom of a man in the moon-rivalling glow. And with the subtle mystery of moonlight it drew him on. Rising silently, he took a step, and though he no longer felt or understood, his eyes strained eagerly to behold the immortal, promising, beckoning mystery. His face and limbs were transfigured into a semblance of divinity by the glowing silver vapors. No man perished there, but a god. Like a flame-enamoured moth, he was prisoned and consumed by the billowing crystal.

When he fell upon the grass, a gleaming, zestful flicker ran through the congealed glow. It seethed rejoicingly, and swirled above the prone figure; gathering upon him like St. Elmo's Fire. A miasmatic halo that sucked and clustered like vampire moths on carrion, the radiance enshrouded him, and his body was limned with brightness.

Under the dark pines the place was evil with feeding light.

*July–September 1935*

# The Priest and the Heretic

Higher among the servitors of the dark Moggua was the venerable priest, Lombei.

He dwelt always within the temple of his deity, that he might remain in readiness for any command of his god, though such had never come.

The temple rose near the broad and slow-moving River of Fear wherein dwell strange denizens; and its walls were builded of black wood of surpassing hardness.

And the floor was constructed of rare black stone from beyond the hills, and no color of any sort was allowed within the sanctuary of Moggua; save only in the inner court.

Here there was a peculiar oily pool wherein the god was said to dwell. Around it ran a blood red coping bearing strange carvings, over whose edges sacrifices were thrown at judicious times.

Now was Lombei, in his 83rd year, approached by a pilgrim from far lands.

"Listen," said the stranger, "there be no gods, for I have defied them all my life, and they have smitten me not."

Dazed and terrified by this heresy, Lombei blinked in aged confusion.

"Listen," said the stranger, "free thyself of enslavement to ancient nursery-tales, and cast off thy god."

Lombei trembled and did not reply. Then, the stranger turned, and said, "I see it is of no use; for you are a fatuous old man." And the stranger left.

Then Lombei muttered in shocked horror and cursed the heretic, and after a time went into the inner court and stared long upon the placid pool.

"If true this be," Lombei observed, "I must cease my priesthood and earn an honest living, for hypocrisy tempts me not."

The pool was very calm.

"If the man be right, all my devotions have been wasted, and I may as well slay myself."

And he looked away in doubt.

But then it chanced that a large bird flying overhead dropped somewhat within the pool, and a ripple spread over the oily surface.

Seeing this Lombei was overjoyed.

"Hidden Moggua, I meant it not. I sorrow at my doubt now thou hast given me a sign."

Thus was his peace of mind restored; and Lombei conscientiously served his deity to the end of his days.

## The Summons

*A Fragment*

"Tahtra-ma; y thiesta, Tahtra-ma; y Thiesta;" came the strange, soundless beckoning—

I hesitated in my stride. About me was the most noxious portion of the city, dim alleys harboring lone obscure shops wherein were vended strange goods. Far down the broken road buildings gleamed alight, and people passed me, huddling against the chill wind. The vague and indeterminate sounds came unceasing, but suddenly above them this new sound, this inexplicable call that had no origin. "Tahtra-ma; y thiesta; . . ."

Stopping, I caught a dim vision of myself in a shop-window. I did not see beyond the glass, I was conscious only of the long, smooth face, the furtive wildness beneath the arching brows. My long recent sickness was apparent, and I was yet unwell. Seeing myself thus, I was half-repelled. My thoughts confused. I strove to clear them; my pace abruptly increasing almost to the point of flight. " . . . tra-ma; y thiesta, tahtra-ma; y thiesta."

Shadows loomed. Whence came this dull, secretive call? I wanted to be alone and calm in my seclusion. Perhaps I should not have come out alone because of the lingering illness. Traces remained in my pallor and unsteadiness. That call should not intrude upon my agitation. I was somehow angered by its lure. Again and yet again came this repetition; never any chance, never any explanation of those cryptic words, and their interminable succession.

Alleys were near and I turned impulsively into a dark one striving to escape those tones. They whispered . . . yet it was not altogether a whisper . . . of dark and curious things. They summoned morbid phantasmagoric visions. It seemed for an instant that I glimpsed leaves and dim tossing boughs against a sky of unholy illumination. Mad thoughts, these. I must cease. Why was my mind so blurred? "Tahtra-ma; y thiesta."

The alley I had entered was wholly unlit. No shops were there, only fat shadows. In the dark I saw nothing, but far ahead at the other end shone the street. I had come into a noisome part of town. Blundering in the lightlessness, my foot struck something soft and horrid. Not seeing what it had been, my mind received a fleeting impression of something small and black that scampered.

I did not doubt that a seizure of my curious and inexplicable illness was upon me, and regretted that I was unaccompanied in these surroundings. This peculiar affliction had mystified the doctors, for it was neither epilepsy nor anything akin save in external appearances. It was connected with the visual trouble with which I had always been afflicted, although it had never previously assumed these recent forms. Nothing had been learned from trephining, but the seizures had ceased. Whatever the cause, it seemed to have been blindly rectified by the surgeons.

Until the operation, a filmy golden haze was gradually obscuring my vision, causing odd and disconcerting distortions of my surroundings, as if I viewed them through a flawed and knotty amber glass. But this was not all. I had also those dreaded spells of giddiness, with deep-toned reverberations in my head. Such reverberations were distinctly not external sounds, yet differed bafflingly from any known phenomena of vertigo. Unpleasant as these recurrent happenings were, I may well have feared them over-much. This was largely due to my inordinate fear of anything conceivably affiliated with madness. There was insanity in my ancestry, and because of this the subject was for me a field of morbid speculation. Brooding upon every fancied sign; ever watchful to find myself breaking down, I led an existence ceaselessly haunted by dread. Fears of this kind formed my first thought when the affliction developed. But the operation upon which I had frantically insisted appeared beneficial, despite the long convalescence. The visual and auditory deceptions vanished; physically I was better than at any previous time, and to my delight, my eyes were even strengthened to a degree not hitherto mine. This evening marked the first recurrence of any illness but the long natural convalescence. So, bewildered in that unhallowed labyrinth of black lanes, I resolved to return home at once if power to do so remained. I must, I thought, avoid if possible the worst extremes of my dizziness in a place as remote, unknown and sinister as this. That the curious sounds and impressions now subtly pouring over me were attributes of my old illness, I did not doubt. This, indeed, was the only natural assumption at the moment. As I hurried on the voice came once more— "Tahtra-ma; y . . ."

It had grown louder—or was it that my delusion had increased? Madness this must surely be. I wanted to think of something clean, but the thing in the alley had been unclean. Now I was far within the tunnel-like street. It wound. The illuminated end was near. I should turn into the light, and stay always within its glow, so that darkness might give me no more bad thoughts. Evil was in the alley, evil was everywhere this night, for the voice came, insinuating, corrupting, loathsome, alluring . . . "Tahtra-ma, y thiesta, tahtra-ma, y thiesta. . . ."

But had I not meant to shake these strange thoughts from my mind? My footsteps echoed upon the cobblestones. This should not be, for I saw a figure ahead, and it made no sound. The form was bent, an old one, carrying faggots. I did not heed him, but as I passed, struggling with an influence oddly like an ingratiating command, and somehow connected with the strange sounds, he raised his head and leered. His teeth were very white in the shadow, and his eyes rolled up disturbingly.

Then he was behind. I was hurrying now, for the command had come more strongly. I was needed. Needed? Wildness. What needed me? Why did the voice trouble me so unendingly? Never did it cease, low but always present, it said "Tahtra-ma, y thiesta."

I was spellbound within a strange delirium. Shadows still, though there was light here. Buildings were too high, there were no doors into which I might flee. Yet this I could not have done in any case. Were not the shops closed? Or, no . . . things escaped my reeling senses. Nothing showed naturally. I was rushing through a dim void, and the streets were mirages. *It needed me . . .*

There was a window, very dirty with many handprints. I stopped and gazed within. This helped to untangle the chaos. A statue was there. I could not tell the shape, although I knew there was a figure. It was naked and riding something, but the mount eluded my vision. I tried, but could not see the thing it rode. Other darks and lights registered, I but sensed them as one senses evil. *As one senses evil—*

This night was evil. I could no longer remember where I had been going. *Tahtra-ma; y thiesta.* It came. The walls were not, nothing was; but the voice; the voice which I must obey, for had it not need of me? *Tahtra-ma; y thiesta.*

If only a new note might come amidst this monotonous repetition. . . . Was I indeed mad? Yes, this must be at last what I had so long feared. I had seen madness in others, but did not understand it before. Madness was odd. I could not think, yet was conscious of the fact, and strove to combat it, strove to think. There was a falling darkness, like fainting, but it was not that. A sound, and spinning.

*Tahtra-ma, y thiesta. . . .*

———————

Where was I now?

This was another, and yet another street. I had no direction save the guiding voice. *I knew I must hurry, for it needed me.* I was on the edge of the city. I did not remember how I had come there, only now the voice was louder.

The forest was not far, I sensed its presence. Soon the paved streets with their huddled rows of houses would thin out and end, and then the roads would give out beyond the last light. In that marginal realm none lived—for the forest had dwellers, and things had fluttered into the city that were not right. "Tahtra . . ."

". . . ma; y thiesta." I became aware of a dank, increasing cold. Now the air had become an indefinable admixture of warmth and chill. It was like a velvet curtain that hindered; enshrouded. Yes, that was right, enshrouded. For was I not partly dead, and living in the Voice? It needed me: therefore, what right had I to be, against its will?

I have said that I was dazed, but this does not accurately convey my curious sensations. Mentally I was in a turmoil of sharp imping-ing thoughts and impressions, yet I could not segregate these con-fused images. My members obeyed with automatic promptness all mental commands, but somehow I felt within a strange dream, for my whole sensation was that of partial hypnotism. Utter lack of the sense of touch had come upon me in a baffling and inexplicable flash.

I do not know how best to describe this curious state—there was in it nothing of the soporific; yet I lacked coherent guidance of my actions, being at the same time wholly aware of the fact. Nerveless fingers touched my moist forehead, as if impelled to the action by some external command. Stumbling, hurrying, I vaguely won-dered—as if accompanying an automaton directed by another's will. And I must repeat that I was not tired in the ordinary sense, being completely conscious during the whole happening. At times I was convinced that the whole thing was a series of distortions produced by the brain-operation. Things flowed in the manner of dreams.

As I neared the city's edge I saw buildings, warehouses. They were last before the forest. What was stored in them? Nothing sane, nothing normal, something incalculably hideous, I knew. Things lay in the street, rubbish and other objects. From the cavern of a small alley something *bubbled,* giving an unspeakably terrifying sensation. It made me feel dizzy. Terror,—and now was the forest. But I must not shirk. *It needed me.*

Dim bushes were all about, and giant, loathsome trees. There were creepers and parasitic growths of misshapen grey. Beneath the moon they seemed to move, but this could not be. *Tahtra-ma, y thiesta.*

Now, all at once, I knew the forest. That radiant sky had come with the voice, long aeons before. Somehow I had seen this fearsome place, and whatever power summoned me must have intended it so. I recognized a certain flashing aspect with terrified shock.

I did not stop, I did not flee, my legs moved on. I was only a submissive, impotent consciousness before whatever fearful thing awaited.

*Aye, Master, I am coming!*

This impulsive thought surged through me, bewildering and dulling my senses and impressions. All that guided me, all that I had of sentient life was for a time that overwhelming urge. As I stumbled through dark thickets it lured me on, ever on to a nameless goal.

The wood was monstrous with ancient trees. No animals dwelt among them, for these black and swollen trunks were exceeding curious in their outlines. They were shunned by the birds, too, and none nested within thez forbidding boughs. The hoary boles rose from dank clusters of unnatural grass and the residue of decayed branches. Upon these heaps of rotten limbs grew here and there small patches of faintly luminous fungi, and desolation and fetor everywhere prevailed. Such plants as could find root amidst this deep-piled ground were oddly misshapen, and partook of the faint luminosity of the putrescent growths. Nor was the foulness of that abominable forest confined to the ground, for those terrible branches, crowded with curious leaves, swayed most unpleasantly against the sky. Scarce ever did the full moon shine upon their tossing heights, and perhaps it were well, for in such illumination they must have been horrid indeed. But although this stronger light was denied them, a dim radiance, like the phosphorescence of some sinister cavern depth, prevailed upon the whole sky. Then, too, the clouds were prone to assume suggestive forms, and pale vapors of unexplained origin were often seen above certain spots of the shunned forest.

Mortals avoided it, and when they had business in the farther valley, chose rather a long and circuitous route, that they might not pass through the threatening shadows that abode beneath the trees.

This narrative is unavoidably impaired and incomplete, for it can be unfolded from only a single angle. I do not know the causes underlying what I shall attempt to describe—I can only relate what appeared to my bewildered senses. I am now relatively certain that my faculties were subtly altered by the operation, *so that I received impressions no one else on earth could have understood.* I was cured of one abnormal condition; but might not that cure have opened certain dormant organs such as abound within the body, making me sensible of things beyond the normal range of the visual and auditory senses? Through the birth of new, special senses might not I not have come to command certain aspects of external reality which none of man's natural senses can grasp and record?

It was while I was staggering feebly amidst the foul, clawing undergrowths of that unhallowed and phosphorescent wood that a change came gradually upon me. I found my pace slackening, and my sense of cloudy seeking diminishing. Presently I realized that I was standing still, with the strange mental vagueness, fatigue, and sense of compulsion suddenly stripped from me. I was my normal self again, though hindered by a feeling of invisible physical restraint, as if unseen walls pressed upon me and limited my motions.

And now there began to beat upon my ears a tide of vibration like the waves of some toneless, prodigious music; a tide that swelled in volume till I was dazed and deafened. It merged somehow with the violently agitated tree-tops, until I fancied for a moment that a storm had arisen. The utter soundlessness of those wild undulations, and the unnatural, menacing solemnity of their rhythms, bespoke a source which could not have been of earth. The music, if such it were, tossed and buffeted the leaves and stirred them to abnormal action. The light in the sky grew more intense, as if some demon-god had bidden the moons of infinity to glow upon the place. The cacophony played before Azathoth in the blackness could not surpass this awful majesty. I wished overwhelmingly to fling myself prone before the inspired and solemn strains, yet I stood erect and wholly motionless, watching the curious glade and the awful shadows. . . .

Meanwhile there had not ceased to sound through me these cryptic words, "Tahtra-ma, y Thiesta; Tahtra-ma, y" until my stupefied thoughts were wearied by their sequence. I could not comprehend the meaning, but I knew they had a very distinct significance, and flitting thoughts told me of no pleasant things. The tongue was not of our land, nor any I had ever heard from the lips of voyagers to far countries. Such words, I felt, were perhaps not even human, but might be the awful syllables of some troll-tongue. Within them, obscurely lurking, were hidden implications half-akin to hints of demoniacal origin. There have been times when I have wondered at their curious meaning, but when I remember fully the events of that awful night, I am glad of my blissful ignorance.

––––––––

For all at once I saw it.

There, within the clearing, was such an abomination as never plagued the good St. Anthony. An immeasurably old and evil thing not of our world but of some infinitely and mercifully remote stellar depth. A form of utter nightmare. And as if bound within some horrid dream, I was frozen, unable even to cry out . . .

Why I, of all the people of the city, was selected by that demoniac entity for its inconceivable uses, I shall never be certain. There are times when I am prone to think that the mind of the—thing—was somehow *en rapport with my own brain;* that by some cosmic fluke of chance, our thoughts were shaped according to remotely similar plans. But I do not know, and all surmise is useless. It is sufficient that I *was* chosen by that incomparably ancient and utterly alien entity for its terrible purpose. Whence it came, I do not even dare to guess, save that the source must have been some shockingly primordial world. Only such a world could have evolved a monster so obscenely complex and maturely terrible. It was older than Stonehenge, and might have manifested itself to the ancestors of the pyramid-builders. It was ancient beyond all human conception or belief.

Nor have I ever decided what it was. Not animal, although it possessed certain attributes of animals, nor wholly vegetable—it was a loathsome and unearthly merging of those arbitrary divisions. There was a ghastly *fungoid* look about it, and I thank the gods that I saw it only in that half-light, for a more distinct view might well have sent me into gibbering madness.

It stood; or crouched—for it was not erect—within the moonlit glade. All about were dark branches, and mottled shadows were cast upon its dim shape. I was unaware of its form for several moments, although my whole nature had at once revolted against the *suggestions* it conveyed. The most hideous feature, I believe, was the eyelessness. That blank, formless face that leered insanely . . . And yet, those nauseous fungoid tentacles, and the contorted and grotesque nature of the entire travesty and insult to sane laws of nature, were even more shocking . . .

However this may have been, and slight as was my glimpse before that peculiar cloud obscured the sky, this momentary impression woke my confused brain into a state of panic-filled repulsion. Had I not been already half-delirious it might have produced an even more terrible effect upon my nerves. As it was, I remember that I shrieked in mortal agony at what I saw.

Yet the thing was not alone. Also within the range of my fear-sharpened sight was a second living figure—and I felt a new horror mixed with sensations too complex to describe when I saw that the figure was human. That the light was indistinct I have mentioned; this prevented my discerning the features, but I knew the shape to be that of a very old man moving rapidly about the glade. I knew, also, why the thing had left its hold on me, for before my eyes a struggle of titanic force was taking place, in which all the evil energies of the monster were absorbed by its efforts against a mortal adversary. All about me I saw the blasphemously twisted boughs of that accursed wood tossing and writhing insanely to the alien pulsing of that wild, toneless music; saw, too, the noxious duel that was fought silently between the unknown ancient and this thing that I felt to be more ancient—this incarnation, older than the very universe, of all the foulness that exists—this thing that before my gaze battled for possession of our world.

For all at once it came to me, dimly, that such was the goal of the abomination. It seemed that I had always known it, as if my mind for one fleeting instant shared the detestable thoughts and memories of the alien, inscrutable thing which had so lately controlled it. I knew somehow—though much of the knowledge clipped away before I could well assimilate it—what that cosmic cacodaemon was, and how it came to be in this nighted and hideous wood on our planet. I knew of its plight, and why it was seeking the aid of some true denizen of a world in which it floundered as a bewildered alien. I knew of its purpose—though so misty are my memories that they flee when I would touch them. This much I remember—that it wished to make some sort of inconceivable lair in our world; wished to contaminate it with the vileness of Yuggoth . . .

Lord Christ! It could have done it, too . . . no question of its power, of its mental mastery. I saw that brave and sturdy greybeard waver, totter uncertainly in the strange strife. I knew he could not defy it longer. What would have happened I dare not even think. That festering monstrosity that glowed even as the rotten fungi. . . .

## A Dream

Through fields of dark and aeon-coarsened weeds a glistening roadway passed. The heavy vegetation crept upon a crumbling surface and forced its way through many cracks. The road was old and little used; for none had cause to traverse its ancient, half-forgotten course. It lay alone beneath the heavy sky of darkened clouds, straight and clearly-defined despite the ruin of the years. Centuries of parching sun and endless rains of leaden skies had alike been powerless to obliterate it.

The wild and desolate plateau ran shadeless to the farthest sight, till dim horizons merged it with a forest-blur of heavy pines. The abandonment manifest in every crack of the rotting surface and the range of towering grasses would cause the thoughtless to deny that man had ever dwelt beside this olden track; but this was false, for on one side there crouched a building of heavy stone, formed with mastery despite its enormous bulk. Crude slabs that in their weight alone might crush an elephant were laid with artful care, and crevices were few about the grey and ancient walls. In lesser cracks and through unglazed windows low above the ground trailed matted vines and clusters of dark leaves, but naught disturbed the squares of pavement in the massive rooms. Men might have lived not long before in that great house where maggots worked themselves through layers of greenish mould, or aeons might have passed since that paving echoed to mortal tread. I do not know, nor is there any record made, for we are careless in this, the world's last age. Humanity is weary and not averse to death.

In a moonless night, when pools of brownish darkness lay among the weeds, I strode along the ancient path, guided by the stars that dimly shone upon the dead plateau. I hastened over fretted chips of roadway where parasitic growths were clawing at my feet; and strode among the ropy vines that looped like serpents in the path. The chill of darkness hastened me, and led by the glimmering lace of distant stars I made my way across the silent and desolate land. The thickness of my clothing fought away the chill of dying Earth, but I knew that I must rest if the sun should find me past this naked plain. I would have lain amidst the grass and slept upon the knapsack that I bore, but they had told me of the empty stone-built houses by the road, and as the ground was wet and dank I hoped to lie within some gaping ruin.

My eyes were weary of the search when I came at last to the dark bulk that loomed against the stars. I saw that others like it lay in rubble nearby, but in my haste I chose the closest, and stood before an unlit portal. The mystery of the night was all embodied here, and I hesitated for a time; but then I made a cautious step, and found myself within.

I had expected signs of vanished life, but only bleakness and hard stone confronted me. The star-light within was small, but I dared not waste my only torch. Groping with my hands for a refuge from serpents, I found a gloomy cavity within the wall a yard above the floor. Climbing wearily in, I set my pouch as a headrest and lay upon the hard surface. Resting thus, there came a surge of sleep about me.

I do not know how long I lay, but in the night it seemed that I woke and looked across the road from a thick window bearing no glass. A curious light played all about the world, and the dark skies were turned to flame. In the maelstrom of the heavens there rose a monstrous tower where no tower had been, and the lightnings of the universe struck in dazzling fury on its height. A surge of light played about the base, and glowing shards were detached as all these forces wreaked their power. For countless minutes the lightning flung its serpent glow, and the tower crumbled in slow coals of radiance. It seemed as if some demon-god were gnawing at its top, as the steady flashes met and fused within the walls. It crumbled slowly, foot by foot, until but half the height was left, and yet the sky was a single furnace of dread force. And as I gazed affrighted, there grew a might *shape* within the pillared coals. The fragments hurtled on the plain, while among them there slowly rose and took shape that awful form which wrung my heart in fear. A seated Titan in the white flame; a thing incredible in size and form. The cindered battlements were gone in gleaming ash about the figure's waist, and from beneath the heaping coals stared sightless the Colossus!

   . . . My dreaming changed, and cold with fright, I tore at my garments and my knapsack, wrenching off frantically every scrap of silver, steel or brass that my fingers found. A subtle instinct whispered that metal was the goal of that sightless, greedy stare, and as I detached each clasp and button I flung it away into the darkness in order that the Colossus might stump and shamble in other places, leaving me unscathed. Thus I fell from dream to mystic dream until I found myself awake and staring at the image of a newly risen moon upon the wall.

   Sweating and trembling from my dream, I sought to guess its portent; and my fright wrought every sound of darkness into circling slumber terrors. Cold, shivering and weary, I lay motionless as the slow moon made its way across the dark.

   As the night passed my terror lessened, and I wondered at the strangeness of my vision. A mist-filled dawn gave courage, and as daylight spread across the plain I looked expectantly where that enormous shaft had been. But there was nothing there except a heap of ancient rubble. If a tower had once risen, all trace had vanished amidst the years.

## A Legend

Dawn marches swiftly away from the island, and it is revealed green in the warm sunlight. Some distance from its borders waves deck themselves briefly with coronets of light, discarding these to drift very lazily across the threshold sands of an unspotted beach. The sky, exhausted for a while, displays only a variety of blues, pallid in the extreme height of the celestial dome, but intensified almost into purple where it curves down to the ocean. There is nothing anywhere else in sight but the calm and verdant island bordered by friendly waves. An indolent peace seems to rest upon it, like a smile on the face of a cherished woman, and if gold and velvet were not such worthless things, we might compare the sunlight to a medley of gilded threads woven upon the green velvet grass. But no weaver has ever made a fabric which would seem other than coarse if it were laid upon the soft sweet grass of the island, and no lapidary has ever fingered gems as intensely coloured as that sea and the fair land it contains.

There are trees upon it, freshly sprung into bud, and glowering bushes which lean down to gaze indolently at their reflections in crystal streams. There are birds and beautifully furred animals; leopards roam through green-shadowed groves inhabited by cocka-toos, whose white wings are the only snow to settle in those boughs. There are buildings of marble, surrounded by white col-umns ornamented with the acanthus leaf; everywhere the elusive nar-cotic scent of flowers snuttering in the wind. There are a variety of wild, countless banks of pale roses, fragile trees, and the wisteria whose drooping flowers are like the clustered waxen cells of a hive.

This island is the outpost of a vast and beautiful world, a world wherein the fruits of unending peace are used to snare the secrets of the universe, a world where man, rendered divine by knowledge, grovels before no imagined and terrifying gods, but seeks himself to unravel the immense patterns of nature, drawn among the evanes-cent stars and copied in the atomic structure of the world. To this island no record of battle has come; no sword has contended for the fertile earth, and there is neither triumph of victor nor screaming of vanquished. Blood has not soiled the clean leaves and grasses of that garden world nor invading foot scarred the sandy beach. The land is secure eternally against the windy rains and the desolating heats which torment and destroy us: it is older than Ilias or Jerusalem or the holy Persian city whose name is forgotten. It is imperishable, though it has not yet had existence; it is immortal though it has not yet been born. It is a world which John Bull dreamed of when he led his ragged legions into London's streets. It is the world for which a thousand rebels fought and perished, sublime in their incandescent vision; it is the world which presently, after more centuries of strife and cruelty, men will unite and build.

## A Memory

### I

I stood with Nalda in one of the lesser Hallways, the gay laughter of revelry yet within my ears. We were both clad in glittering pleasure-garments and the bat-cloaks that had recently become the fashion. I wanted to laugh again and tell Nalda of a wonderfully comic thing, but the solemn, unexpected look upon my companion's face made me uncomfortable. I did not wish to be serious, for when one is serious, the drabness of reality is intolerable.

The white metal walls shone clearly with a frosted silver glow, so that we were ill-concealed. Our cloaked forms must have been easily visible from the main hall where folk were hurrying by, and anyone chancing to look would easily have seen us there. We did not wish this: even though no one could know what we intended. There were few places where one might remain unseen in the glowing city, and although no one had entered the passage in which we stood, Nalda was apprehensive.

This devious, madcap matter must be over hastily, and still thinking of the gaiety we had left, I assented only half-seriously.

We determined then, to go into the deepest levels of the City for that which we sought. This plan of Nalda's was audacious. My friend would have it that we make a descent into the lower floors where dwelt the glortups. It was a wild, disturbing notion, and yet it fascinated me.

Conceive, if you are able, this giant city of ours! an entire metropolis welded into one single structure, higher than man had ever built before, and sinking far into the earth—so far that the very number of the levels was forgotten. The gleaming spire was lovely in the sunlight—silver-white, and jeweled with many windows. It had been centuries of centuries in the making, as intercourse with the outside world became less needful. Half-forgotten wars began the fortifying, and reared those giant walls no foe could pierce. Outlying districts had been abandoned to the forest growth, and all the people dwelt thereafter within the walled enclosure. Growth became vertical rather than upon the earth's surface, and floor by floor the giant structure rose as each new level was needed. It paralleled the building of a single tower, but this ultimate tower was mighty past all thought. And these things happened likewise in an hundred places throughout the land, and men congregated into feudal towns, so that they no longer spread over the green countryside and along quiet roads in little houses, for all were centred now within those giant spires. There were battles, and lands were wasted, and everywhere the forest came again or ruined, crumbling towns; for nature ever triumphs in the struggle for possession. A great many people were slain, and much secret lore of ancient years was lost, so that those who were left after the weary centuries of war no longer knew how man might fly or travel through the ocean's depths or do the other wondrous deeds of their fathers.

The cities ever fought among themselves and wished secretly to conquer one another, for each had drawn away from all the rest, becoming sufficient unto itself in this new and curious life. When at last respite came from those unending battles, none remembered the freer life beyond the walls, but continued in the manner of those who first began the towns.

Synthetic foods were everywhere employed, and since there had been no place for livestock in the cities, the tame beasts of older years grew wild and roamed the land ferociously. There were wolves—though none could tell whence they had come—and herds of clumsy, savage cattle. The cities by this time rarely held communication with one another, although at gradually lengthened intervals folk would go to other towns for special purposes. But even this fell off in time, so that at last the man was rarely met who knew the feel of grass beneath his feet.

And then one day some forgotten genius mastered the secret of
light, and created an artificial radiance more powerful than the sun,
and as inexhaustible. The last need of the old world was gone, for
dazzling synthetic beams lit and warmed our tiny world; and the
old windows were converted into thick walls. Only at the very top a
few cloud-piercing stories were left as they had been, and this was
only that curious ones might view the outside from this eyrie. For
now, of course, none went into the green and desolate wilderness
which had replaced man's traces on the outer earth. A crumbling
block of masonry, overgrown with knotted vines—a fragmentary
road that came and went beneath the clustering weeds; these were
all the eye perceived when telescopes scanned the country. Our fathers were comfortable in this haven, and there was no reason to go
beyond the walls.

Two centuries had gone since any strove to penetrate that unpeopled wilderness around us and seek even the nearest of the other
cities. Then at last a group of daring youths set out to find what
things had happened in the intervening years. The town they
sought was a great port of commerce in the old days, and lay upon
a gulf some fifty miles distant. There had been a highway when
traffic was regular between the cities, but during the long wars and
the years of abandonment this road had deteriorated into a mere
footpath beset by tangled shrubs. Here and there smooth patches
suggested the former pavement, but for the most part it was gone.
Upon this desolate path the youths set out, armed with sharp
weapons hanging at their belts. Man had believed from ancient tales
that once he had the gift of flight, but now there were many who
did not credit this. In any case, no flight-machines were left, and
the cloud-castles were given again to the birds. All travel now must
be afoot, and in this wise the group departed, feeling strangely free
on reaching the open fields that their fellows had never known.
Many eyes were on them in the upper tower; but after they reached
the wilderness and disappeared within, they were not seen again.
From that time no one wished to venture out, and there were no

human shapes upon the verdant sod about the City.

It was not many leagues before the sea began, for the ancient town was built for trading with a vanished port. How curious and lonely it all was—the tall, grey shaft in the glow of a colder sun than our fathers knew, still and dominating, brooding near the tossing oceans where no vessels sailed. The sea itself—powerful, surging, rolling; harbouring a force that overwhelms the senses, yet never a living thing to watch it; the coarse-grained beach all naked of any mark but that of the beast. The sea—yet with none to behold it tossing in anger on the rocky coast, or to spy its lesser heavings from without that shaft above the wilderness. . . . The white-piled clouds and the unutterably lonely piercing cry of some unseen waterfowl, borne by the beating wind—These were all that broke the emptiness beyond that sealed Door.

Yet there were things which led the people in our Tower to believe that life must persist elsewhere. Curious lights as of many torches in a procession were once seen winding against the dark horizon . . . a writhing maggot of light which no telescope could resolve. It had crawled beyond the tangled forests far across the leagues of moonless night, and had vanished and returned intermittently. And another time these curious lights had come near and passed close beneath the Tower, so that men might have unbarred the Door and gone without to see who bore them. Yet somehow this was felt to be unwise, for they did not know what might be encountered. And afterward, when all the fearfulness had died, those who had seen these things could not be sure that the night had not deluded them, for of such nocturnal happenings no traces could be glimpsed by those who looked afterward, by day, from the high windows.

All this had been in the long ago—half-forgotten through the centuries—till the recent years of my own life. When I was a child I had heard queer whispered tales of old, and had sought to learn more concerning the hinted marvels. I searched through clasped tomes and studied crumbling vermin-haunted records on dim shelves. Yet after

all my delving I found nothing to confirm or shed light on the leg-
endry which had grown furtively within the Tower, so concluded
that this lore was wholly fable; spun in idleness by the aged.

## II

I do not know when or how it was that the slave-things called
glortups came. Our people did not remember. None were certain
whether those squat, brownish-green little monsters that mimicked
the aspect of humans and the features of toads were created in the
wonderful experiments of our ancestors; shapen from plastic slime
with forgotten arts—or whether they were transplanted from some
nameless place in the ancient years when men flew among the
clouds. There were no records in the mouldy tomes of our race, and
it almost seemed as if they had come suddenly, from their unknown
source, in the time after our culture began to decline. It was many
centuries since anyone kept records, and the recollection of man is
short. They had been here always, said those whom I questioned,
and it was enough that they were present to work. Besides (with a
shrug) they were only . . . glortups. And whenever I sought to learn
more of their origin I met the same reply. I was not satisfied, but
no one could tell me anything further.

So maimed and repulsive were they that many of the masters
could not bear their presence, and no glortup was allowed to come
upon the highest levels. Perhaps it was well, for there, in the radiance of the higher towers, was the eyrie of the City; the heart of the
complex and infinitely delicate mechanism that, all undirected, op-
erated our tiny world. The chaos of tangled wires, of flaming tubes
and palpitating rods was such that no man could know it all, and
had not our ancestors wrought enduringly, all the motion of the
Tower would have slowed in failing years. Few and old were the
ponderous machines entrusted below to the glortups, and they
were cruder in make, of thick iron cast in heavy parts, so that little
short of malicious mischief could harm their massive segments.

But I do not think that any master really felt such provisions a necessity. There had been fear of rebellion in the past, but naught had ever come of it. It was merely needful to torture a few of the slave-things by the Electric Prong, and all the rest were dutiful again. Wisdom pointed out, of course, that absolute control of centres of importance was essential to our safety, and this rule was everywhere effected. But the vital point, the point which no one seemed to heed, was that our slaves had come to be a basic need; a masonry of toil and servitude that was the Tower's base.

Of late several acts of curious vandalism had occurred, acts which could not have been other than deliberate. The Council could not understand what led the stupid glortups, for the subtlety of these events bespoke a reasoning far beyond that of the slave-things. The possibility was felt that some unique intelligence had been spawned among them; some secret aberration that directed these malignant activities from a concealed lair. There were countless places in her vile, stinking warrens of which we knew nothing; places frequented only by the numberless generations of the glortups. And below them were many levels where no one ever went whence my friend and I were bound. In such a reeking, lightless den might hide this thing whose existence we suspected. Hence might have been directed the purposeful destruction whose existence became more and more unmistakable. At times there were rumours among our people that the thick metal wall lying between our city and that of our slaves had been pierced in a hidden place, and that glortups went in secret throughout our city during the night, traversing silent glowing halls when none observed, and slinking about the levels on strange missions. Other incredible tales said that the glortups went by dark into the outer world; that they had chipped the masonry from hidden doors, and at certain times made curious trips into the obscure realms lying beyond. I did not think that this was so, nor did I have that latent fear of the slaves which many admitted; yet I realized that a deep and sinister intellect had subtly begun to work and scheme, an evil brain that sought our overthrow.

There were many who would have sealed the Door which shut

our world apart, but so long as there was no open defiance, the Councillors were loath to alter matters, despite recurrent fears. Yet even they could not deny that matters progressed steadily toward an unknown goal. A heavy bolt of whitened steel was shot when the sleeptime came, and in the light many guards kept watch over the slaves, but unrest stirred throughout the dark.

The causes of our subtle fears were complex and oddly related. Singly, they were meaningless, but when they were viewed as one, disturbing patterns formed. There were, for example, certain futile gougings in the metal walls of the slave-world; and certain curious marks and gashes on our great machines, as if to mark them for unknown purposes, although glortups were not permitted near them.

A fearful thought, to know that evil, slant-eyed monsters skulked about deserted halls, and planned their subtle deeds while painted revellers frolicked feverishly within our rotting world. Cloaks glittered gorgeously, and high saturnalia reigned—while all around the dark ones lurked, stealthily awaiting something. Corruption spread its evil roots from floor to silver floor, as if a gangrenous disease were eating through all the Tower. Yet still the piled-up terraces stood in majesty while flashing years went by.

Aware of all this evil, Nalda and I were yet resolved upon passing into the darkness of the glortup-world. No human foot had trod that path for many dusty years—to monster-folk alone were these nighted labyrinths familiar. Nalda had braved these unknown perils years before, as one of a watchful, well-armed band; but now the memories were dim. The chief impression that remained was one of night-steeped crypts, all the blacker through contrast with the dazzling, man-made radiance which poured from hidden sources to give the upper world a ceaseless day.

### III

Although we had enquired secretly and in many subtle ways, we found no guide for our forbidden mission. Some of those among the younger group were willing and most eager to accompany us, but Nalda thought that two might gain the glortup world where more would only bring detection. And thus, since there was little cause to wait, we set out lightly clad and weaponless,—as had ever been our custom.

Delay might bring about some interference, and so we joined the stream of traffic that passed the way we wished. The hanging cloaks upon our shoulders hid our jeweled garments, and no one gave us any notice. Amidst the throngs we moved in quiet haste, and soon the giant Door loomed close. The opening was thrice my height, and smooth as polished glass upon the inner edge. When the period of sleep was sent upon the city, and the halls were dimly silent, stalwart guards swung the Door outward until it met the distant ceiling; and it was the closing lips of a silver monster. The young guards kept watch throughout the darkness. At night here would be no chance for us to pass, but in the day the risk was smaller.

But as we drew near that vast portal, a fear came upon me, and I was trembling lest we be stopped. The barrier stood open as a train of glortups bore foodstuffs into the City. I did not see what happened, but there was trouble of a sort, for a swift flurry of motion passed among the black-clad guardians, and one of them ran his angry spear through the belly of a slave. The maimed thing dropped its burden and fell writhing on the floor, with foulness oozing from its wound. We stood agape, but Nalda saw that for a moment no one watched, and so we passed unseen into the glortup-world.

I stood then, in a world unknown. For a thousand years this place of slaves had grown and spread in darkness, so that the plan and shape of its labyrinthine passages was lost to mortals. There, in filth and gloom, they spawned, those twisted slaves, and flocked in evil throngs upon strange missions. Some might ask why we did not obliterate those rotten levels, and put the slaves to torch and spear, scouring the City clean of this corruption. The time was gone when we might have done this—our race was softened now and paid more heed to gold and silver spices and silken robes than to the menace from below. The glortup-world was vast and cata-combed, like a hill of monstrous ants that naught could slay. *They* were not our slaves: although they kept a servile pretense, we knew it to be a mockery.

Standing there in pale gloom lit by many torches, we hesitated, for neither knew the way, and it was grimly dark before us. But we must penetrate the shifting gloom. Nalda touched my arm, turning away, and in a while the door was lost to us as we joined a throng of busy slaves. Most were bound in the direction whence we had come, conveying various articles for the use of the masters, while others returned empty-handed or bearing some frankly pilfered del-icacy. They scarce accorded us a glance, and then it was more one of indifference than surprise at our presence. Once in a while those bands of masters had come among them, and they took us for part of such a group.

I am certain that we should not have been allowed to make this journey, had any known of it. But no one was aware that we had come, for we had slipped away in quiet. We learned where a pillar stood that marked the descent into the lower levels, and it was soon before us. The opening was dim and black, and scarce ever a slave entered it, though a few came out as we peered into its depths. Then we descended the thirty-odd stairs and entered into the city of the glortups.

As we hurried on, a number of the things stared hatefully at us, not with enough interest for menace, but with a vague resentment that we feared. I had begun to regret our folly, but Nalda spurred me on. It was not far to the next of those many stairways, and we passed the intolerant eyes of the slave-folk with a rapid pace. Upon this anciently built plane we came on ponderous machines. The glortups were trusted for their care, as there was little to go wrong, and no damage might be done them. They occupied a vast dim room, and flashed amid incessant grindings. There was a tremen-dous creaking and groaning and clashing of bright wheels, and clat-tering noises echoed through the sound-filled air. From an unseen source came endless tumbling sounds of maddening duration.

I was dazed and confused by these contrivances. Hurrying cables intermeshed into a meaningful rhythm, dynamos spat their glittering fire; wheels and cogs and clashing metal were everywhere about us. As I stood with my companion there was a small movement across the cellar. Something other than the machines had shifted, but it may have been a guard.

The floor trembled and buzzings poured like a wind about us. Nalda led the way through a forest of bristling machines, stooping below swift cables, and by a winding course avoided the devices. Once I was fascinated by the odd shadows, and barely avoided a sinister beaked device that swung scythe-like past my head. The glittering blade ascended as rapidly as it had come, and disappeared upon its course, but for a frightened moment it had seemed deliberate to me.

As we passed through a thick door of metal we were confronted by a one-eyed slave. He stared insolently, and turned abruptly into an alcove. I did not realize what he intended until Nalda seized my arm and we began that precipitate flight into the nether world. We flung ourselves down the broad, unaccustomed steps; and all the time I listened strainingly above our heavy breath for the sound of pursuit.

It was darker here upon this second level, and no slaves were about. There was a terrible silence and calculated emptiness, and I was racked with fear; but in a little while courage returned, and we passed down the mystic corridor to the next stair.

This, however, was lit by torches, and I saw that we had come upon the eating-level of the slaves. Some were squatting in small rooms and sprawled upon rough benches. They held bowls of coarse food, from which the steam arose; and I thought that I saw one gnaw upon a bone, though this cannot have been. They were engrossed in gluttony, and did not seem to notice us. Something in their postures, however, caused me to suspect that they were not as preoccupied as they would seem. This interest in the bowls was too marked, too planned, and I felt that they watched us intently from beneath dark brows. This all seemed as if the things expected us, as if their lack of interest veiled other thoughts.

For a moment, as we passed silently along the corridor by those red-lit rooms, I did not see the door we sought; but then my eyes detected it beyond the gloom at the passage-end. My companion followed me, watching my jeweled collar for a guide. When we reached the place, we were forced almost to lower ourselves down the tiny metal stair beneath the hinged cover, and after we had descended the dismal steps, a shadow came very silently above the opening. Nalda did not notice, but when I looked up, I saw that the glortups had replaced the metal slab. We could not retrace our way.

I did not say anything of this, but I was keenly aware of some cautious malice that the glortups planned.

From there the planes were more dark and evil, shadow-steeped and labyrinthine. Far down beneath the earth we came at last to a level which lay deep in dust, where doorways leading into secret alcoves were rusty and ajar. There was something terrible in these long-deserted alleys and dark passages beneath the pressing earth. It typified the downfall of our race and the fast-approaching end to the revelry above us. Our race had scorned the knowledge of the past and fallen into ignorance, and even yet they did not see those dim shadows lying upon the path ahead.

Down still. Our way led into these remote and desolate levels where not even glortups came. These walls were cracked with the weight of aeons, and the pavement had forgotten human tread. It became a nightmarish and interminable descent from dim corridor to corridor until I was dazed with climbing downward.

You ask me what we sought in these unpeopled cellars? All that I recall is our certainty at the time, the assuredness that we should not fail in that dim quest. Of its nature I can tell nothing but that it was forbidden to us, and that we risked much to go. My weary memory holds little more . . . the dreams are fading rapidly; and I recall but a small part of that phantasmagoric descent. I know that once my companion fell and crushed the mouldering rail about an interminable stair, so that it broke and fell into a lightless shaft. And once I thought that I had found a sign of something living. But I knew that it could not be, that I had seen some fungus, and that it was not a crust of bread that lay within the shadow; but cold fears crept into my heart.

Now the city of the masters was lost to us as yesterday, for we were deep in these forgotten levels. But in spite of the desertedness and the thick dust that lay everywhere about, a strange *awareness* haunted me. I felt that somewhere in these catacombs our coming was awaited—but what lay waiting, I did not know. And I strove in vain to overcome this fancy.

There was a broad flight of stairs sinking into the gloom before us, and I saw that they were made of stone. Why this rude material had been employed by the vanished masons was not clear; but shortly it broke upon me that we were no longer in the levels beneath the city of our forbears, but in some level of subterranean crypts. This place was mined with a vast system older than the Tower itself, and from the ponderous masonry I judged that we were far within those black and illimitable warrens.

The sight of that wide stair and the impassive void of the hall beyond made an ineffable impression upon my weakened senses. We looked upon this grey expanse from a platform at the turn of a railless stair, and though only thick dust confronted us, there was something overwhelmingly frightful in that view. I thought that I felt a little draught of chill air, but it could not have been, for the dust was undisturbed. There was no rubble in that unfathomed hall, but far down its length the black entrance of another passage opened on the left.

As we stole along the ancient corridor, I saw once more a shadowed object by the wall; and this time there could be no error. And it was not buried in the deep-piled dust, but lay before us, oozing hot pitch and little curls of smoke. A recently extinguished torch was smouldering in the path. But whence had come such an object, in this fungus-haunted vault?

Unwarned, I pierced the awful veil of time and realized in chill, vampiric fear where these places led, and where we were. In an ecstasy of terror I knew why the tunnels were so oddly built, and why they differed from those our fathers made above them. These nighted burrows were not built by men at all—they were there before.

I realized this in a frenzy built up by countless subtle queernesses. I knew now what race had catacombed the earth—I knew the terrible secrets of our own people. The place from whence the glortups came was known to me, and I knew with what they leagued and planned; and what had borne those curious torches through the dark wilderness. The revelation enshrouded my soul in terror, and I shrieked aloud because of what was in these sunless corridors; because of the monstrousness that had lain these centuries beneath the City, and because of the miasmatic contagion that it spread. As I strove to speak there came a sound that should not have been, and Nalda heard, and turned to flee, but clustering shadows loomed like formless giants, and the darkness was a hampering veil.

Thus we came at last upon the evilness that lurked beneath the rotting Tower.

## Pursuit of the Moth

Laughing joyously, the youth Sigrill pursued his companion through briar and thicket-hedge. They held him snared, these pricking weeds; and while he sought to disentangle himself, the other slipped away; his lithe body parting the brush as if he passed through cobwebs. On the edge of the grove Amno paused and tauntingly displayed the bow he stole in mockery. "You will not easily regain your weapon," he tantalized, "for you must overtake me first, and I am fleet as the moth!" Saying this, he vanished.

Yet ensnared amid those thorny hedges, Sigrill was half-angered at this slim companion who had so neatly sent him blundering. As he gingerly freed himself, the youth caught glimpses of a wondrous meadow that lay beyond the wood, basking verdantly in the stillness of a summer day. It was the calm and pleasantly inactive season that comes in the year's midst, when there are yet gay blossoms lingering from spring; in a time before the green land has felt that dry searing heat of August. It is then, more than any other time of year, that a true peace descends upon the earth; and in the golden haze of a summer noon there comes surcease to all the enmity of life.

Finding this a boredom to their boundless youth; the two had set out in hunt of any game that might unwarily emerge. The sun was not obscured by any cloud, and the day was fortunate. Having lunched on wild figs and those other fruits which are known within the forest, for several hours they wandered amongst the twisted boles that rear and pile throughout the moss-grown jungle. Although quiet winds dispelled those noxious swamp-mists, and though beyond an arabesque of twining boughs he saw the reassuring sky of gold and blue and violet; Sigrill was disturbed. To find a cause for this uneasiness was difficult, for nowhere was there aught to give alarm or dread. It was only a strangeness in the atmosphere, a curious and portentous disquiet that lurked unseen. He found himself not wholly liking that merry taunt from Amno . . . *I am fleet as the moth.* He was disturbed, too, at the absence of that weapon which customarily swung about his shoulders. So, abandoning the efforts to release himself unscratched, Sigrill plunged in force through all the creeping growths that hampered his way.

Stepping beneath a low-bent bough overhung with parasitic orchids, he reached the forest margin and found a firmer soil beneath his tread. The shallow grasses of the meadow rustled almost imperceptibly, and a draught of warmness touched him; but beneath that empty sky of violet there was no sign of his companion as far as he could see. facing the broad unbroken plain; on either hand and to his back there reared the mighty jungle, where Amno might be hiding. For a moment he considered, and then began to skirt those crowded, shadowy trees. Behind vegetation at his left a man might readily conceal himself. Without alarm or anxiousness the huntsman searched. Into many clumps and thicket-darknesses he peered, calling for surrender more angrily than in jest, but there was no reply save that of the soughing wind. He did not pause, and so at length had searched for many yards along the jungle-edge, shouting as he went.

Now he was perturbed in fact, and did not smile, but shouted with a real dismay; and when he heard no answer yet, searched in wild and frantic ways.

But as he called and looked about, he saw upon the miry ground a set of human tracks, and these he traced in anxiousness to where they had led amidst a clump of dark and gloomy trees.

The trail marked out a narrow path among shroud-hung boles and past dark piles of rotting underbrush, and did not waver in the course. Wondering that Amno pursued this curious route, the other followed with hastening steps; and did not think about the dangers threatening one who bore no arms or club.

Now the deepness of a black morass was on him, and he scrambled clumsily from weed to slime-rooted weed, with naught to light his way. Beyond the trunks of cypresses a faint illumination came, as if some horrid rottenness were glowing in putrescent filth. Stagnant pools of tepidness gave forth a noxious stench, and there was nothing but dark and the splashing of his boots within the sticky mud. He made his way reluctantly into the murky glen, fearful that his friend had rashly come into this place. And Sigrill felt that hidden eyes were fixed upon his path, though a loneliness was everywhere. He did not falter, but trailed his friend through long and devious windings, perplexed at the sureness of the tracks. It almost seemed as if they fled—(or did they follow? he was not sure) upon a destined course, over which gnarled vines shut out the bright sky. Confusion reigned: the uncontrolled tumult of a loathsome swamp. But now there loomed ahead the bulk of some defensive wall, bearing a single pillar-flanked gate; and beyond this gate was a dim fortress.

The castle rose till giant cypresses were overtopped, and it was hung with vines of centuries, whose secret roots had cracked their supporting stones. This monstrous growth of clinging plants concealed it from the plain—that clean and grassy field so vividly in

contrast with this foetid tower. Wondering that a crumbled pile
rose where only plants should be, Sigrill halted briefly upon the
path of dark loam. He did not like the pillars of the ruined gate, for
they were twined with bloated creepers; yet between them showed
hasty footsteps, and he knew that Amno had passed before him.

As Sigrill resumed his stride a luminous grey moth flew up star-
tlingly, and beat soft wings about his head. They were great wings,
and he was forced to strike at it. Brokenly, it fell upon the ground,
and fluttered crippled wings until he kindly crushed the writhing
form beneath his heel.

At the dim portal of the vacant place there hung no door, but
fragmentary planks were piled upon the sill. The youth was urged
ahead by footprints leading into the lightless maw of this revolting
wreck. What things had built it as a lair or when, he dared not
think, for it was old; far older than the jungle, and menacing in
each aspect of its dim and sinister bulk. But Sigrill prayed in silent,
and upon the air he drew an ancient Sign of holiness. Having thus
prepared for any evilness within the place, he entered.

At first, because of the gloom, he did not see the objects piled
in heaps of gorgeous rubble, but in a little while beheld all forms of
glorious ruined things, unsurpassed in richness. There were gem-set
chalices, and broken furniture of curious make, inlaid with golden
leaves. A single triangular window-pane of lapis-lazuli set unnaturally high above the tiled floor gave light, whereby he saw the rotten
rags of wondrous tapestries sagging from mildewed walls—weavings
of some perished loom whose figured richness stank in foul decay.

But from the blurred and grimy fragments he discerned things
passing strange, and was afraid at what they traced in coloured
thread. There came an overwhelming fright upon the youth as one
patterned shape stirred faintly, but half-crying out, he saw that it
was not the tapestry which moved, but a silver moth upon it—a
moth such as he had seen before the murky gates. Large as his two
hands it was, and glistening wonderfully in the light from that blue-
gleaming pane. Fluttering a moment, it descended in a swift erratic

flight, and lighted on the quiet face of that which Sigrill had not spied: the limpness of a youthful corpse on piles of ruined rag.

*May 5, 1935*

## At Night

It was very nearly dusk when we reached the house of the four old people. The fields about us were purpled with darkness, and a pear-shaped moon came faintly in the northeastern sky. Below the dim satellite I could discern a group of crouching trees, who held among them that ancient and disreputable building. Low, black, and sinister, it seemed a fitting harbour for the incredible wrongs attributed to the pallid inhabitants.

As we sneaked toward it, like a pair of thieving cats, both of us were silent. Our motions were as soundless as falling snow, because we dared not be found so close to that house. We had come this unpropitious night to find a cause for the vanishment of our friend, Elshard. Three days before we knew that he had ridden on the highway beyond the grassy field, but since then, no word of him had come. It was a dark night when he rode his weary steed that way, and the pine-surrounded cottage was on the other side of that field, and the strange people had bad legend in our village; so Yarrh and I had come aspying.

There was no light in the side of the house to which we came, but a small lamp shone in the cellar, and from this came the voice of the old men and that beldame who guarded their house. We lay in the bushes to watch, but there was only angry talk, and we saw nothing unsavory in the glare of that lamp beyond the dirty window.

From where we hid, the place seemed very large, and the pines showed only a little over that hunched roof. But there was a single tree on this side of the house—a tree that was not an elm or an oak or a maple. In the moonlight it stood guardian to the black house, hovering wickedly misshapen and bloated limbs above the crumbling shingles.

I had not known a tree to be there, and since we lay concealed for a time, my gaze returned to it. The yard was bladeless sand, but the dancing moonlight peopled it, and when the rays strained through the high leaves, there were odd patterns of shadow on the ground. The bark of that immense tree was bulging and contorted, so that where it outlined on the sky my fancy drew bestial, writhing shapes. Here, on the high limb, a chimera moved, below it was a formless ape; while on another limb I saw fat serpents. And all were living, straining for release from the imprisoning bark.

I toyed with this mirage a while, and was near to showing Yarrh when he silenced me in haste. After a quiet interval in which I saw the cellar light was gone, an old man came around the corner of the house, carrying a great loaded sack upon his wizened shoulders. We did not stir, lest he should turn and see us, and my breath was painfully abated. Going beneath the lowest branches, in a place where they bent to meet the ground, he passed from view, and then returned unburdened. After a brief, pleased consideration of the tree, he went around the house and left the yard in emptiness.

When we were sure that he had gone, Yarrh and I stole out to see what his strange burden was. And what it was I think we knew already—for Elshard had not been very large.

I looked up at the vibrant bulk of foliage and a thousand leaves peered back. Then I was afraid, but Yarrh had gone too close, and my restraining hand was late. Rustling, uncoiling in a serpentine animation, the boughs reached out and fixed themselves most horribly to the hands of Yarrh, and to his face. His screams were lost in the embracing bark; the bark that spread like a cancerous growth along his limbs and over his body. As if it rooted somewhere beneath his skin, the bark erupted over my poor friend, absorbing him, so that in a brief shocking moment he was as one with the twisting, contorted branch. Struggling somewhat, the new human-shaped protuberance was a sentient prisoner; a prisoner unreleasable; a prisoner with Elshard and those other victims of the guardian tree.

*February 9, 1936*

# The Root-Gatherers

*A Sketch*

The red sun was nearly lost behind a welter of dark trees, and night thickened about us. It was then I first noticed that my mother had a dim fear of the ancient lost place through which we must go. I did not mind seeing ruined buildings; in truth rumours of the corpse-town had fascinated my young ears. You see, I had accompanied her only a few times to hunt food-roots, and had never before gone the way lying directly through the city. Tubers grew well in the clay caverns beyond that place of ruins, and in order that no one else might find them, my mother always chose a time when she could go unobserved. This was in the brief period before nightfall, while the tribe was engaged in cooking.

About us spread once cultivated fields where straggling bean and pea-vines persisted after a time past reckoning, but since man did not care for them, or fight the weeds, few plants bore anything edible. A horde of pale blossoms, hued like the summer evening, and bearing five points, overspread leagues of unused soil and crowded onto the rotten highway. This land about us, these ancient, sun-covered fields, we knew had once been great and flourishing; but in a forgotten time something wrong had happened. We are the children of the old race, but no one cares now about the ancient things and the world of dead memories. Such things they say are of no use, for they cannot help us to obtain food. Only two or three of us take interest in the past. Perhaps it is a fortunate thing, because those who do are half-restive in the life about them.

A last reflection from the sky spread a golden mantle over the fields as we came to the wood of black fir-trees which hinted at the nearness of the first ruin. Their foliage shut out the ending glory of the sun, and for a breathless period we hastened through premature night. I pushed my way among the bushes, following my mother, and soon the ebbing daylight sparkled rewardingly again in leaves of summer greenery.

When we were beyond the trees I looked at the small figure beside me, and felt a pang because of half-recollected stories of our ancient grandeur, when we had made cities like the dead one before us, and did not fear storms and animals. But then a glimpse of the most outlying ruin changed my thoughts, and wonder and astonishment hid from me the knowledge that we were frail and lonely and trivial amid surroundings that thought of a vanished day.

Forgotten now was our humble errand and the dust of the road. Before us lay a fallen tower, very nearly complete, girt with thin pillars like fingers clasped about it. The base of this brick spire lay near us and the little wood, but what remained of the highest tier was half buried, very far away. It had been fashioned strongly, and had fallen like a chimney, intact save where a few centuried pines (lean and tortured) found root-hold in the encircling facade.

There was nothing to show the purpose for which it had been made, and tradition only knew of it that men had drawn the lightning there in magical ways, and sent out again the glory of the skies in a throbbing halo. My regret that we have no memories is a pang more difficult than hunger, for hunger can be satisfied, but for the nostalgic beckoning of old centuries there is no assuagement. I would like so much to fill out the gap of years which binds us to the past, when men built that old city; and to know the hues and forms of a life vanished utterly. But there are only ruins on which to speculate, fragments of a life existing nowhere, and the people of that place are lonely in the desolate grave of night. A rain of centuries has obliterated most of the traditions about them and all that I may ever recapture is as nothing when it is weighed against the ignorance of our time. Forest and wooded glen, and tales of ancient huntings are the joys of my race.

There are two ruins which even yet hold for me the greatest lure, and I saw them both, that day, now likewise gone into the forgotten abyss of time. The first is that Gargantuan tower of slim embracing pillars, whose foundation—jagged on the sky—seemed to my childish eyes much like a crowd of vultures, and the other, a metal bridge farther on the way, seen only as one nears the city. The bridge is not so great in height as the tower must have been, but it spans a great sluggish river. Men have used it forever when they wished to go into the place of ruins, and wild things scurry over the perilous span in darkness. Sometimes apes and bears are tracked across the old bridge, and slain upon it, though since my youth these are grown scarce.

We came to it later, when the broken tower was out of sight. It was lost overhead in perspective and darkness, and I beheld the corroded girders with a vague fear. The end near us was choked with trees, and beneath it the river flowed green, with spots of diseased yellow. There were five arches upon pillars of old brick, for the river is wide in that part, and had been that way even when the city was built. The weedy stream forms a lagoon where great rushes and lilies grow, and there is only a stirring of the tired water. It is a vivid and chromatic scene that I remember—the dead green surface and the vague glitter of the bridge at dusk—though years have gone since I was there last.

I looked about as we started across the ruinous structure, and saw a few pale stars where a girder had fallen away overhead. They watched like indifferent eyes, through the faint evening, from a timeless vantage point. Vague emotions moved in me, and I felt again the regret that ruins must lie unpeopled and forgotten. It was a brief sensation that the noises of a dying thing might arouse; not pity, for pity is then of no use, but an ineffable emotion as near to sorrow as the mist is to rain. It was not sharp enough to analyze, but I have kept the memory of a child who felt, beyond the netted, broken girders, the regard of those unseeing stars.

There was only in places a floor, so for the most part we walked on iron beams. In the blackness under us the water rustled past some obstruction which I did not see, and on the curving shores was a cluster of stooping trees. The far end of the bridge was in shadow, but I knew from my mother's words that we should come out between the metal ankles of a guarding statue into the vast silent ruins of a city. Tottering in the gloom, the old bridge was like a man whose ribs are sharped by the years. As we traversed it, I looked up in apprehension, and saw that above us tons of insecure metal swayed like a broken spider web. I feared that it would fall, but it had been suspended in that fashion before memory, and yet the cables are intact and the girders whole.

Then we came into the city, passing below the mute colossi whose downward gaze had the frightening indifference of all ancient things. There was an aspect of *waiting* about the metal statue, whose head touched the darkness and the increasing stars. No one has guessed when it was made and set there as guardian of the bridge. It is of the same material, and built of cunning segments, rather than sculptured. Looking briefly at the high, indistinct face, I turned away from the bridge and the nameless crouching giant to go into the ruinous streets.

Here was Doom. The shards of a city that once knew merchants and toilers and the glittering rich—peopled now with memories and shadows and the whisper of the breeze. Silent now were the streets whose paving had sounded with the trample of multitudes; silent also the tumbled houses. There were no high structures, these had fallen unmarked during the years of neglect. The air was stagnant and weary, and the dark holes in the street and buildings were like the orifices of a nameless skull.

A moon had come up out of the chaos of stars, and swung above the fretted outline of the ruined city, where an immemorial silence reigned. No throb of bird-wing, no rustle of furred feet disturbed the still evening. There were only stars attendant on the moon, and a bluish silence which filled the town like water.

For centuries the vines and roots of jungle things had accumulated about the city, enveloping it and gnawing at outlying districts. For centuries the bubbling hues of sunset had glazed with yellow lacquer those dark streets, and crept along unseen walls. Throughout the multitudinous days of its collapse there had been clouds over it and bright skies and rains: the thunder of the elements had beaten down on it, and sun and storm had battled, each claiming it his fortress. But that night, all was fled save silence.

I saw what once had been a shop—the front was crumbled, and a rotten beam lay half across the opening, but there was a litter of incredible wreckage within—goods that had been fashioned for purchasers dead a thousand years, despised even by the beast. Someone had come there and sorted out the useful, undamaged things, but like the rest, these lay in an unclaimed pile. Perhaps the scavenger was there a day before us—perhaps he had become the prey of some animal eight hundred years ago. There was nothing to tell why he had not borne off his spoil.

I would have liked to go into some of the buildings which ranged spectrally along the road. Now one, and then another took my fancy, but we had no time if we meant to end our mission by a safe hour. There was one pile of white marble standing alone in a little field, as if it had been a temple or a strong man's house. And I saw another; round, with many bordering pillars, like an immense spider; whose purpose I could not understand. I would have explored these had there been no hurry. But I knew that we must get back before there was too much moonlight, and the beasts came out. They are very terrible at such times.

And so we went on, and found many roots in the caverns beyond the city.

*June 1936*

# A Dim-Remembered Story

*Dedicated to H. P. Lovecraft*

*Prologue*

I have seen the castle of Yrn, which shall rise in undreamed years, and I have been at night in the wood which usurps a curious ruin. I have witnessed the master-things at their gigantic play, and I have known that last abyss wherein my faltering body might not live. Now I shall write of what happened, and of how these things befell me.

Time, of all things, is most elusive; for no one can know what it actually is. Perhaps time is a creation of Man—and Man is a brief thing upon a fragile sphere. His world is but a single blossom in the garden of the firmament. It might be that if there were no life, Time would not exist. The crystal stars would then remain in their careless pattern—the night sky would be as great and jewel-set, but if no thing watched, if no heart moved in all eternity, by what should Time be reckoned? A scientist has written: "Suppose that everything in the universe should halt—all life cease, the planets pause in their orbits, the atoms and electrons cease their flow. Time would be suspended and when motion set in again it would appear to us as the next instant, and we should be unaware of the occurrence." He suggests, too, that possibly Time does not run a smooth course; that it may ebb and surge like any stream. In each such abeyance there might be long eternities.

With this is my story linked. What I would say may forever elude me, because it is difficult to put such things in words, but I am getting down this narrative in the hope that someone may understand, or at least believe, it.

In looking down earth's centuries, our minds can summon all the vanished things—the filth of Villon's Paris, or the tumult of dead Carthage, or monster-swamps which have seen no mortal in secret Asia. Pageants are re-staged for us, the noise and colour of forgotten worlds are fixed eternally. Yet because we cannot reach them, they seem beyond recovery; their ecstasies wholly lost. To you now who scan this page, I say they are not gone, nor do I affect a paradox. Augustus yet prevails in uncrumbled Rome, and Christian warriors storm the bearded foe of Acre, on that bright dust-filled day nine centuries ago. In Poseidonis there are lunar rituals, and Russia's Ivan holds a bloody scepter. These worlds are only around some crook in the lane of eternity, hidden by a bend in the path along which our own frail world passes.

Our age is a given point in the inexorable journey—if we might look ahead, we should see it blotted out by a succeeding epoch. Then our towns and continents will be as one with those lost earths. Yet our wars and loves and passions, the shapes and hues of our existence are set, fixed, in some unknown way. All things that have been, all that shall be, are together recorded. It is as if everything in earth's history, each phase and aspect of life, had been ordained at the great start of things. As if they had occurred, perhaps, at one mighty instant, so that the beginning and the end are merged. Or as if each century were an earth separate in space and time and matter. A thousand earths—a world repeating itself beyond counting, so that things may exist in many avatars and many ages. Worlds beside us that we cannot reach.

And so with those latter events of earth's career, in the land before us, we shall come upon them in a destined sequence, through the rise and triumph and perishing of cultures, through the great sweep of history, as autumn succeeds the full summer, and tired leaves fall where once fell blossoms. But if the way might be opened, the door unsealed, we could go into other realms, to see and know forbidden things. They are as real, those future years, as any which our far journeying has passed. This fact I know with a poignancy none other can share. Do not say the land ahead does not exist, simply because you cannot see it.

Look tonight at the stars. Let them overwhelm you in the postures of their bright dance. Face the vastness which they dot like silver bees, and sound with your own brain the mystery, hazarding at the inscrutable plan of things. Then you will comprehend my tale.

## I.

### *That Is Not Dead . . .*

Each muscle of my body twitched weakly as I recovered consciousness. For a moment, as I lingered in the void between sleep and life, there was a sense of floating—a feeling of disembodiment that increased as I neared reality and awakening. It was as if I drifted idly among clouds of red and purple, of green and orange and yellow, mingled with yet other prismatic hues for which I can find no name. I moved in pleasant languor through a thousand-coloured realm, knowing it as half a dream and I a dream within it. About and above me were shapes like those made in our eyes by gazing too long at the sun. I was ambiguously conscious that all these forms had such an origin, that they were but a visual rendering of things whose true nature eluded my sight and comprehension. Then all the horizon of seething colour faded swiftly, dropped into organizing patterns, and ebbed about me. Everything was clear in an abrupt stab of light.

Hot bands were tight about my throbbing head, and I was unable to rise from the bank of moss whereon I lay. A verdant greenness smote my retina and shot through trembling eyelids. The green of a forest luxuriant in plants and trees. This wealth of ferns and matting vines and thick, olive-coloured trunks was pierced with gilding sunlight. I blinked painfully, and all the jungle wavered into brightness. Everywhere this monstrous forest loomed, dripping pale sunlight into leafy strongholds. My weakness seeped away as I sprawled prone in the rich sward.

How may I convey to you the mysterious beauty of this afternoon wood? Keats would have worshipped it like a Druid-priest. It was a green-carpeted gallery guarded by rows of dark, polished pillars, or a tapestry of gold on silk. There were somewhere bird-voices in ardent song, and I heard the pleasantly harsh cry of a carrion fowl. But I did not see the fluttering wings, nor could I discover anything living.

After a little I attempted to rise, but Gulliver bound in Lilliput could not have had more difficulty. A sword of pain was thrust into my aching head, as if some blow had felled me. My thoughts were blurred, and somehow fearing, as I stood wearily to gaze about me. How had I come into that ancient wood? Clustered with great bushes among oak boles, it seemed almost tropical in that glamorous light. Trees leaned in on me, alight with the failing sun, as if they would impart some woodland secret. It was like waking into a dream of Arden, or some strange forgotten wood of Arthur's time. It was as fabulous and richly foliated as lost Eden might have been. On every side the great trees rose; above, their tops were so netted as to hide the cobalt sky. They lingered, waiting and silent—tall goblins circling me with outstretched arms. This wood was strange and mystical. In the lingering afternoon dark shadows spread, and tried to blot out the pools of light strewn everywhere.

In what manner had I come to be there? Alien and inscrutable, my surroundings gave no clue. It was painful and annoying to stand bewildered and impotent in a strange place. Deprived of recent memories, weak and bruised, how was I to leave the place and reach the city? If the visions of a sleeping mind were made reality—and reality this was—one might know my baffling sensations. I had never anywhere before seen the place, yet now I stood upon the grass within a strange, faintly sinister forest, searching with confused eyes for some familiar sight.

The blind eyes of the forest peered back. Leaves and mosses seemed to watch me, and tortuous black limbs to await my action. I had wandered many times over half-lost roads and through dark, unpenetrated regions in the Kansas hill-country. Perhaps, in a state of partial amnesia, I had got into a secluded portion of the woodland. I could in no other way account for the odd surroundings in which I found myself. And if that were so, a few hours' walk should take me to some house or roadway. At either of these, I would be all right. On the road I might hail some passing car, or at a house I could quietly learn my position, saying that I had become lost from a party of campers. By this I should attract little attention to myself, which was best, if my memory were indeed gone. Already darkness was settling upon the great world, and this enchanted sunlight would ebb into dusk before the hour was past.

So, perplexed and irritated and perhaps a little afraid, I wandered into another glade, surrounded by dark bushes. From that place, which was as unfamiliar as the first, I made my way through snaring briars, until I came to a third. Each of them was to me a street in an unfamiliar town; and I added to my bruises the flick of sharp vines. Soon the futility of this aimless walk forced itself upon me, and though I could see no smoke, nor any trace of habitation, beyond the avenue of sunset trees, I determined that my course should lie in one direction. If I should walk long enough, there must certainly be an end to the unpierced forest.

With this thought, I chose a random direction—to the left of the misty, tree-hidden sun, and walked into the brightness. The vegetation surrounding me was very rich, and I wondered that it should remain untouched by men. In these modern times the places seemed fabulous—a wealth of timber that knew no axe. Hoary and untramped, it had been neither cut nor touched by man, as fallen, decaying trees attested.

I had walked some little time before I realized the dangers those unplumbed thickets might conceal. I had seen nothing; not even the flutter of those abounding singers; but some thin voice of inner consciousness whispered, *tread quietly;* and a little breeze soughed past, laden with the mysterious scent of the forest.

The rich profusion of the trees began to thin, and I saw the late sky behind dappling greenery. The silence of this vast clear world was rendered more noticeable by the noise of birds, but for some while they remained beyond sight. Now, as I paused a moment, one plump bluejay lit with unexpected quickness on a dark bough before me, and cocked his speculative head. There was something unusual in the short body—something that troubled me, though what it was, I did not know. Startled by the small creature, I smiled at my fright, but when he was gone, my wariness was increased.

Then, at once there was no sound but that of quivering branches, until I heard above it the heavy rustling of some large animal, very near. The wood became to me a place of terror, and the bright sunset failed to assuage my nocturnal fright. I had seen nothing; yet I felt now an unreasonable apprehension, and fled among the oaks and foetal pines. If there had been a real danger, if some creature had trailed my path, that noisy flight imperilled me. It was only an excessive nervousness that caused my dark terror, for nothing followed. After an inward struggle, I slowed my pace, forcing myself into a normal walk. But when I came upon a stout limb beneath the trees, I took it with me as a club.

The trembling of dusk overshadowed the forest when I came upon the second living thing that my long walk revealed. It was, I am certain, a rabbit; though of what breed I hesitate to say. There was only a glimpse of the round grey body before it plunged into the underbrush, but I was greatly disturbed by that sight. When I speak of it, there exists no comparable experience whereby to judge. The little animal was not visibly deformed: it moved with reassuring naturalness, yet there was something definitely wrong about those short, thick legs, and the flattened tail. It was a rabbit, but such a rabbit as might have lived in the years before man's existence, or as the product of cautious experiment in some gleaming laboratory. It was not the sort of animal that should roam a Kansas field.

Yet it was not until I saw those other objects that I received the full shock of implication. Walking in the dim light of that forest, I came upon profuse numbers of wild yellow roses, frail to the touch. And as the red-gold sun hovered in a last farewell, I found among the blossoms a singular thing.

At first glance it was no more than a rock, albeit a rock of curious evenness and regularity. But as I examined it the fact became apparent that this moss-hidden block, beneath the guarding thorns, had been shaped by deliberate hands. There were traces of an ornate and ineradicable carving. Despite the fleeing daylight, despite the verdant patina of forgotten centuries, I saw a design that was not traced by capricious weathering. This stone was patterned, and had once formed part of a massive wall. I knew this because of the other stones that I found close by. Some were drifted over by decaying leaves and insect-haunted mould, or split by usurping roots. These also were from some lost ruin, the magnitude of which was disturbing. Not because the blocks were so large, but from the number and position of those which were uncovered, and from that greater number betrayed by an exposed corner, or an uncovered edge, I saw that a mighty tower had fallen very long ago in this place. Long ago—and Kansas is a new country. Only a century has gone since white men settled there, and the Indian had no such masonry.

The tower had not collapsed from age and imperfection—that much was clear from the disposition of the ruins. Some force had crushed those blocks into the black soil of the forest; strewn them (like scattered toys) over a great area.

I stood aghast before this evidence of an old, unrecorded catastrophe, and the fears that were to come later began smouldering in my brain. Fragile blossoms piled their fragrant petals over the old ruins, and great trees were sprung everywhere amid them. But even the hoary fingers of time might not conceal what had happened in that place, when the forest was young.

Here a deep gouge, as if made by a clumsy Titan, marred the flowering sod: in another place a whole fragmentary wall, whose stones were broken *across,* lay beneath aspiring bushes. Whatever had happened—an explosion, an earthquake,—the memory of that flaming day had lingered through dark centuries, while vines and flowers crawled and bloomed above the shards of a cryptic doom.

As I have said, the antiquity of this ruin began to trouble me. The fact alone that I was so far from any road seemed disquieting. Perhaps this is the best time to speak of those dim, unshaped fears that crowded my dazed mind. Can you conceive the bitterness of my position? This was not amnesia, for I knew my identity and all the countless details of my commonplace life. There was no stumbling in my reason—I could have described even the pattern of the metal-work in that elevator I so often entered, or the chipped door of my small office. Yet there was some dim barrier . . . a veil enshrouding whatever lay immediately before my wakening.

You know, it was an odd place I found myself in. A place whose existence was unfamiliar to me—and night was close. Then, too, I had discovered things which hinted at a gulf between this place and my previous life. I do not mean that I had any assurance, then—but somehow, everything seemed very unusual in the gloom.

Disturbed and perplexed though I was, there was at first no panic in my bewilderment. Instead, I had an intense and half-suspecting curiosity about a place harbouring such things as I had seen—a place strange, too, in other, less obvious ways. Not even the countless trees seemed normal, though what was unusual about them I could not decide.

Now I shall tell you things as they happened. To this, I will append what I have since guessed or learned. Only in this way can you understand anything of my reactions and emotions. Gradually there was forced upon me the realization that I had undergone something enormously removed from man's experience. In all the years of our race there has been no one else who can narrate such a tale. It was, viewed in the perspective of what we call normality, as alien and cat-astrophic as the approach of some celestial derelict laden with fiery death. It involved abstrusenesses that might baffle Jeans or Edding-ton, perplex the greatest of our scientists. For it was a looping, of the real world with another no less real, but more distant than the mind can hold. Distant not in the scale of miles and light-years, but in another, less tangible, less conceivable, fashion.

I do not wish to evade, but my fingers are reluctant to form the incredible words; though I underwent the experiences for which those words would stand. Trembling in the grasp of a cosmic nos-talgia, my whole frame was wrenched by a shocking, tremendous emotion. I suspected, now, that I was lost indeed; lost forever in some alien eternity. There was a dark whisper of *wrongness* in the darkling glade and that land which surrounded me . . . something hinted incredibly by the aspect of those old fragments and the ruin whose existence had not been mentioned in the town where I grew up, being unknown to anyone of my time. Something hinted again by the nature of the bird that I had seen, and by that curiously—evolved—rabbit.

Though I was spared at first the certainty of my belief, the devastation of that awful knowledge, my whole outlook, my reactions and numb feelings were twisted horribly, like those of a man who has escaped an hideous death, only to realize that he will be maimed during the rest of his life. It was so overwhelming, so incredible, that I was at first unable to realize the blight induced by that change. Recognition of that might only come when I had pondered the matter, and seen in each aspect of life how great and monstrous a transition I had undergone.

Then, while I was torn with grief and horror and dull acquiescence, I heard the clank of metal upon stone. The feeling induced by this sound—ordinarily a common one, and unworthy of notice—is indescribable. For a brief moment I hoped, wildly and incredulously, that all my fears had been the result of a weary body and a mind depressed by unknown surroundings. I wanted dreadfully to believe this, yet in the end I knew that I was unable. What lurked in my outraged brain was a verity, as actual as any memory or knowledge. Such a change in my surroundings, in the very structure and appearance of common plants and animals could mean but a single thing, and that one thing I feared to believe, the while I knew that ultimately I must.

Acceptance of such things does not come fast. There were left to me long periods of suspense and torment—moments which were more terrible, I think, than certainty would have been. It was not until I saw the castle of Yrn that I knelt before the daemonic knowledge and the accompanying pain.

I heard, as I have said, some metallic object ringing through the forest. And hearing it, I knew in a flash of joy and surprise which no fear might stifle, that some one else, some mortal being, had caused that sound in the lonely and morbid wood. This was confirmed by the clear voice of a woman, among unidentifiable sounds.

In a brief moment I hastened through the shadows, coming to a clear space not twenty yards from where I had stood and thought myself alone. The forest resembled a rich wash-drawing by some Dutch master, while a few woolly blossoms trembled about me, shedding their fragrance in the enchanted glade. By the curbing of a stone well there was a figure, blurred in the dark. I knew that it was a woman—the woman whose laughing voice had come to me. She was cupping water in a bowl, and pouring it into a squat red jar that stood beside her.

The hour, if I had been in the city, was that in which street lamps begin to flare out with their mellow, insecure glow, driving the blue and translucent shadows of evening from streets made abruptly mysterious. There, in the forest, I remember that it was very dark, and objects were melting into a blurred unity. I dared not frighten the woman, and so I called out to her from the shelter of an oak. My voice broke the rustle of evening in a harsh, unexpected way, as if I listened to a stranger, and not as if I spoke myself.

"Don't be alarmed," I repeated, showing myself frankly. But she had dropped the clay vessel in a start of fear, and it splintered on the well-top. She looked up and watched my hesitant advance. My clothing was lamentably torn and soiled, and upon my face were many thin scratches, so that I did not wonder at her distrust. As I walked toward her she drew back with something of defiance in her broad, strong face. Her features were not delicate, nor wholly pleasing, but they held an honest, competent quality, like the face of a young peasant woman.

"*Na troiten,*" she cried anxiously, and her voice quavered. "*Na troiten.*" And her dark eyes searched my face, as she stood motionless.

Then, after a gaze that was also an inspection, she spoke again, and though a sullen resentment darkened her voice, there was less of fear within it.

"*Td'lo,*" she observed suddenly in a syllable I cannot form. "*Na troiten!*" And she laughed, somehow like a grey bird, reassured.

My brain was sick from that smouldering fear, and perhaps she realized something of my plight, for she spoke not unkindly, and called to some unseen companion.

As she stood before me with an enquiring regard, a younger girl clad also in garments of heavy grey entered the clearing. The two of them considered me, and spoke together. Then the younger addressed me, but I could only shake my head despairingly.

Fat boughs swayed about us, whispering of the oncoming night. This was far upon us, and the women were veiled by smudging blue. The elder woman touched my arm—her face was broad and somehow bovine without actual ugliness—and turned away. There was nothing to do but follow.

Of my confused mental state, I can hope to convey but little. The sudden, unwarned severance from reality—or what I had known as reality, for if such things might happen, what then was reality?—caused me to experience emotions that few can ever have known. Perhaps it were best to follow only the surface impressions of that frighteningly strange event. I cannot ever tell of the rapture of despair that thronged my dull brain.

So I followed the two grey-clad figures, mysterious in the young moonlight. They might have been the sisters of Clotho as they stole, tall and silent, like dim wraiths through the listening forest. At times the new-spread darkness hid them from me, so that it was difficult to see the path they took.

There is a dim, elusive spirit in the new evening, when the naked realities of day are veiled, and hidden things steal forth to caper with the bat in pearl-grey shadow. The sunlit, familiar aspect of nature is concealed, and mystery breathes in each sentient tree. The ecstasies of dusk are sounded by each exuberant frog and shrill, secretive insect. But quickly the dark triumph of night was banished by a flower-white moon that spun high in the steel chambered heavens. The cold orb served as our penetrating torch, and by this light I trod the leafy earth. Whatever season ruled this land, it wove the rich death of autumn with blossoming springtide. The chill that caressed me was no harbinger of frost, but a breath of fear from my own heart. My flesh tingled in the seeping moonrays, for it is strange to follow hidden figures in the darkness.

## II.

### —*Which Can Eternal Lie,*

From their sturdiness I knew that these women led hard lives. Their stride was more assured than mine, as if from customary walking of fields. They knew a simple existence, like the Viking women, or the wives of a pioneering race. Vaguely, almost unconsciously, I identified them with the folk of medieval times—not those of palace gardens, but the sturdy peasant class who made ale and loaves for warring men.

Suddenly, the forest dropped away, and we stood in the flowers of a grass-smooth plain. All about us blooms nodded in the pallid light. White iris beneath the moon. It struck a rich nostalgia in me, for that glow was fascinatingly uncanny. A deluge of death-white pallor shimmered in the air, enveloping the guides like a horde of merging wraiths. How am I to tell of the lunar magic wrought before me? Like clustering moths, the fragile iris melted away to a jewel-dim sky. The moon had frightened all the stars, until they fled in trailing sparks; ahead the firmament was bright with them—each of a dead world of jewelled cities hurtling to oblivion.

The women pointed, and I made out a shape that blotted away the sky. The dusky battlements of a crag-hung castle. Rising mountainously from the shimmering field, it pierced the sky with wall and turrets crouching monstrously against the silken universe.

What hands had reared that dark pile I could not guess. Kobald-builded, in the darkness the citadel seemed vaster than any building on earth. Only gods might live in such a place of wonder, overlooking mortal worlds. But these cryptic guides were women, and they were leading me through silver fields toward a roadway in the sky. For it seemed that. Sheer as the wind-haunted trails that wind to monasteries in Tibet, the ribbon looped through netted stars.

Up that trail we toiled, the women silent ghosts on the rocky slope. The castle-walls, high above me in the glittering moon, were guarded by a natural fortress of sheer cliffs, save in this one place where the trail was made. It would be a strong foe whose army scaled the grey spires.

Let me tell what I remember of the precipice-upthrust castle when I first beheld it in the warm night. There were many smaller and a single great tower rising with protruding turrets like a faery stronghold on the moon-blotting mountain. The place was built of storm-dark blocks, broidered with aeonian moss. We trod a narrow road between sentinel boulders, and to either hand beyond those boulders, the sustaining cliff fell into darkness. I did not wish to look into the shuddering void, and kept my eyes upturned. The peak on which the castle reared was a flat-topped cone, steeper than the pyramids of sun-baked Egypt, and guarded on all sides by the plain.

I was sick with weariness when we stood at last before the gated wall. The night had been like the colour of lost dreams, and I half-expected some mailed warrior to confront us in that curiously medieval arch. But instead, the elder woman swung wide a nail-studded door.

A long grey-hung chamber lit with the orange flame of candles was revealed as that door swung back. The woman entered before me blotting out the rich light.

For a moment their faces were hidden from me, and I wondered at the ever-present grey. From a night-dim wood to dark castle hung with smoke-hued tapestries I had been led by figures in the garb of corpses. This colour was oppressive, and my heart was glad of the mote-spinning light. About me there were many candles, on heavy tables of carved wood and upon figured chests that stood against the wall. The closing door disturbed their patient flame ever so slightly, and as they settled into calmness, I saw beyond my guides a man in rich garments.

As he faced me the women drew aside, and I stepped out of the gloom. He was a man who but recently had passed his youth, and the plump face had not yet lost a certain handsomeness. This huge man was clad in a curiously extravagant fashion quite in contrast to the quiet grey of the women, and his short thick fingers were ringed with great seals. Something about his dress reminded me of the gaudy costumes of the fifteenth century, but his clothing, while very colourful in orange and crimson silk, was less grotesque. Over tight breeches embroidered with a pattern of ferns he wore a waist-long coat with puffed sleeves and stiff cuffs of elaborate lace like that of his collar. A massive chain of flat gold links hung over his vast shoulders and lay upon his chest. Each segment of this chain bore a curious cypher.

The man's hair, heavy and flaxen like that of the women, hung loosely about his collar, clipped in a rough fashion, so that it did not veil the burning of his eyes. There was a mistrusting civility in that gaze, and his thick mouth seemed tinged with latent cruelty. He spoke to me in a voice of great suspicion.

Since I comprehended nothing of his words I shook my head wearily, and the two women burst into shrill chatter. From their gestures I judged they told of how I had been found in the shadowed wood, and of my ignorance regarding their tongue. At any rate, the man did not attempt to speak to me again. Instead, he gave me a strange look and indicated that I was to stay in this room. Then, as I seated myself upon a thick chest of reddish wood, he drew aside a heavy curtain and left me. The women followed, looking back at me in a secret triumph for which I was at a loss to account. It was as if they were pleased at having trapped some malignant but valuable animal.

I remained there for a time, inspecting the room with great curiosity. That such a medieval place might be set in any modern wood was unthinkable—I was as completely severed from the world that I had known as if I had found myself upon another planet. That vertigo, the sense of an ebbing tide that fell away from me as I woke, had tangled all my thoughts, and I only knew that if I had been a victim of amnesia, my wanderings had been far and strange to bring me to this place.

The room was long and narrow, and where no shadowy tapestries were hung, a bleak rock of the same hue was revealed. The roof was vaulted, like cathedrals I had seen in ancient towns, and there was not anywhere a window. This place was old, with the echoes of antiquity in the dark halls and chambers. Great chests of red and brown wood formed all the furniture, save a very solid table in the center of the room; and large hides that had the texture of ape-fur were spread upon the floor.

I had no idea of what these people intended, but despite their curious attitude, I hoped that I had been accepted as a guest for at least this night. While I awaited their return, numberless candles dwindled into little rills of wax, and my weariness increased.

Rising at length, I went to look at those dim hangings, and found that pale designs were worked in threads that tiny spiders might have webbed. The scenes depicted were of great strangeness, and seemed to form a series commencing at the curtained door. But when I tried to catch their theme, I was unable to follow the narrative unfolded. On the first of them a figure knelt before a vibrant glow that radiated swathingly about his averted head and upflung hands. The tapestry was worked with great skill, and I was enchanted by its beauty. Another was a forest-scene with great dim rocks ranged about as if they had once formed the base of a ruined tower; while others dealt with various subjects whose relationship was vague, as if some pictured links were lost. And the last of the weavings was a mad potpourri of seething colour, like a war-lock's brew. I think they must have been very old, for some were stained and half-rotten to the touch.

I turned back to the massive table. It was crusted with wax from a candelabrum, and a platter laden with foodstuffs had been set upon it by a quiet servant. There was no meat, but many vegetables were stewed together (some of them unlike any that I had seen) and I fell to eating hungrily. Before I had finished, the man who had become my host returned, and I saw his crimson coat beside me as I looked up.

He plucked my sleeve, and leaving the grey-hung chamber, led me through a dark passage. The low-burning taper in his thick hand did not flicker, for here were no more windows, the room I left. Yet from the plain I had seen a multitude of lights, so there must be windows elsewhere in this shadowed pile—perhaps in the place where guardsmen and warriors had their quarters. No thin arrows might pierce these unbroken walls. I thought of the towers above, grey in the darkness, save where moonlight drove the shadows into fluttering clots; and I thought again how mighty must a foe be to overtop these walls. The place was built to withstand prodigious attacks—yet I had seen no garrison, nor any man save this scarlet-cloaked figure. In what tumultuous halls were the fighting men, and who served this cryptic lord? Were the women menials, or did they share his rank and dignity? These questions plagued me as we neared a heavy door secured by an elaborate system of iron bolts and chained rings.

My host bent over the catch—I did not see how it was managed—and swung back this time-assaulted door. Then he gave to me the candle, and vanished in the gloom. I awaited his return, but after a time, when he did not come back, I stepped across the threshold, and found myself in a small chamber roofed by pointed arches. There was a low couch with woven spreads, and beyond this a window in the facing wall. Tiny stars hung in the unglazed opening, and there were hints of man's fire beyond. I set my candle on a wooden bench, and looked through the narrow window-slit.

It opened above a walled court, empty and silent in the snowy moonlight. Beyond these walls I saw the plain, still as if overtaken by charmed death, save where iris rippled in the breeze, like the glitter of waves over a dark lake. A woman's voice, singing, disturbed the stillness. What she sang I shall not ever know, but it was lonely and thin, and pierced my very soul with rapture. The round moon with its burden of ancient death was not so tragic as this melody; lamenting the inevitable doom of loveliness, like a mournful Pierrot in autumn's garden. It remembered dimly the scents and colours and the ecstasy of paradise. It was the dirge of water-steeped Atlantis, or the cry of a tortured lover in the night. Long after the voice of passionate despair had ebbed into oblivion, the silence rippled with its memory, and I scrutinized the black horizon to find a key to the singer and her melody.

When I lay at last upon the pillowed couch, sleep came over me, but it was fraught with troubling dreams.

### III.

*And In Strange Aeons . . .*

It seems, now, very difficult to make the statement that I have lived for three days in a remote castle, lost in some century for which there is scarcely a name. I have little doubt but that I shall fail in my attempt to convey the peculiar shock of my knowing that to be a reality; yet it was a thing as actual, as incontrovertibly real, as the existence of that dusty-sun heated road you rode on today—as certain as the live pounding ocean on a brilliant day.

It was with that curious detachment that comes when one awakens in a strange room that I beheld the morning. My weariness had abated, but a vertigo of strangeness clung oppressively to me. Remembrance of my isolation came. My world was lost as aeon-buried Ur, as the obliterated palaces that perished before Cortez. This morning memories were clearing, and the wrench of my bewildering transition throbbed in a hot brain. I realized wholly; and realizing, accepted the fact, that something—God knows what, for even yet I am uncertain—had precipitated me into realms that only madness can accept. The nostalgia of old centuries overhung me, and momently I feared a confirmation of that besetting dread; feared that I should know absolutely and completely that my old life and surroundings were lost to me—that I was destined to live and perish in this incredible alienation.

Yet, in a while, I was able to force myself from these reflections, and rising, looked from the narrow window. Even the greatest of sorrows cannot last. So brief are man's emotions that when the height of fear or passion has been reached, that emotion ebbs like a tide slipping oceanward.

The sky was gaudy once more, and everywhere leaves of sanguine hue invaded the green ranks. The army of marching trees was flecked with blood. Summer's garment was cast off, and the very grasses were astir in some ineffable expectancy. Over a sky like the rich enamel of an inverted cup there moved a caravan of tumbled clouds—slow and infinitely majestic.

In the courtyard whence that song had come, a young man now walked slowly beneath me, carrying a thin spear. The fresh sun was quieting, and my darkness-nurtured fears perished like fungi brought into the light from an unclean hole. Morning was new, and I was strengthened by the reassurance of day. For a long time I gazed into the dim hills, which were broken by outlined leaves of the closer forest. I must have stayed there a long while, for the sky became a faded powder-blue, and the scattered clouds like chargers whose silk manes overspread the heavens.

My attention was drawn again to the young man below me. He also gazed over the surrounding world, but with a keener scrutiny than mine—a gaze suggesting watchfulness, as if he were a castle guardian. Beneath the foreshortened curls of browning hair, his young body was clad in a green and yellow tunic; and on his metal belt hung a thick blade, hilted with coloured stones. He laid the spear upon a low wall, and toyed with the keen blade of this smaller weapon. I had thought both primitive, until it came to me that all battling must be afoot in this strange place, and from the walls of such a castle a sword might be very potently destructive.

In the vast sky there was no glitter of aeroplane, and only hunting birds glided above the forest. Otherwise, the swollen clouds were white. In this land were there none who had conquered the air? Were all men and all strongholds so near to barbarism?

The man in the courtyard disappeared, and dawn was forgotten by a molten sun. Unanswered, mystified, I left my room in search of the castle lord.

And so for three days I dwelt in the castle, sleeping in that arched room whose shadow is yet on me. In that time I found little explanation of my disturbing change. Roaming through dark halls, I found chambers as old as memory; overhung like all the castle and the land with the wraith of some enormous change. These rooms were furnished unendingly with chests, though they held only dust. Some were used as chairs and some as tables, though most of them were long disused. Apish hides concealed the floors, and there were a few decorative hangings of extreme age. The place had obviously been made to house a great multitude, but now the windowless rooms were given into the keeping of spiders.

I saw no books, but in a high room I found by torchlight the fragments of a damaged manuscript, written in unreadable characters. It bore no pictures and I was unable to discover anything familiar in the text. Of alien tongued warriors I saw many, but the two women did not reappear. So, alone, I peered from dizzy windows at hilly forest-land that rolled away to opalescent mist, and descended forgotten stairways where rubbish hampered my footsteps. There was much that I did not ever understand. The incongruities of this narrative are due only to my faulty comprehension, a situation so different from that which I had known. I was inarticulate and lost, as any savage taken from his tortuous jungle to a dazzling slave town.

When the third day came, I had grown somewhat accustomed to the strange place, and knew the names of the castle-lord and his great fortress, which was Yrn. But there was nothing to show me positively into what years I had come, or the nature of that land. And now I shall not know. The wood, the castle—and that greater thing which came after—these are only fragments in a great mosaic whose design is concealed. This much I know or have surmised. By the natural calendar of stars and forest-growth and other changing guides, I have tried to judge the century and year prevailing in that place of Tomorrow. And it is such that I hesitate to accept it, despite the weight of evidence. It is thrice farther from us than we are from the Thinite Kings of Egypt; it is deeper in the coming years than any past thing of which we have record.

Not centuries, but dozens of centuries barred me from my own world. There are things of great wonder to me, but none so terrible as this. I think that civilization sank to low ebb in that unknown span of years. Brought on by wars unchronicled, by some misty Armageddon of fire and battle and great lumbering machines, the lands and governments were broken into chaotic fragments of which this castle was a part. There must have been others like it, but of them I can only know a little. Countless subjects baffle me—there is so much that I desire to learn of that mysterious place now lost to me forever.

Whether even a guess of a hundred centuries is right, I do not know. Perhaps I underestimate—it may have been a thousand centuries away. Between that time and my own the fires of war spread over a mourning earth, and there were battles so great and terrible that a new Dark Age set in. Mankind slipped far in those years . . . perhaps he may not regain his old supremacy. That also is scribed in the unseen and unguessed volumes of coming things.

All traces of the city that I had known were gone. There were no ruins. No rusty girder or asphalt fragment remained to mark the town now buried underneath a settled wood. Knowledge of the intervening years depends upon the length of time in which a mutation can develop. The bird and hare which I saw (and whose aspect first set loose the roving of my fear) had altered subtly, but considerably. I do not, of course, have any evidence but that it was a local change. Under the new conditions of that vast, crouching forest, evolution may have quickened, so that in a relatively short period those variations might occur. Whatever the answer to this may be, is also a clue to the date of that age into which I was flung.

Some while ago I made a plan of the castle as it was. There were nearly sixty rooms, flanking long hallways, and they were above one another to the extent of three and sometimes five stories, with small tower-rooms. Most of these were empty, though at one time a great host must have quartered there. I found signs carved over certain doors, in the time-blackened wood; which gave me great wonder, for like the words of these people these were unknown. No trace of the English tongue has gone to them, who are our descendants and the inheritors of earth.

On this third day the lord of Yrn was absent when I rose, and I did not see him afterward. To him I came from the outside, and left as strangely. The mystery of my coming and disappearance must have been great to him. For neither time was I warned—abrupt and sudden, the change came, and I was flung through time and space and universes in the great transition.

There were steps leading to a northern tower, and I stood on these when it came to me a second time. At first I seemed to fall, as if the steps had slid beneath me, and a noise like breaking surf was in my ears. The stairs before me writhed; grew dim in a blur of floating colours. Then came a wave of darkness, and a shock that tore my vitals, wrenching each cell of my flesh. It was at once pain and ecstasy and terror. When it returned, all things merged before my sight, and a great radiance supplanted the hall and the many dark steps. A blur of light, as if some god crouched before me, so glorious that my eyes were dimmed. Vibrating, throbbing, this glow set up a curious rhythm which passed to my inmost tissue and was echoed there. I was enslaved by the pure and glowing energy of the hueless light. It was mightier than the power which churns out earth in the frail universe. My heart jerked dizzily, and I felt an expectant lightness. Then I was devoured by the live, hungry radiance, so that in the final vertigo of consciousness my body was distant and my flesh numb.

## IV.
### *Even Death May Die*

I was caught up in the backwash of that incredible change. Like a swimmer in unknown waters, I was embraced by a moving wave. And upon the peak of that wave I was borne . . . carried into the heart of a black, unsailed ocean. Swiftly, I was swept into that sea, while the image of the castle swayed in my memory like a curtain in the breeze. And then, in a crescendo that was neither visual nor audient, the curtains of the universe rolled back, and before me was the stage upon which universes enact a brief, tragic drama.

Here, all the stars were changed. I was in some altered cosmos—the cosmos of future aeons, when not one star shall remain as we know it. It was hideous and stupefying to find no recognized orb in that realm. The night sky was great, larger than my vision could embrace, and everywhere about me was star-flecked darkness, and at my feet a chasm of night.

I say above and below, for these are terms that come to mind, but there were no true directions. My spirit swung as the hub of a radiating universe.

Freed of matter, I had become a naked consciousness; and this thing is wonderful. My body had passed to its own land, while my spirit, my intellect, my comprehension, dropped to the far abysses before it could return and join with flesh again. Only thus, you understand, could I have experienced the journey into that waiting Ultimate.

Gradually, I seemed to move—blown before a wind out of nowhere . . . and approach the clustered universes, shuddering with stars. To every side, fixed and still in the eternal night, they spread as I moved among them. And drifting ceaselessly, after a great period I found one thing which I had known; one spot dear and marked for me in the indifferent, half-forgotten years of Earth. Like a bubble of heated glass, our sun glowed small and red. And when I saw at last, within the unknown deeps, that solar pinpoint, there revolved about it no longer any Earth. The worlds were gone, and our sun dead with the cool of night. Chasms sprawled where anciently green fields and cloud-strewn skies had shut away the ravenous black. Mankind was a dream, and the earth a bright, nostalgic memory. There was no record of how our world perished. Somewhere in the great maze a star winked out. Only that, and all of humanity was gone—the splendid dreams, the bravery of that race which I had known (long since) when it was young. Man, great, assured, and invincible, was now obliterated. For him a last sunset had dappled the orange sky, flared up in false dawning, and sunk at length to embers. Cold embers that no breath might re-quicken. The horror of that long-evaded Night had cast its shadow over Earth, and she was gone now. Her fragile vision of supremacy had been as naught; her gods and citadels, with all lovely things, gone. Perhaps, for a while after Man was dead such things as Egypt's pyramids endured for cenotaphs to the lost race. Perhaps, here and there about the dead world (now cold eternally, in the End of things) some traces of humanity survived a while.

Yet they all crumbled before the sun's death; and that great em-ber shot her last rays upon an empty land. Perhaps a few green things were left . . . a few toughened forms of earlier vegetation; plants and vines that struggled like reptiles to remain in the dim sunlight. These things may have been left—but Man was gone. The splendour of his race was forgotten, and the lordly trumpets mute. Then, when unmeasured centuries were done, earth had ceased, and her sun lingered briefly as a cinder, unmarked, in the blackness.

My position was alien and frightful. Lost forever and remote in a hallway of the gods, guided by no thing that man had seen, and facing the horror of the Inevitable, I knew an emotion that mixed ecstasy and terror, and yet other things for which there are no words. How I went from that place, for what centuries my brain was numb, I do not know, but in a time I saw again the unknown and hateful stars above me, glittering like the hoar on some rock-chiselled tomb in a silent land of snow and night.

Everywhere was the black abyss. A monstrousness that grew and burrowed through the cosmos, engulfing faint worlds and brit-tle suns; sundering and destroying them. A nighted area where Nothingness grew powerful on substance.

Eternities it swelled before me, until I saw that each of the strange new galaxies was vanishing. A last handful of stars melted away in gradual aeons. Reluctant, they went like guests at an end-ing banquet, until I was alone. Unaccompanied now, I drifted on that unknown ocean through which lay no chartered course; and where the ships of worlds had destroyed themselves on reefs of darkness. Brave, small voyagers, with no captain and no beckoning goal! Tiny wormish lights that crept awhile upon the fields . . . lights that were now forever extinguished.

So I was left in ages of black so great that only blindness might conceive it. It was not an absence of light . . . it was a tangible negation, an unending hue like the shadows of a demon wing. Or it was a crypt—the burial ground of forgotten orbs whose brief lives were glut in the maw of that triumphant abyss.

There would never anywhere again be worlds. I watched for centuries, conscious of this fact. Confronting me was the sum, the purpose and destiny of the galaxies that had spotted that void. My soul shrank from the cataclysm before me, and trembling my consciousness waited; as if I sat before a darkened stage, seeking the rise of a curtain. But the comedy was played, and all the actors gone. Blank, hideous, supreme, devastating, the eternal naught remained.

I waited, beset with monstrous fancies. Then my searching eyes found a dim light swelling beyond the limit of vision. What it might be, or how far away, I could not tell. There were no worlds to judge by, no scale for measurement. But the light grew; and I saw it to be composed of many separate glowing objects. In that vast chasm their progress was torturingly slow, yet no comet might attain such a speed. It was only that their road was the road of eternity.

I could not, yet, distinguish what form the lights assumed. Was it a band of celestial vagrants? A lost group of wandering stars? There was no answer save only that which patience might bring. Then, for a little, I feared that I was not in the path of the approaching forms, dreaded that they might take a distant course. Gradually, however, they became clear. A band of racing lights, perhaps half a hundred of them. Lights only: hued in green and red and purple. Globular forms of *adhering vibration* . . . elementals. There were before me only the simple balls and that nothingness in which they moved. Pristine matter in a pristine cosmos. They had shape—the simplest; and substance. What that was is beyond ken.

And they had colour. But there was no complexity, no kin in their forms to the forms of Earth.

The balls were living. As I watched, they grew tremendously, and shifted like phantasmal sea-things. How much of consciousness they had, I cannot guess. They lived and moved, but their sentience was too different from my own for one to comprehend the other.

Each ball gave off a faint glow, so that as they hung before me they made a coloured pool . . . a dancing, tossing mass of gem-hued radiance. It is hard to fit words to such alien things, and to such a sight. I was a mote in the great desolation. My world was gone, and with it, all worlds. Yet here before me, in the ultimate chill of a naked void, there clustered a group of living lights. Things from infinitely beyond Space; creatures from a place which no faltering word can make real. I feared them, not because they were evil-shaped, or because of their actions, but because they were great— for such greatness is terrible. There was more than fright upon me as I watched the globes at play. They built themselves in pyramids, and rapidly strung out, like a huge necklace athwart eternity. A myriad forms of unearthly geometry diverted them as they rolled and built, separated and shifted in kaleidoscopic array.

About this eerie tableau I felt a dreamful familiarity, as if I had known before the mad gyrations of those living colours. I wrenched a painful memory from darkness; plunged backward into a fearful mind, until I came upon the impression of that vari-coloured bubbling through which my awakening mind had seemed to fall, and first beheld the earthly forest, so long vanished.

Here, at the end of time, when all celestial landmarks were obliterated, when the very firmament had altered, was the same group of tossing colours on a millionfold scale. These playful monstrosities, whose very conception was perverse, gambolling in deformed symmetries, were akin to what I had seen in the land of unconsciousness.

Then, before I could know what ultimate goal the creatures might have, before I might comprehend that quest, which led them across the fields of Infinity, an emotional illness came upon me, and I was sick in a dull, indescribable fashion, revolted by the wrongness of that lurking universe. Thus bitter and forlorn is that despair which awaits us.

As my mind turned—for I might not faint, having no body—it was like seeing black cliffs rise and curve away overhead. I lost all sense of vision, and seemed pressed on every side by a buzzing darkness. Then, slowly, deliberately, everything wheeled about me, so that I hung like a perishing wretch upon the edge of a great chasm. A chasm deeper than the pits of hell, and more evil. Again, with swifter motion, my surroundings revolved; and then life became a series of hideous revolutions backward through time and space. I seemed to experience anew each joy and pain that I had ever known: again and yet again I lived a tortuous life, and the dark years sped in rhythm with a lurching cosmos.

### Epilogue

I have begun, lately, to judge something of the force motivating my transition, and to gropingly conceive the nature of those . . . objects . . . inhabiting the lost void to which my dream bore me. Their cosmic errand is unknowable, as is the inconceivable dimension of their reeling, prismatic lair. They are, I believe, the dominating life-form, the ultimate inheritors of our universe. Perhaps they even created it. In a part of space lost past the reach of light-years; a place where the farthest comet never swings, these creatures have their world. A nighted world in no sense like our earth-wrought planets . . . a world upon the black Rim—a world that no mind can believe or even dimly picture. It must be a place of very wrong dimensions, existing in some alien eternity. I cannot hazard the nature of such a place, or know whether it be in the aeonian past or vague futurity. It was in only our small portion of infinity that I saw the evanescent forms of the master-things, journeying through galaxies as I might wander along a pebbled beach. But I do know this: that all the laws and barriers of our cosmos are as nothing to them, dwelling as they do in a realm oblique across eternity. For their purposes the master-things somehow turned aside the stream of years, diverted for a space the succession of ages from the rusty channel wherein they flow. And in that celestial maelstrom I was sucked, twisted about, so that when their Gargantuan play was over, I was flung from Time's unknown waters upon the rock-girt coast of alien years. From my own life I was caught up by a violating law, whose course left me for a little upon the future world, and then swept me to the far black reaches of God's infinity. My voyaging was lone and terrible. It took me past the chaos of suns and stars, beyond the nethermost limits of a perishing universe. And in the end I saw those Supreme entities, whose servants are the gods. They linked the end and origin of things, they formed a million-ruled universe as playground, and then set those rules aside.

My first transition was of flesh, but the other passes such material change. When I was swept into the naked and lonely Ultimate, it was as an ego, an intelligence, a consciousness. My flesh could bear the change and stress of thrice five hundred years, but it was for centuries that I swung in the unplumbed void. Years or centuries of aeons—I do not know. Yet it was for a very long while that I watched the symphony, the ecstasy and harmony, of the abyss-things. Visually, perhaps I was not absent at all from my own world. Perhaps I only *flickered* in existence; but in that time I saw a new land and a new universe. I spent a million years in space, or if you like, three days in the old castle.

I am told that I fainted on the street that morning and remained unconscious for some while. I was taken to my brother's home, and remained in a coma for several hours. During this time, my body scarcely held life . . . the pulse was dim and faint, the muscles limp as if I were newly dead. Then, before I woke, groaning as if in torment, I flailed my arms about in mysterious battle.

I know what happened in that time, and I shall tell what I am able. When I fell upon the pavement, I had *already* made the flight into a future world. I had experienced the imperceptible brief physical absence from the year and the world of my people. Yet my first transition, as I have said, was bodily; and the second one of soul, spirit, intelligence—call it what you will. I do not wish to indulge in spurious mysticism, for I merely seek the narration of a verity. So, you will understand that when my outward shape returned to 1936, to the month and day, perhaps to the second from which it came, the *other* component of my entity was swept immensely farther, parting wholly from my body, into the sucking whirlpool of time, whose flotsam is the stars. Into the great distances I went, to Infinity and her sheer end. It was ordained that, like a pendulum, my spirit must complete the far swing, where matter could not go. And thus for a while was my body returned, untenanted, to earth; while I knew the terrors of the abyss, and all the pain thereof.

But somehow more than to any other part of that adventure, my thoughts return to the old castle beyond an unknown wood. It is frightening to think that it will not be built for over fifteen thousand years, for I can remember the sunlight on the open court and the green deeps of that surrounding wood more clearly than this room in which I write. I lived in that castle when it had begun to crumble, and I felt the breeze come over swinging vines and old trees when I stood before the narrow window of my arched chamber. Yet my bones shall be wind-borne dust, and I shall have known rebirth in grass and flowers and dark roots, many centuries before masons lay trowel to the first stone of that edifice. The place where it will rise, in more than a dozen tens of centuries, is now an active city, with steel and glass and concrete walls that seem very permanent. But I know them as ephemera, for my eyes are haunted by the nocturnal wood, by the dark sunset of that land wherein I shall never again be. It saddens me to think of the bright sunshine and the fresh wind that will come long after I am worm-infested. Having seen it I know that in this world about me I can nevermore find zest, desire, or consolation.

But the room is growing chill, and I do not think that I shall write any more.

# The Night Ocean

*With H. P. Lovecraft*

I went to Ellston Beach not only for the pleasures of sun and ocean, but to rest a weary mind. Since I knew no person in the little town, which thrives on summer vacationists and presents only blank windows during most of the year, there seemed no likelihood that I might be disturbed. This pleased me, for I did not wish to see anything but the expanse of pounding surf and the beach lying before my temporary home.

My long work of the summer was completed when I left the city, and the large mural design produced by it had been entered in the contest. It had taken me the bulk of the year to finish the painting, and when the last brush was cleaned I was no longer reluctant to yield to the claims of health and find rest and seclusion for a time. Indeed, when I had been a week on the beach I recalled only now and then the work whose success had so recently seemed all-important. There was no longer the old concern with a hundred complexities of colour and ornament; no longer the fear and mistrust of my ability to render a mental image actual, and turn by my own skill alone the dim-conceived idea into the careful draught of a design. And yet that which later befell me by the lonely shore may have grown solely from the mental constitution behind such concern and fear and mistrust. For I have always been a seeker, a dreamer, and a ponderer on seeking and dreaming; and who can say that such a nature does not open latent eyes sensitive to unsuspected worlds and orders of being?

Now that I am trying to tell what I saw I am conscious of a thousand maddening limitations. Things seen by the inward sight, like those flashing visions which come as we drift into the blankness of sleep, are more vivid and meaningful to us in that form than when we have sought to weld them with reality. Set a pen to a dream, and the colour drains from it. The ink with which we write seems diluted with something holding too much of reality, and we find that after all we cannot delineate the incredible memory. It is as if our inward selves, released from the bonds of daytime and objectivity, revelled in prisoned emotions which are hastily stifled when we would translate them. In dreams and visions lie the greatest creations of man, for on them rests no yoke of line or hue. Forgotten scenes, and lands more obscure than the golden world of childhood, spring into the sleeping mind to reign until awakening puts them to rout. Amid these may be attained something of the glory and contentment for which we yearn; some adumbration of sharp beauties suspected but not before revealed, which are to us as the Graal to holy spirits of the mediaeval world. To shape these things on the wheel of art, to seek to bring some faded trophy from that intangible realm of shadow and gossamer, requires equal skill and memory. For although dreams are in all of us, few hands may grasp their moth-wings without tearing them.

Such skill this narrative does not have. If I might, I would reveal to you the hinted events which I perceived dimly, like one who peers into an unlit realm and glimpses forms whose motion is concealed. In my mural design, which then lay with a multitude of others in the building for which they were planned, I had striven equally to catch a trace of this elusive shadow-world, and had perhaps succeeded better than I shall now succeed. My stay in Ellston was to await the judging of that design; and when days of unfamiliar leisure had given me perspective, I discovered that—in spite of those weaknesses which a creator always detects most clearly—I had indeed managed to retain in line and colour some fragments snatched from the endless world of imagining. The difficulties of the process, and the resulting strain on all my powers, had undermined my health and brought me to the beach during this period of waiting.

Since I wished to be wholly alone, I rented (to the delight of the incredulous owner) a small house some distance from the village of Ellston—which, because of the waning season, was alive with a moribund bustle of tourists, uniformly uninteresting to me.

The house, dark from the sea-wind though it had not been painted, was not even a satellite of the village; but swung below it on the coast like a pendulum beneath a still clock; quite alone upon a hill of weed-grown sand. Like a solitary warm animal it crouched facing the sea, and its inscrutable dirty windows stared upon a lonely realm of earth and sky and enormous sea. It will not do to use too much imagining in a narrative whose facts, could they be augmented and fitted into a mosaic, would be strange enough in themselves; but I thought the little house was lonely when I saw it, and that like myself, it was conscious of its meaningless nature before the great sea.

I took the place in late August, arriving a day before I was expected, and encountering a van and two workingmen unloading the furniture provided by the owner. I did not know then how long I would stay, and when the truck that brought the goods had left I settled my small luggage and locked the door (feeling very proprietary at having a house after months of a rented room) to go down the weedy hill and on the beach. Since it was quite square and had but one room, the house had required little exploration. Two windows in each side provided a great quantity of light, and somehow a door had been squeezed in as an afterthought on the oceanward wall. The place had been built about ten years previously, but on account of its distance from Ellston village was difficult to rent even during the active summer season. There being no fireplace, it stood empty and alone from October until far into spring. Though actually less than a mile below Ellston, it seemed more remote; since a bend in the coast caused one to see only grassy dunes in the direction of the village.

The first day, half-gone when I was installed, I spent in the enjoyment of the sun and the restless water—things whose quiet majesty made the designing of murals seem distant and tiresome. But this was the natural reaction to a long concern with one set of habits and activities. I was through with my work and my vacation was begun. This fact, while elusive for the moment, shewed in everything which surrounded me that afternoon of my arrival; and in the

utter change from old scenes. There was an effect of bright sun upon a shifting sea of waves whose mysteriously impelled curves were
strown with what appeared to be rhinestones. Perhaps a water-
colour might have caught the solid masses of intolerable light which
lay upon the beach where the sea mingled with the sand. Although
the ocean bore her own hue, it was dominated wholly and incredibly by the enormous glare. There was no other person near me, and
I enjoyed the spectacle without the annoyance of any alien object
upon the stage. Each of my senses was touched in a different way,
but sometimes it seemed that the roar of the sea was akin to that
great brightness, or as if the waves were glaring instead of the sun,
each of these being so vigorous and insistent that impressions coming from them were mingled. Curiously, I saw no one bathing near
my little square house during that or succeeding afternoons, although the curving shore included a wide beach even more inviting
than that at the village, where the surf was dotted with random figures. I supposed that this was because of the distance, and because
there had never been other houses below the town. Why this unbuilt
stretch existed, I could not imagine, since many dwellings straggled
along the northward coast, facing the sea with aimless eyes.

I swam until the afternoon had gone, and later, having rested,
walked into the little town. Darkness hid the sea from me as I entered, and I found in the dingy lights of the street tokens of a life
which was not even conscious of the great, gloom-shrouded thing
lying so close. There were painted women in tinsel adornments, and
bored men who were no longer young—a throng of foolish marion-
ettes perched on the lip of the ocean-chasm; unseeing, unwilling to
see what lay above them and about, in the multitudinous grandeur of
the stars and the leagues of the night ocean. I walked along that
darkened sea as I went back to the bare little house, sending the
beams of my flashlight out upon the naked and impenetrable void. In
the absence of the moon, this light made a solid bar athwart the walls
of the uneasy tide; and I felt an indescribable emotion born of the
noise of the waters and the perception of my smallness as I cast that

tiny beam upon a realm immense in itself, yet only the black border of the earthly deep. That nighted deep, upon which ships were moving alone in the darkness where I could not see them, gave off the murmur of a distant, angry rabble.

When I reached my high residence I knew that I had passed no one during the mile's walk from the village, and yet there somehow lingered the impression that I had been all the while accompanied by the spirit of the lonely sea. It was, I thought, personified in a shape which was not revealed to me, but which moved quietly about beyond my range of comprehension. It was like those actors who wait behind darkened scenery in readiness for the lines which will shortly call them before our eyes to move and speak in the sudden revelation of the footlights. At last I shook off this fancy and sought my key to enter the place, whose bare walls gave a sudden feeling of security.

My cottage was entirely free of the village, as if it had wandered down the coast and was unable to return; and there I heard nothing of the disturbing clamour when I returned each night after supper. I generally stayed but a short while upon the streets of Ellston, though sometimes I went into the place for the sake of the walk it provided. There were all the multitude of curio-shops and falsely regal theatre-fronts that clutter vacation towns, but I never went into these; and the place seemed useful only for its restaurants. It was astonishing the number of useless things people found to do.

There was a succession of sun-filled days at first. I rose early, and beheld the grey sky agleam with promise of sunrise; a prophecy fulfilled as I stood witness. Those dawns were cold, and their colours faint in comparison to that uniform radiance of day which gives to every hour the quality of white noon. That great light, so apparent the first day, made each succeeding day a yellow page in the book of time. I noticed that many of the beach-people were displeased by the inordinate sun, whereas I sought it. After grey months of toil the lethargy induced by a physical existence in a region governed by the simple things—the wind and light and water—had a prompt effect upon me; and since I was anxious to continue this healing process, I spent all my time outdoors in the sunlight. This induced a state at once impassive and submissive, and gave me a feeling of security against the ravenous night. As darkness is akin to death, so is light to vitality. Through the heritage of a million years ago, when men were closer to the mother sea, and when the creatures of which we are born lay languid in the shallow, sun-pierced water, we still seek the primal things when we are tired, steeping ourselves within their lulling security like those early half-mammals which had not yet ventured upon the oozy land.

The monotony of the waves gave repose, and I had no other occupation than witnessing a myriad ocean moods. There is a ceaseless change in the waters—colours and shades pass over them like the insubstantial expressions of a well-known face; and these are at once communicated to us by half-recognised senses. When the sea is restless, remembering old ships that have gone over her chasms, there comes up silently in our hearts the longing for a vanished horizon. But when she forgets, we forget also. Though we know her a lifetime, she must always hold an alien air, as if something too vast to have shape were lurking in the universe to which she is a door. The morning ocean, glimmering with a reflected mist of blue-white cloud and expanding diamond foam, has the eyes of one who ponders on strange things, and her intricately woven webs, through which dart a myriad coloured fishes, hold the air of some great idle thing which will arise presently from the hoary immemorial chasms and stride upon the land.

I was content for many days, and glad that I had chosen the lonely house which sat like a small beast upon those rounded cliffs of sand. Among the pleasantly aimless amusements fostered by such a life, I took to following the edge of the tide (where the waves left a damp, irregular outline rimmed with evanescent foam) for long distances; and sometimes I found curious bits of shell in the chance litter of the sea. There was an astonishing lot of debris on that inward-curving coast which my bare little house overlooked, and I

judged that currents whose courses diverge from the village beach
must reach that spot. At any rate, my pockets—when I had any—
generally held vast stores of trash; most of which I threw away an
hour or two after picking it up, wondering why I had kept it. Once,
however, I found a small bone whose nature I could not identify,
save that it was certainly nothing out of a fish; and I kept this,
along with a large metal bead whose minutely carven design was
rather unusual. This latter depicted a fishy thing against a patterned
background of seaweed instead of the usual floral or geometrical
designs, and was still clearly traceable though worn with years of
tossing in the surf. Since I had never seen anything like it, I judged
that it represented some fashion, now forgotten, of a previous year
at Ellston, where similar fads were common.

I had been there perhaps a week when the weather began a
gradual change. Each stage of this progressive darkening was followed by another subtly intensified, so that in the end the entire
atmosphere surrounding me had shifted from day to evening. This
was more obvious to me in a series of mental impressions than in
what I actually witnessed, for the small house was lonely under the
grey skies, and there was sometimes a beating wind that came out
of the ocean bearing moisture. The sun was displaced by long intervals of cloudiness—layers of grey mist beyond whose unknown
depth the sun lay cut off. Though it might glare with the old intensity above that enormous veil, it could not penetrate. The beach
was a prisoner in a hueless vault for hours at a time, as if something
of the night were welling into other hours.

Although the wind was invigorating and the ocean whipped into little churning spirals of activity by the vagrant flapping, I found
the water growing chill, so that I could not stay in it as long as I
had done previously, and thus I fell into the habit of long walks,
which—when I was unable to swim—provided the exercise that I
was so careful to obtain. These walks covered a greater range of sea-
edge than my previous wanderings, and since the beach extended in
a stretch of miles beyond the tawdry village, I often found myself

wholly isolated upon an endless area of sand as evening drew close. When this occurred, I would stride hastily along the whispering sea-border, following its outline so that I should not wander inland and lose my way. And sometimes, when these walks were late (as they grew increasingly to be), I would come upon the crouching house that looked like a harbinger of the village. Insecure upon the wind-gnawed cliffs, a dark blot upon the morbid hues of the ocean sunset, it was more lonely than by the full light of either orb; and seemed to my imagination like a mute, questioning face turned toward me expectant of some action. That the place was isolated I have said, and this at first pleased me; but in that brief evening hour when the sun left in a gore-spattered decline and darkness lumbered on like an expanding shapeless blot, there was an alien presence about the place: a spirit, a mood, an impression that came from the surging wind, the gigantic sky, and that sea which drooled blackening waves upon a beach grown abruptly strange. At these times I felt an uneasiness which had no very definite cause, although my solitary nature had made me long accustomed to the ancient silence and the ancient voice of Nature. These misgivings, to which I could have put no sure name, did not affect me long, yet I think now that all the while a gradual consciousness of the ocean's immense loneliness crept upon me, a loneliness that was made subtly horrible by intimations—which were never more than such—of some animation or sentience preventing me from being wholly alone.

The noisy, yellow streets of the town, with their curiously unreal activity, were very far away, and when I went there for my evening meal (mistrusting a diet entirely of my own ambiguous cooking) I took increasing and quite unreasonable care that I should return to the cottage before the late darkness, though I was often abroad until ten or so.

You will say that such action is unreasonable; that if I had feared the darkness in some childish way, I would have entirely avoided it. You will ask me why I did not leave the place since its loneliness was depressing me. To all this I have no reply, save that whatever unrest I felt, whatever of remote disturbance there was to me in brief aspects of the darkening sun or in the eager salt-brittle wind or in the robe of the dark sea that lay crumpled like an enormous garment so close to me, was something which had an origin half in my own heart, which shewed itself only at fleeting moments, and which had no very long effect upon me. In the recurrent days of diamond light, with sportive waves flinging blue peaks at the basking shore, the memory of dark moods seemed rather incredible; yet only an hour or two afterward I might again experience these moods once more, and descend to a dim region of despair.

Perhaps these inward emotions were only a reflection of the sea's own mood; for although half of what we see is coloured by the interpretation placed upon it by our minds, many of our feelings are shaped quite distinctly by external, physical things. The sea can bind us to her many moods, whispering to us by the subtle token of a shadow or a gleam upon the waves, and hinting in these ways of her mournfulness or rejoicing. Always she is remembering old things, and these memories, though we may not grasp them, are imparted to us, so that we share her gaiety or remorse. Since I was doing no work, seeing no person that I knew, I was perhaps susceptible to shades of her cryptic meaning which would have been overlooked by another. The ocean ruled my life during the whole of that late summer; demanding it as recompense for the healing she had brought me.

There were drownings at the beach that year, and while I heard of these only casually (such is our indifference to a death which does not concern us, and to which we are not witness), I knew that their details were unsavoury. The people who died—some of them swimmers of a skill beyond the average—were sometimes not found until many days had elapsed, and the hideous vengeance of the deep had scourged their rotten bodies. It was as if the sea had dragged them into a chasm-lair and had mulled them about in the darkness until, satisfied that they were no longer of any use, she had floated them ashore in a ghastly state. No one seemed to know what had caused these deaths. Their frequency excited alarm among the timid, since the undertow at Ellston was not strong, and since there were known to be no sharks at hand. Whether the bodies shewed marks of any attacks I did not learn, but the dread of a death which moves among the waves and comes on lone people from a lightless, motionless place is a dread which men know and do not like. They must quickly find a reason for such a death, even if there are no sharks. Since sharks formed only a suspected cause, and one never to my knowledge confirmed, the swimmers who continued during the rest of the season were on guard against treacherous tides rather than against any possible sea-animal.

Autumn, indeed, was not a great distance off, and some people used this as an excuse for leaving the sea, where men were snared by death, and going to the security of inland fields, where one cannot even hear the ocean. So August ended, and I had been at the beach many days.

There had been a threat of storm since the fourth of the new month, and on the sixth, when I set out for a walk in the damp wind, there was a mass of formless cloud, colourless and oppressive, above the ruffled leaden sea. The motion of the wind, directed toward no especial goal but stirring uneasily, provided a sensation of coming animation—a hint of life in the elements which might be the long-expected storm. I had eaten my luncheon at Ellston, and though the heavens seemed the closing lid of a great casket, I ventured far down the beach and away from both the town and my no-longer-to-be-seen house. As the universal grey became spotted with a carrion purple—curiously brilliant despite its sombre hue—I found that I was several miles from any possible shelter. This, however, did not seem very important; for despite the dark skies with their added glow of unknown presage I was in a curious mood that flashed through a body grown suddenly alert and sensitive to the outline of shapes and meanings that were previously dim. Obscurely, a memory came to me; suggested by the likeness of the scene to one I had imagined when a story was read to me in childhood. That tale—of which I had not thought for many years—concerned a woman who was loved by the dark-bearded king of an underwater realm of blurred cliffs where fish-things lived, and who was taken from the golden-haired youth of her troth by a dark being crowned with a priest-like mitre and having the features of a withered ape. What had remained in the corner of my fancy was the image of cliffs beneath the water against the hueless, dusky no-sky of such a realm; and this, though I had forgotten most of the story, was re-called quite unexpectedly by the same pattern of cliff and sky which I then beheld. The sight was similar to what I had imagined in a year now lost save for random, incomplete impressions. Sugges-tions of this story may have lingered behind certain irritatingly un-finished memories, and in certain values hinted to my senses by scenes whose actual worth was bafflingly small. Frequently, in flashes of momentary perception, we feel that a feathery landscape (for instance), a woman's dress along the curve of a road by after-noon, or the solidity of a century-defying tree against the pale morning sky (the conditions more than the object being significant) hold something precious, some golden virtue that we must grasp. And yet when such a scene or arrangement is viewed later, or from another point, we find that it has lost its value and meaning for us. Perhaps this is because the thing we seek does not hold that elusive quality, but only suggests to the mind some very different thing which remains unremembered. The baffled mind, not wholly sens-ing the cause of its flashing appreciation, seizes on the object excit-ing it, and is surprised when there is nothing of worth therein. Thus it was when I beheld the purpling clouds. They held the state-liness and mystery of old monastery towers at twilight, but their as-pect was also that of the cliffs in the old fairy-tale. Suddenly reminded of this lost image, I half expected to see, in the fine-spun dirty foam and among the waves which were now as if they had been poured of flawed black glass, the horrid figure of that ape-faced creature, wearing a mitre old with verdigris, advancing from its kingdom in some lost gulf to which those waves were sky.

I did not see any such creature from the realm of imagining, but as the chill wind veered, slitting the heavens like a rustling knife, there lay in the gloom of merging cloud and water only a grey object, like a piece of driftwood, tossing obscurely on the foam. This was a considerable distance out, and since it vanished shortly, may have not been wood, but a porpoise coming to the troubled surface.

I soon found that I had stayed too long contemplating the rising storm and linking my early fancies with its grandeur, for an icy rain began spotting down, bringing a more uniform gloom upon a scene already too dark for the hour. Hurrying along the grey sand, I felt the impact of cold drops upon my back, and before many moments my clothing was soaked throughout. At first I had run, put to flight by the colourless drops whose pattern hung in long linking strands from an unseen sky, but after I saw that refuge was too far to reach in anything like a dry state, I slackened my pace, and returned home as if I had walked under clear skies. There was not much reason to hurry, although I did not idle as upon previous occasions. The constraining wet garments were cold upon me; and with the gathering darkness, and the wind that rose endlessly from the ocean, I could not repress a shiver. Yet there was, beside the discomfort of the precipitous rain, an exhilaration latent in the purplish ravelled masses of cloud and the stimulated reactions of my body. In a mood half of exultant pleasure from resisting the rain (which streamed from me now, and filled my shoes and pockets) and half of strange appreciation of those morbid, dominant skies which hovered with dark wings above the shifting eternal sea, I tramped along the grey corridor of Ellston Beach. More rapidly than I had expected the crouching house shewed in the oblique, flapping rain, and all the weeds of the sand cliff writhed in accompaniment to the frantic wind, as if they would uproot themselves to join the far-travelling element. Sea and sky had altered not at all, and the scene was that which had accompanied me, save that there was now painted upon it the hunching roof that seemed to bend from the assailing rain. I hurried up the insecure steps, and let myself into a dry room, where, unconsciously surprised that I was free of the nagging wind, I stood for a moment with water rilling from every inch of me.

There are two windows in the front of that house, as on each side, and these face nearly straight upon the ocean; which I saw now half obscured by the combined veils of the rain and of the imminent night. From these windows I looked as I dressed myself in a motley array of dry garments seized from convenient hangers and from a chair too laden to sit upon. I was prisoned on all sides by an unnaturally increased dusk which had filtered down at some undefined hour under cover of the fostering storm. How long I had been on the reaches of wet grey sand, or what the real time was, I could not tell, though a moment's search produced my watch—fortunately left behind and thus avoiding the uniform wetness of my clothing. I half guessed the hour from the dimly seen hands, which were only slightly less indecipherable than the surrounding figures. In another moment my sight penetrated the gloom (greater in the house than beyond the bleared window) and saw that it was 6:45.

There had been no one upon the beach as I came in, and naturally I expected to see no further swimmers that night. Yet when I looked again from the window there appeared surely to be figures blotting the grime of the wet evening. I counted three moving about in some incomprehensible manner, and close to the house another—which may not have been a person, but a wave-ejected log, for the surf was now pounding fiercely. I was startled to no little degree, and wondered for what purpose those hardy persons stayed out in such a storm. And then I thought that perhaps like myself they had been caught unintentionally in the rain and had surrendered to the watery gusts. In another moment, prompted by a certain civilised hospitality which overcame my love of solitude, I stepped to the door and emerged momentarily (at the cost of another wetting, for the rain promptly descended upon me in exultant fury) on the small porch, gesticulating toward the people. But whether they did not see me, or did not understand, they made no returning signal. Dim in the evening, they stood as if half-surprised, or as if they awaited some other action from me. There was in their attitude something of that cryptic blankness, signifying anything or nothing, which the house wore about itself as seen in the morbid sunset. Abruptly there came to me a feeling that a sinister quality lurked about those unmoving figures which chose to stay in the rainy night upon a beach deserted by all people, and I closed the door with a surge of annoyance which sought all too vainly to disguise a deeper emotion of fear; a consuming fright that welled up from the shadows of my consciousness. A moment later, when I had stepped to the window, there seemed to be nothing outside but the portentous night. Vaguely puzzled, and even more vaguely frightened—like one who has seen no alarming thing, but is apprehensive of what may be found in the dark street he is soon compelled to cross—I decided that I had very possibly seen no one, and that the murky air had deceived me.

The aura of isolation about the place was increased that night, though just out of sight on the northward beach a hundred houses rose in the rainy darkness, their light bleared and yellow above streets of polished glass, like goblin-eyes reflected in an oily forest pool. Yet because I could not see them, or even reach them in bad weather—since I had no car nor any way to leave the crouching house except by walking in the figure-haunted darkness—I realized quite suddenly that I was, to all intents, alone with the dreary sea that rose and subsided unseen, unkenned, in the mist. And the voice of the sea had become a hoarse groan, like that of something wounded which shifts about before trying to rise.

Fighting away the prevalent gloom with a soiled lamp—for the darkness crept in at my windows and sat peering obscurely at me from the corners like a patient animal—I prepared my food, since I had no intention of going to the village. The hour seemed incredibly advanced, though it was not yet nine o'clock when I went to bed. Darkness had come early and furtively, and throughout the remainder of my stay lingered evasively over each scene and action which I beheld. Something had settled out of the night—something forever undefined, but stirring a latent sense within me, so that I was like a beast expecting the momentary rustle of an enemy.

There were hours of wind, and sheets of the downpour flapped endlessly on the meagre walls barring it from me. Lulls came in which I heard the mumbling sea, and I could guess that large formless waves jostled one another in the pallid whine of the winds, and flung on the beach a spray bitter with salt. Yet in the very monotony of the restless elements I found a lethargic note, a sound that beguiled me, after a time, into slumber grey and colourless as the night. The sea continued its mad monologue, and the wind her nagging, but these were shut out by the walls of unconsciousness, and for a time the night ocean was banished from a sleeping mind.

Morning brought an enfeebled sun—a sun like that which men will see when the earth is old, if there are any men left: a sun more weary than the shrouded, moribund sky. Faint echo of its old image, Phoebus strove to pierce the ragged, ambiguous clouds as I awoke, at moments sending a wash of pale gold rippling across the northwestern interior of my house, at others waning till it was only a luminous ball, like some incredible plaything forgotten on the celestial lawn. After a while the failing rain—which must have continued throughout the previous night—succeeded in washing away those vestiges of purple cloud which had been like the ocean-cliffs in an old fairy-tale. Cheated alike of the setting and rising sun, that day merged with the day before, as if the intervening storm had not ushered a long darkness into the world, but had swollen and subsided in one long afternoon. Gaining heart, the furtive sun exerted all his force in dispelling the old mist, streaked now like a dirty window, and cast it from his realm. The shallow blue day advanced as those grimy wisps retreated, and the loneliness which had encircled me welled back into a watchful place of retreat, whence it went no farther, but crouched and waited.

The ancient brightness was now once more upon the sun, and the old glitter on the waves, whose playful blue shapes had flocked upon that coast ere man was born, and would rejoice unseen when

he was forgotten in the sepulchre of time. Influenced by these thin
assurances, like one who believes the smile of friendship on an enemy's features, I opened my door, and as it swung outward, a black
spot upon the inward burst of light, I saw the beach washed clean
of any track, as if no foot before mine had disturbed the smooth
sand. With the quick lift of spirit that follows a period of uneasy
depression, I felt—in a purely yielding fashion and without volition—that my own memory was washed clean of all the mistrust
and suspicion and disease-like fear of a lifetime, just as the filth of
the water's edge succumbs to a particularly high tide, and is carried
out of sight. There was a scent of soaked, brackish grass, like the
mouldy pages of a book, commingled with a sweet odour born of
the hot sunlight upon inland meadows, and these were borne into
me like an exhilarating drink, seeping and tingling through my
veins as if they would convey to me something of their own impal-
pable nature, and float me dizzily in the aimless breeze. And con-
spiring with these things, the sun continued to shower upon me,
like the rain of yesterday, an incessant array of bright spears; as if it
also wished to hide that suspected background presence which
moved beyond my sight and was betrayed only by a careless rustle
on the borders of my consciousness, or by the aspect of blank figures staring out of an ocean void. That sun, a fierce ball solitary in
the whirlpool of infinity, was like a horde of golden moths against
my upturned face. A bubbling white grail of fire divine and incomprehensible, it withheld from me a thousand promised mirages
where it granted one. For the sun did actually seem to indicate
realms, secure and fanciful, where if I but knew the path I might
wander in this curious exultation. Such things come of our own natures, for life has never yielded for one moment her secrets; and it is
only in our interpretation of their hinted images that we may find
ecstasy or dulness, according to a deliberately induced mood. Yet
ever and again we must succumb to her deceptions, believing for
the moment that we may this time find the withheld joy. And in
this way the fresh sweetness of the wind, on a morning following

the haunted darkness (whose evil intimations had given me a greater uneasiness than any menace to my body), whispered to me of ancient mysteries only half-linked with earth, and of pleasures that were the sharper because I felt that I might experience only a part of them. The sun and wind and that scent that rose upon them told me of festivals of gods whose senses are a millionfold more poignant than man's, and whose joys are a millionfold more subtle and prolonged. These things, they hinted, could be mine if I gave myself wholly into their bright deceptive power. And the sun, a crouching god with naked celestial flesh, an unknown, too-mighty furnace upon which eye might not look, seemed almost sacred in the glow of my newly sharpened emotions. The ethereal thunderous light it gave was something before which all things must worship astonished. The slinking leopard in his green-chasmed forest must have paused briefly to consider its leaf-scattered rays, and all things nurtured by it must have cherished its bright message on such a day. For when it is absent in the far reaches of eternity, earth will be lost and black against an illimitable void. That morning, in which I shared the fire of life, and whose brief moment of pleasure is secure against the ravenous years, was astir with the beckoning of strange things whose elusive names can never be written.

As I made my way toward the village, wondering how it might look after a long-needed scrubbing by the industrious rain, I saw, tangled in a glimmer of sunlit moisture that was poured over it like a yellow vintage, a small object like a hand, some twenty feet ahead of me, and touched by the repetitious foam. The shock and disgust born in my startled mind when I saw that it was indeed a piece of rotten flesh overcame my new contentment and engendered a shocked suspicion that it might actually be a hand. Certainly, no fish, or part of one, could assume that look, and I thought I saw mushy fingers wed in decay. I turned the thing over with my foot, not wishing to touch so foul an object, and it adhered stickily to the leather of the shoe, as if clutching with the grasp of corruption. The thing, whose shape was nearly lost, held too much resemblance to what I feared it might be; and I pushed it into the willing grasp of a seething wave, which took it from sight with an alacrity not often shewn by those ravelled edges of the sea.

Perhaps I should have reported my find, yet its nature was too ambiguous to make action natural. Since it had been partly *eaten* by some ocean-dwelling monstrousness, I did not think it identifiable enough to form evidence of an unknown but possible tragedy. The numerous drownings, of course, came into my mind—as well as other things lacking in wholesomeness, some of which remained only as possibilities. Whatever the storm-dislodged fragment may have been, and whether it were fish or some animal akin to man, I have never spoken of it until now. And after all, there was no proof that it had not merely been distorted by rottenness into that shape.

I approached the town, sickened by the presence of such an object amidst the apparent beauty of the clean beach, though it was horribly typical of the indifference of death in a Nature which mingles rottenness with beauty, and perhaps loves the former more. In Ellston I heard of no recent drowning or other mishap of the sea, and found no reference to such in the columns of the local paper— the only one I read during my stay.

It is difficult to describe the mental state in which succeeding days found me. Always susceptible to morbid emotions whose dark anguish might be induced by things outside myself, or might spring from the abysses of my own spirit, I was ridden by a feeling which was not fear or despair, or anything akin to these, but was rather a perception of the brief hideousness and underlying filth of life—a feeling partly a reflection of my internal nature and partly a result of broodings induced by that gnawed rotten object which may have been a hand. In those days my mind was a place of shadowed cliffs and dark moving figures, like the ancient unsuspected realm which the fairy-tale recalled to me. I felt, in brief agonies of disillusionment, the gigantic blackness of this overwhelming universe, in which my days and the days of my race were as nothing to the shattered stars; a universe in which each action is vain and even the

emotion of grief a wasted thing. The hours I had previously spent
in something of regained health, contentment, and physical well-
being were given now (as if those days of the previous week were
something definitely ended) to an indolence like that of a man who
no longer cares to live. I was engulfed by a piteous lethargic fear of
some ineluctable doom which would be, I felt, the completed hate
of the peering stars and of the black enormous waves that hoped to
clasp my bones within them—the vengeance of all the indifferent,
horrendous majesty of the night ocean.

Something of the darkness and restlessness of the sea had penetrated my heart, so that I lived in an unreasoning, unperceiving
torment, a torment none the less acute because of the subtlety of its
origin and the strange, unmotivated quality of its vampiric existence. Before my eyes lay the phantasmagoria of the purpling clouds,
the strange silver bauble, the recurrent stagnant foam, the loneliness
of that bleak-eyed house, and the mockery of the puppet town. I no
longer went to the village, for it seemed only a travesty of life. Like
my own soul, it stood upon a dark enveloping sea—a sea grown
slowly hateful to me. And among these images, corrupt and festering, dwelt that of an object whose human contours left ever smaller
the doubt of what it once had been.

These scribbled words can never tell of the hideous loneliness
(something I did not even wish assuaged, so deeply was it embedded in my heart) which had insinuated itself within me, mumbling
of terrible and unknown things stealthily circling nearer. It was not
a madness: rather was it a too clear and naked perception of the
darkness beyond this frail existence, lit by a momentary sun no
more secure than ourselves: a realisation of futility that few can experience and ever again touch the life about them: a knowledge that
turn as I might, battle as I might with all the remaining power of
my spirit, I could neither win an inch of ground from the inimical
universe, nor hold for even a moment the life entrusted to me.
Fearing death as I did life, burdened with a nameless dread yet unwilling to leave the scenes evoking it, I awaited whatever consum-

mating horror was shifting itself in the immense region beyond the walls of consciousness.

Thus autumn found me, and what I had gained from the sea was lost back into it. Autumn on the beaches—a drear time betokened by no scarlet leaf nor any other accustomed sign. A frightening sea which changes not, though man changes. There was only a chilling of the waters, in which I no longer cared to enter—a further darkening of the pall-like sky, as if eternities of snow were waiting to descend upon the ghastly waves. Once that descent began, it would never cease, but would continue beneath the white and the yellow and the crimson sun, and beneath that ultimate small ruby which shall yield only to the futilities of night. The once friendly waters babbled meaningfully at me, and eyed me with a strange regard; yet whether the darkness of the scene were a reflection of my own broodings, or whether the gloom within me were caused by what lay without, I could not have told. Upon the beach and me alike had fallen a shadow, like that of a bird which flies silently overhead—a bird whose watching eyes we do not suspect till the image on the ground repeats the image in the sky, and we look suddenly upward to find that something has been circling above us hitherto unseen.

The day was in late September, and the town had closed the resorts where mad frivolity ruled empty, fear-haunted lives, and where raddled puppets performed their summer antics. The puppets were cast aside, smeared with the painted smiles and frowns they had last assumed, and there were not a hundred people left in the town. Again the gaudy, stucco-fronted buildings lining the shore were permitted to crumble undisturbed in the wind. As the month advanced to the day of which I speak, there grew in me the light of a grey infernal dawn, wherein I felt some dark thaumaturgy would be completed. Since I feared such a thaumaturgy less than a continuance of my horrible suspicions—less than the too-elusive hints of something monstrous lurking behind the great stage—it was with more speculation than actual fear that I waited unendingly for the day of horror which seemed to be nearing. The day, I repeat, was late in September, though whether the 22nd or 23rd I am uncertain. Such details have fled before the recollection of those uncompleted happenings—episodes with which no orderly existence should be plagued, because of the damnable suggestions (and only suggestions) they contain. I knew the time with an intuitive distress of spirit—a recognition too deep for me to explain. Throughout those daylight hours I was expectant of the night; impatient, perhaps, so that the sunlight passed like a half-glimpsed reflection in rippled water—a day of whose events I recall nothing.

It was long since that portentous storm had cast a shadow over the beach, and I had determined, after hesitations caused by nothing tangible, to leave Ellston, since the year was chilling, and there was no return of my earlier contentment. When a telegram came for me (lying two days in the Western Union office before I was located, so little was my name known) saying that my design had been accepted—winning above all others in the contest—I set a date for leaving. This news, which earlier in the year would have affected me strongly, I now received with a curious apathy. It seemed as unrelated to the unreality about me, as little pertinent to me, as if it were directed to another person whom I did not know, and whose message had come to me through some accident. None the less, it was that which forced me to complete my plans and leave the cottage by the shore.

There were only four nights of my stay remaining when there occurred the last of those events whose meaning lies more in the darkly sinister impression surrounding them than in anything obviously threatening. Night had settled over Ellston and the coast, and a pile of soiled dishes attested both to my recent meal and to my lack of industry. Darkness came as I sat with a cigarette before the seaward window, and it was a liquid which gradually filled the sky, washing in a floating moon, monstrously elevated. The flat sea bordering upon the gleaming sand, the utter absence of tree or figure or life of any sort, and the regard of that high moon made the vastness of my surroundings abruptly clear. There were only a few stars pricking through as if to accentuate by their smallness the majesty of the lunar orb and of the restless shifting tide.

I had stayed indoors, fearing somehow to go out before the sea on such a night of shapeless portent, but I heard it mumbling secrets of an incredible lore. Borne to me on a wind out of nowhere was the breath of some strange and palpitant life; the embodiment of all I had felt and of all I had suspected—stirring now in the chasms of the sky or beneath the mute waves. In what place this mystery turned from an ancient, horrible slumber I could not tell, but like one who stands by a figure lost in sleep, knowing that it will awake in a moment, I crouched by the windows, holding a nearly burnt-out cigarette, and faced the rising moon.

Gradually there passed into that never-stirring landscape a brilliance intensified by the overhead glimmerings, and I seemed more and more under some compulsion to watch whatever might follow. The shadows were draining from the beach, and I felt that they took with them all which might have been a harbour for my thoughts when the hinted thing should come. Where any of them did remain they were ebon and blank: still lumps of darkness sprawling beneath the cruel brilliant rays. The endless tableau of the lunar orb—dead now, whatever her past was, and cold as the unhuman sepulchres she bears amid the ruin of dusty centuries older than man—and the sea— astir, perhaps, with some unkenned life, some forbidden sentience— confronted me with a horrible vividness. I arose and shut the window; partly because of an inward prompting, but mostly, I think, as an excuse for transferring momentarily the stream of thought. No sound came to me now as I stood before the closed panes. Minutes or eternities were alike. I was waiting, like my own fearing heart and the motionless scene beyond, for the token of some ineffable life. I had set the lamp upon a box in the western corner of the room, but the moon was brighter, and her bluish rays invaded places where the lamplight was faint. The ancient glow of the round silent orb lay upon the beach as it had lain for aeons, and I waited in a torment of ex-

pectancy made doubly acute by the delay in fulfilment, and the un-
certainty of what strange completion was to come.

Outside the crouching hut a white illumination suggested vague
spectral forms whose unreal, phantasmal motions seemed to taunt
my blindness, just as unheard voices mocked my eager listening.
For countless moments I was still, as if Time and the tolling of her
great bell were hushed into nothingness. And yet there was nothing
which I might fear: the moon-chiselled shadows were unnatural in
no contour, and veiled nothing from my eyes. The night was silent—I knew that despite my closed window—and all the stars were
fixed mournfully in a listening heaven of dark grandeur. No motion
from me then, or word now, could reveal my plight, or tell of the
fear-racked brain imprisoned in flesh which dared not break the silence, for all the torture it brought. As if expectant of death, and assured that nothing could serve to banish the soul-peril I confronted,
I crouched with a forgotten cigarette in my hand. A silent world
gleamed beyond the cheap, dirty windows, and in one corner of the
room a pair of dirty oars, placed there before my arrival, shared the
vigil of my spirit. The lamp burned endlessly, yielding a sick light
hued like a corpse's flesh. Glancing at it now and again, for the desperate distraction it gave, I saw that many bubbles unaccountably
rose and vanished in the kerosene-filled base. Curiously enough,
there was no heat from the wick. And suddenly I became aware that
the night as a whole was neither warm nor cold, but strangely neu-
tral—as if all physical forces were suspended, and all the laws of a
calm existence disrupted.

Then, with an unheard splash which sent from the silver water
to the shore a line of ripples echoed in fear by my heart, a swim-
ming thing emerged beyond the breakers. The figure may have
been that of a dog, a human being, or something more strange. It
could not have known that I watched—perhaps it did not care—but
like a distorted fish it swam across the mirrored stars and dived beneath the surface. After a moment it came up again, and this time,
since it was closer, I saw that it was carrying something across its

shoulder. I knew, then, that it could be no animal, and that it was a man or something like a man, which came toward the land from a dark ocean. But it swam with a horrible ease.

As I watched, dread-filled and passive, with the fixed stare of one who awaits death in another yet knows he cannot avert it, the swimmer approached the shore—though too far down the southward beach for me to discern its outlines or features. Obscurely loping, with sparks of moonlit foam scattered by its quick gait, it emerged and was lost among the inland dunes.

Now I was possessed by a sudden recurrence of fear, which had died away in the previous moments. There was a tingling coldness all over me—though the room, whose window I dared not open now, was stuffy. I thought it would be very horrible if something were to enter a window which was not closed.

Now that I could no longer see the figure, I felt that it lingered somewhere in the close shadows, or peered hideously at me from whatever window I did not watch. And so I turned my gaze, eagerly and frantically, to each successive pane; dreading that I might indeed behold an intrusive regarding face, yet unable to keep myself from the terrifying inspection. But though I watched for hours, there was no longer anything upon the beach.

So the night passed, and with it began the ebbing of that strangeness—a strangeness which had surged up like an evil brew within a pot, had mounted to the very rim in a breathless moment, had paused uncertainly there, and had subsided, taking with it whatever unknown message it had borne. Like the stars that promise the revelation of terrible and glorious memories, goad us into worship by this deception, and then impart nothing, I had come frighteningly near to the capture of an old secret which ventured close to man's haunts and lurked cautiously just beyond the edge of the known. Yet in the end I had nothing. I was given only a glimpse of the furtive thing; a glimpse made obscure by the veils of ignorance. I cannot even conceive what might have shewn itself had I been too close to that swimmer who went shoreward instead of into the ocean. I do not know what might have come if the brew had passed the rim of the pot and poured outward in a swift cascade of revelation. The night ocean withheld whatever it had nurtured. I shall know nothing more.

Even yet I do not know why the ocean holds such a fascination for me. But then, perhaps none of us can solve those things—they exist in defiance of all explanation. There are men, and wise men, who do not like the sea and its lapping surf on yellow shores; and they think us strange who love the mystery of the ancient and unending deep. Yet for me there is a haunting and inscrutable glamour in all the ocean's moods. It is in the melancholy silver foam beneath the moon's waxen corpse; it hovers over the silent and eternal waves that beat on naked shores; it is there when all is lifeless save for unknown shapes that glide through sombre depths. And when I behold the awesome billows surging in endless strength, there comes upon me an ecstasy akin to fear; so that I must abase myself before this mightiness, that I may not hate the clotted waters and their overwhelming beauty.

Vast and lonely is the ocean, and even as all things came from it, so shall they return thereto. In the shrouded depths of time none shall reign upon the earth, nor shall any motion be, save in the eternal waters. And these shall beat on dark shores in thunderous foam, though none shall remain in that dying world to watch the cold light of the enfeebled moon playing on the swirling tides and coarse-grained sand. On the deep's margin shall rest only a stagnant foam, gathering about the shells and bones of perished shapes that dwelt within the waters. Silent, flabby things will toss and roll along empty shores, their sluggish life extinct. Then all shall be dark, for at last even the white moon on the distant waves shall wink out. Nothing shall be left, neither above nor below the sombre waters. And until that last millennium, and beyond the perishing of all other things, the sea will thunder and toss throughout the dismal night.

# Birthday

Mrs. Doris Byttner rolled over on a pillow that had worked its way nearly off the bed, rubbed her eyes, and went through the gestures of the half-wakened sleeper. There was only a vacant spot where her memory should have been. She did not know into what scene she emerged, nor what abandoned realm was left beyond the borders of consciousness. For a time she lingered this way, reluctant to waken. Then she writhed down in the lumpy bedclothes, and opened one eye by itself. Wonderingly it surveyed the room, as on a thousand previous mornings, and then remained still. Presently the other joined it from a cheek red and wrinkled by sleep. They stared into invisibility, searching for some recollection. And presently, having found it, they considered the knowledge. It was August tenth, 1928, and it was her birthday. Not that that meant much. Sometimes she was the only one who remembered, and once even she had forgotten. The Byttner family wasn't much on celebrations. Most of their celebrating was done, lone wolf style, at public dances and speakeasies. Nevertheless, it was her birthday.

Since nobody else was going to do anything about it, she wondered if her tin compact had enough change to buy herself a present—just out of sentiment. Wondering was as far as she got, because she knew very well what it contained: three dimes and a quarter, in addition to the crumbled remains of a cake of powder. She kept her finances in there because they were never extensive enough to warrant a purse, although squeezing it shut on too many nickels had broken the little mirror, so that only a sliver remained by which to do her nose. Mrs. Byttner kept on the go all the time, but her cash did not undergo much fluctuation. The blue pocketbook with the fancy clasp, given her by a long-unseen sister two years ago, still reposed in the dressing-table, in spite of her daughter's calculated efforts to adopt it. Swollen only by yellowing tissue-paper, it was likely to stay there two years more. Mrs. Byttner liked to keep it nice—in case she had any use for it, although generally her tidiness was more a wish than an actuality. The room bore sullen witness to this; but what was the use of putting things away for the space of one night? She left them where she took them off in her course about the room, and resumed them along the same route. Nobody else saw them except her family, and they were much worse.

The eyes shifted imperceptibly, as if to another thought. She'd have to call last night her birthday-party, she thought in amusement. As if she'd had a birthday-party in twenty years! And with this a sweep of memory came out of the previous night . . . her pimply young escort, the poorly-lit dance-hall, and the café where they had all adjourned to drink sour coffee and keep the yawning proprietor awake long after he wanted to close. She'd never even been certain of her partner's name—he was just somebody handed to her by Marjorie. who was probably afraid to dance with anyone that lacked durability. "You're the life of this party, Doris; can I put a friend in your custody?" she had bubbled. "I'll try not to batter him up too much. Do you want a receipt?" was her reply, and everybody laughed. But with such an informal introduction it was no wonder she'd missed his name. She danced with so many people. Probably everybody in town except her husband. He never went out; and he didn't pay any attention to what she did. It was very irritating. He never even got jealous of her retinue of pasty younger men. Nobody paid much attention to the people who weren't young enough to be smart and dashing, but were afraid to stop their colourless gaiety. "I'm going to keep going as long as I can," she had often said, "I don't want to sit in a greasy kitchen and watch my husband read the sporting page with his suspenders down." Mr. Byttner's household garb was rather lacking in appeal—particularly the dirty undershirt, which he refused to send to the laundry. "You go on, Doris," he always said to her when she got started on this track. "You'll have a better time without me, and I'm too tired."

Once in a while she thought that it was too bad to go off and leave her husband in an empty house every evening, and she would stay home a night, or maybe two nights. But when she did this he read the endless newspaper and scratched under his chin while she sat and stared bleakly at him. He paid little attention to her, and the clock ticked raucously; now and again he would adjust his newspaper with a slight rustle: otherwise the house was still. She couldn't get any sleep before midnight, and so there would be nothing to do but read Flora's magazines, when she might have been out dancing. There was no reason to stay home on his account. Generally she and Flora left right after dinner without doing the dishes, although grease is less inviting when it's cold; and they cooked everything in grease except the spaghetti. Dish washing, like cooking, was shunted off on whomever felt least like arguing, and the two of them, struggling in the kitchen, did less work than she might have done alone. But they had much in common. Both had discovered that pepper was useful in disguising poor cooking, that if you use too much grease it pops out and makes peculiar rings on the electric coils, and that it's much easier to cook the same things every day because you can always add yesterday's left-overs, so that nothing is thrown out. Sometimes a fragment would be passed over for successive days until it got too shrivelled or too powdery, depending on its nature, and then it went into the cat's food, but generally they got along pretty well, and it was possible, at times, to persuade the heir of the household to do the dishes.

The businesses of housekeeping attended to, they would go to their rooms, and amid a shouted conversation, apply rouge and hurry into Flora's dresses and Mrs. Byttner's uncostly jewelry, telling each other whom they were going out with, and arguing over the car. Flora generally lost in this, because there was nobody to come for her mother, while a random group generally stopped in for her. Flora's friends were always willing to take her along; Doris had to get herself about. In that circle of left-over maidens and parts of families each was too much engaged in clinging on himself to bother about Flora's mother. They were all glad to see her; she was so amusing and never minded playing the piano while the rest danced, but nobody quite wanted to go around and take a married woman out for the evening while her husband read the newspaper. She kept on with them and meant to continue doing so, but it was wearing to dye her hair every week and then keep dabbling unevenly at the roots where it kept growing out a sickly colour.

The glassy eyes moved again, and surveyed an aged clock with little rosebuds painted on the base. It was nine-fifteen, and somebody ought to be getting up to put the coffee on. Flora had come in last, and ought to be getting a little sleep if she meant to play tennis after lunch. Her office-minded husband would be gone long ago. He never remembered birthdays, not even his own. A man like that gets tiresome at first, and them simply becomes a vegetable sprouting vaguely in the background while his wife is out hankering after the gay life she wanted twenty years before. Doris missed it in 1908, because there was Flora to take care of, but Flora breezed along and took it in her stride, along with a half-conscientious attempt at college, which her mother hadn't got. Doris had encouraged her. Let the girl enjoy herself. She might marry a vegetable, too, who took a negative view on everything and still managed to depress everybody.

Mrs. Bytnner had been fool enough to marry what looked like a good job, and found its progress glacial "It's a lot more sensible, Doris, to take a man you can get with a steady income, instead of waiting until you get left behind," her sister had said, and Henry had had a fascinating little red mustache, in those days. It had grown so thin he had to shave it off, later. The ruddy face had grown pasty, and he had become indifferent to her after Flora's birth. A vegetable that would have been afraid to get out of its garden. So the upbringing of the children had devolved on her; and she had encouraged them to be independent, since that was what she wanted for herself. As a result they had raised themselves, indifferent to the father because their mother was indifferent, selfish because she gave them more than household finances could spare. When she found out that they were steering themselves at a pretty fast clip, she tried to interfere, but they sulked and hinted she was envious. After that, she was hesitant about her maternal duties, and since all her firmness had oozed out in the twenty years with Henry, all she did was watch them. Presently this left off, too, and she found herself suddenly freed, with nothing to do but keep Henry in running order. In that chaotic household she was a little mystified when Flora brought friends in and didn't introduce them to her. She felt that Flora was ashamed of her, and helped to drag Henry from sight whenever the doorbell rang, while she was in her small untidy room and waited, hoping that someone would miss her and ask her to come out and meet everybody. They didn't. Gradually, then, it had dawned on her that she might go around herself, since everybody was overlooking her. Henry took her to the movies when Clara Bow was on, but he had never danced.

When she began to hunt up her own amusements he raised no objection. Those amusements, the circles open to a woman who was lost between two generations, were an echo of the pleasures of nineteen. Feverishly, not willing to admit themselves fossilized, reluctant to sit in kitchens and too zestless to look in other fields, the parents imitated their children, and pretended to have a hell of a good time. Tired eyes took on a sparkle from the light of glittering restaurants, spiritless flesh forgot itself for a few short hours in the intoxication of dancing. Doris put on her sprightly expression along with her too-short evening gown and her nail-polish. When the car swung out of the garage, she was already half-eager with the expectation of moving again in an evening of laughter where people thought her clever. Henry didn't think her clever any longer. He hadn't even asked her opinion when he shaved off his mustache and began leaving his shoes in the bedroom when he read the sport column. Why he read this was a mystery, because he couldn't throw a beanbag, and didn't want to learn how. All he wanted was somebody to cook spaghetti and scrape the grease off the pans so it wouldn't get to smelling bad. He gave her an allowance, and never a cent more. The allowance was enough, but the method irritating. Flora picked up her spare cash doing typing. Mrs. Byttner hadn't been smart enough to learn anything like that, so there was no way of getting back at Henry.

This reflection brought her around, as she lay in a cotton night-gown decorated with faded unidentifiable flowers, to the fact that fifty-five cents wouldn't even buy a good handkerchief. Not that she particularly wanted a handkerchief, but that was what everybody gave everybody else for a present. Since the hands of the clock progressed, Mrs. Byttner hurried through a decision of what kind she might have bought if she had been shopping, and sat up to survey the room. It had been the children's room at first, but she had taken it and given hers to Flora several years ago. It was not an entertaining thing to consider, since only vague cleaning attempts had been made on the previous day. A straightening process was unavoidable. She would have to do this after she had gotten Flora up and made the coffee.

As she balanced on the edge of the bed and combed her hair, discovering that another tooth was broken out of the comb, her daughter gave a strong, melodious yawn and set about obscure thumping noises in the next room. The comb had been part of a wedding present, but was the only survivor. Not much had survived that wedding. Her scant hair subdued by a complicated system of bobby pins (she still wore it as long as it would go), there was powder to apply; and this demanded a mirror so as to permit the studied inspection of various contortions. Screwing her face up as if in actual pain, she was dusting the white powder on, and considering the appropriateness of chili for breakfast when her eye paused with the same fixed indifference it had shown previously. She did not put the grimy powder-puff on the table, but held it listlessly. Among the litter of small bottles, chipped pseudo-ivory toilet articles, and discarded hairnets a badly-wrapped package intruded itself. Flora had been the last in—she must be responsible for the object. "Well! So my hard-hearted daughter did remember," she exclaimed in surprise. She did not open it; the contents were of no importance. Probably a set of cocktail napkins, or something peculiar to put ashes in. But she was pleased as she began again the cloudy attack of the powder-puff, and looked admiringly at the blue tissue-papered box.

It did not occur to her to inspect it just yet. She meant to get more excitement than that out of a birthday present. Taking a final swoop at her face, she discarded the fungoid object, and hunted out a dressing-gown that had once been lavender. There were dishes left in the sink, and somebody had to get them out of the way to make room for coffee. Deciding hastily on pork-and-beans, which could be heated with little trouble, Mrs. Doris Byttner thumped on her daughter's door and went to the kitchen. She was thirty-nine years old.

# Nightfall

Now I, who am the last survivor, shall slay myself. There is no reason for delay; this tower, woven about with clouds, is very tall, and below it dark waves throng amid the rocks. The ocean is bare and ominous, holding no variation: to its farthest edge the pattern is the same—wave and rock, rock and wave—until the eye is dimmed by the repetition. These coasts have known the wave in sunlight and darkness since they emerged, slimy and raw, from beneath earlier waves—presently, when I and my death are a long time over, they will descend once more, and there will be nothing for the waves to beat on, so that at last they will be defeated. Meanwhile, they are horrible as one by one, malign, deliberated, they take shape, collect themselves and mount with increasing rapidity to shatter their edges of foam upon red sandstone. The coast is pitted until it resembles a gory, petrified sponge.

I do not know why I listen for such a long while—the balcony window is open, and the balustrade will not impede me. In the long shaft of the tower underneath me no person moves; they are all gone away. Save for myself this tower regarding the sea has forgotten mankind. The elements exult, knowing that we are defeated and that in an hour or less, when I am ready, there will be not one left to watch.

It is a damp wind that blows through the room, and the bronze sky has become so dark that it will soon be tangled with the waves. Far out they are building into a storm—a final and cataclysmic attack upon the tall, pallid tower, deserted by man. They advance with the noise of a mob.

A step, and the little balcony is all that holds me back. It is no substantial barrier, but I shall very naturally pause in fear and contemplation, and lean over it to stare at the unreflecting water and the intricate, baffling pattern of its tread. I must be certain to leap out, so that it will be the submerged cleft and not the rocks I strike. One moment, hesitant and still part of life, I shall contend with instinct, and then step off, to fall down shafts of black air in hideous descent, swifter than the darksome stain *inside* that wall. The ocean's lifting mouth will suck me in, and for the remaining instant of entity walls will rush past and up, the shore rises up like a sky. And then a torturing compression of my lungs, vainly closed; a trickle of blood inside them, and the cool, surprising breaths of water as my flaccid body investigates the deep.

*May 27, 1937*

## Origin Undetermined

I have been reading the singular document Heywood Roberts left, and wondering if it should be published. It may have some value to students of psychology, since it deals with an uncommon sort of mental disorder from the victim's own point of view; indeed, it is unique—I do not know how to classify such abnormal imaginings. The delusion from which he suffered must have appeared very real and terrible, since he chose such a fearsome method of escape. That he was a suicide can no longer be doubted; the basement of the

Nelkin Gallery of Art has disclosed certain evidence confirming such a view. No heirs are known to me, and since the appended text was addressed in my care, I believe that my authority to circulate it will not be questioned. Should any relative of the deceased encounter it, I trust that he will not object to my action.

A certain amount of explanatory matter must be affixed to this record, in which fact and madness are strangely mingled. In 1912 and 1913 I knew the deceased more than casually, both of us then being students at the Cassia Medical School in Detroit. He seemed then to promise a brilliant career as surgeon, but afterward he gave this up altogether, victim of a mood which, if it were not quite the Freudian impulse to self-destruction latent in us all, was at least an impulse to conscious and unpreventable destruction of his own opportunities. I have seen this curious, lamentable impulse driving others; they seem predestined to unenviable fates. I still recall my earliest impression of him . . . a roundish head surmounting an awkward body; dark eyebrows and mustache; and a vaguely Oriental quality about the pale fleshy face, though he was Nordic enough in reality. His chin was not strong, and there was something weak about the corners of his mouth. He spoke interminably in complicated and remotely stilted sentences—the almost pedantic English of a foreigner who does not grasp our idiom—and though his speech was full of ideas and enthusiasms, there was often too much of it. He was as erratic as he was brilliant, a youth who had discarded the inane philosophy in which he was reared, but who had not yet evolved a workable substitute. He might have become a criminal as readily as a surgeon, a feverish drunkard as readily as a scholar. Yet in the end he did not succumb, as I feared he might, to the brief and fiery intoxications of a dissipated life. There was a balance wheel somewhere in him, and it asserted itself, enabling him in time to reach a prominent place in the field he chose to work in. This field was archaeology. Long before Roberts abandoned medicine, his fertile imagination played with the shards of our forgotten past, with desert cities in which the legends of humanity had birth, with

Akkad and Persepolis, with Knossos and Karnak, where chiseled spearmen watch the sunlight move across fields baked hard eight thousand years ago. The wreckage cast up from the expanding sea of Roman conquest, the stupendous tombs of Egypt, and more than these, the secret, jungle-beset palaces of Central America, were a greater reality to him than the world he read of vaguely in books and newspapers. It is scarcely odd that he gave up his medical studies; he was not realist enough to be a doctor.

After I had lost sight of him for a decade he wrote to me one day, his letter disclosing that he had become curator of Central American antiquities at the Nelkin Gallery of Art. I saw him many times in the succeeding years—he had shaken off his early unsteadiness, and become deeply absorbed in his new work. Some of his extensive information regarding primitive surgical practices held especial interest for me, and once or twice he was flattering enough to ask my opinion regarding knives and scalpels excavated by field expeditions sent out by the Gallery. But there was nothing about him to indicate that such an incomprehensible breakdown lurked ahead.

Early in March of last year Roberts called my office, the nurse answering him, but in a moment passing the phone on to me. I took it and was at once disturbed by the quality of his voice. He did not, apparently, realise that Miss Phillips had left, for he continued with a strange, broken plea:

"Got to do it. I can't tell you how vital it is. God! It's already started. If you turn me down . . . no choice left. It works fast. If you saw what it does . . . this means my life. I'm coming over now . . ."

"Heywood!" I shouted, astonished by his frantic rambling. "What's the matter? I didn't get you." But a sharp click informed me that he had hung up. I tried to ring him back: there was no reply.

Then Miss Phillips spoke. "Who on earth was that, do you know?" Disconnectedly, I explained, and she reflected a moment. "It was something about poison or infection, I think. Perhaps I'd better get ready in case he comes over." She busied herself with the contents of the glass-shelved cabinet.

I spent the next quarter hour dialling places he might have called from. His office at the Gallery was silent, and such people as I did reach knew nothing of the matter . . . I was still engaged this way on the arrival of the man himself. He snatched the door open, glaring distractedly into space—the seal of fright set heavily upon him. He looked, I swear, like a dying man who has peered through the black corridors of destiny. The nurse and I were silent, appalled by his eyes. Fear is a communicable thing, and he was radiant with it. A moment he stood, almost quietly, but it was the quiet of a bowstring when the arrow is poised for flight. His turbulent gaze sought me, and there was no madness in it. Here was a man gripped by shadow hands, but a sane man. He closed the door and slid into a chair beside it.

"I know you didn't understand me," he said. "I guess I sounded crazy—God! I am crazy, with fear . . . But you must listen now. I am in danger; believe me. It's a kind of poison, and it works fast. I can't tell you what it is. You've never heard of it. It's tropical . . . very rare. And it doesn't show up until the last. It will be too late when you can . . ."

He thrust his left hand out across the desk where I sat, and turned it slowly. The ring caught light from overhead, glittering in our eyes. The flesh bore no mark, no wounds, no discolouration.

Roberts spoke again. "You've got to amputate."

The absurdity of this roused me. "Don't be an idiot, Heywood! If you are poisoned, there must be antidotes. I'm not going to tell you to calm down . . . you know that excitement only increases your danger . . . but I am going to tell you not to say crazy things like that. What was it, anyway? Was it a snake?"

He shook his head. "I knew you'd object—you don't know what it's like. No, it wasn't a snake. It's . . . something old," he added, half to himself. "Something people don't remember anything about . . ."

"Old? Connected with your work? Tell me."

"There isn't time. There isn't time," he cried in agony, and then subsided. "Well, I'll tell you part of what happened, to show you why you've got to do it." After a momentary hesitation he went on.

"You know we get a lot of weapons over at the Gallery, from the Guatemala excavations. Parker has sent up some splendid finds . . . I don't know if you've read about them. The papers gave his discovery of those Mayan altar-tombs a big write up. Anyway, he sent a final crate from that site up by steamer in August. Most of it came from one grave of the Old Empire, about two or three hundred B.C. A magnificent piece of luck. There were even bits of fabric wrapped around a bronze knife. It was this knife . . . I've always been careful with stuff like that, the Indians make strong poisons . . . But at first I was busy with the weavings. I put the knife aside all winter, until this morning, when I wanted to clean it. When I took it out of the cabinet it slipped to the floor. By some devilish luck I cut my hand a little. Less mark than a razor would make, but I was afraid of it, and went downstairs for iodine. While I was out of my office I left the knife on my desk. I had the door locked. I didn't think about anything else." He paused.

"You want me to amputate your hand because you scratched it, and you only *think* the knife was poisoned two thousand years ago?" I hoped to shame him out of his extravagant mood. But he went on:

"We have a cat there, a large white one called Arky. Well, Arky had the run of the place—he lives in the basement—and he must have been in the room when I left. When I got back he was on my desk, licking the blade of the knife. He raised his face and stared at me as I came in, and arched his back for me to pet him. I took the knife away, and he growled as if I had taken his dinner. Then he jumped down and hid under a cabinet. I tried to coax him out, but he wouldn't come. Finally I decided the harm was done if there'd been anything on the blade. That was right after I came to work.

"About an hour later I heard Arky scratching around as if he wanted to get out, and then he gave a peculiar yowling shriek. Animals make funny sounds when they're hurt. I suspected what was wrong with him—it made me wonder if iodine was strong enough for my cut . . . and in a few minutes he crawled out, dying. Then I knew my own danger. Whatever was on the knife was still strong. *And I had cut myself.* I called you then." Here he ceased, looking vaguely at me, and said, "You must do what I want."

"That is not what happened," I said.

He started to protest, and knew that I was unconvinced. "No," he admitted, strangely cool. His passion had sunk down within him, leaving only a reflection in his fevered cheeks. "That's only partly true. I can't tell you any more. But I have not lied about the need for amputation. You must cut off my hand."

I looked at Miss Phillips, wondering at this unreasonable persistence. She took my part. "You can't ask him to do that! It is perfectly sound. I don't understand, but I think you are reasonable. If you are poisoned, the Doctor can treat you. Let him try."

Roberts leaned forward savagely. "Christ! Won't you hurry? I can't waste more time. Cut if off!"

"It would mean the end of my reputation," I said.

He made a choking sound. "You mean you haven't got any reason? There's reason enough, if you only knew . . . I'll give you one."

Before I saw what Roberts was up to, he had pulled a revolver from inside his coat. Miss Phillips emitted a faint scream.

"Are you threatening me? I have no anaesthetic," I protested. "My instruments aren't ready."

"I can stand it," he replied.

Then he held his palm over the mouth of the gun and pulled the trigger.

I never saw him after the operation. Until I saw the manuscript written out of his torment, I did not think I even wanted to hear of him. Now I am doubtful. Perhaps what he made me do was necessary; I do not know. The initial lie he told me has shaken my trust in him. So little proof exists! The Maya urn is back on exhibit, but nothing may be learned of it. As for the cat named Archaeology, I am told it disappeared some days ago. The guards have given it up, and the bowl of food in the cellar is not likely to be touched if there is any truth in what Roberts wrote. I would like to believe that he was the victim of some dark mood, and that he wrote these pages from his broodings and delusions alone. But why would a man shoot his own hand off?

## The Manuscript

Although you surmised that much of my story was a lie, I could not have said anything else. Now I am writing because I have reached the ultimate link in a nightmare chain of godless and terrible events. What I will say must inevitably seem a greater lie than the lies I have told you, but I think that writing it out will be a relief to me.

As you know, my special interest lies in Central American ceramics of the prehispanic period. Most of our stuff comes from expeditions financed by the Gallery, but occasional pieces drift in from Europe. This may surprise you, but it can be easily explained. During the last century many sites in the Old Empire region were irresponsibly excavated, and pieces were taken away without adequate record of their origin or the circumstances of their discovery—a vital point in archaeology. Some of these objects went to museums, but others were cast adrift as mere curiosities, shelved ultimately in littered shops or the houses of parvenu magpies. In any case, various pottery fragments, some of them infinitely tantalising because of what might have been learned from them if their histories had not been lost, do turn up. In the past we at the Gallery have not bought anything of note this way, but late in February we obtained a magnificent decorated urn, *unbroken,* about seven inches high, and decorated in a style akin to that of the Nazca ware in South America. Its colour and dimensions, however, seemed to link it more closely with Mayan traditions, and without any actual assurance I judged it to be such, marking the exhibit card *Origin Unknown.* A feather-helmeted man, concealing his face behind tense fingers, was painted in exquisite outline about the piece, which came from a Jewish dealer in Hamburg—a man of remarkable erudition driven out of the country by Nazi terrorists. He was compelled to break up his private collection in order to finance his escape.

The urn was capped with hard baked clay, never broken off. Whatever it might contain, it was not heavy, and I speculated on its contents, not daring to tamper with the seal. I toyed with the notion of making an X-ray, but did not follow this up from sheer lack of time. No especial caution was taken in exhibiting the piece, despite its fine qualities, and it was finally placed in a separate case in Gallery 3.

There are several rooms in the basement of the Gallery, and in one of them I fixed up a cot several years back, sleeping there as often as I do at home. I have stayed in the building for as much as a week when my work demanded it. About ten days ago I had been over-working consistently, and being too tired to go home, I slept in this basement room. I had prepared a report for the Board of Trustees, and the confounded thing stuck at every point, so that I was not finished until two a.m. The watchman saw my light at that time, but says that it had gone out when he came around again. My brain was utterly clogged—a physical and mental indolence against which I had struggled for days seemed to dominate me. I could perform only routine actions—extinguishing lights, locking my office, and descending to my room. All these in a dream-like stupefaction.

I went over the report through hours of uneasy slumber, awaken-ing somewhat after dawn more tired than when I lay down. My in-ordinate weariness had waxed rather than abated, and some area of memory seemed deliberately shut off from the rest of my mind. Many things sink down out of reach in the waves of sleep—more, I have been thinking, than we shall ever suspect. As I opened my eyes on the bleakly furnished room there was a feeling that something had eluded me when I woke—something which had accompanied me very close to the waking world. I seemed to remember being a witness, or perhaps even a participant, in some distressing action whose nature I could not recall.

I saw it was nine o'clock, almost time for the main doors to open. I shaved and put on my clothes, going at once to my office. My intention was to get money for breakfast down the street, but I went no farther, for as I thrust the key in the door, hasty steps clamoured on the tiled floor of Gallery 3, and Williams, the guard, appeared. His youngish, thin face was clouded with dismay.

"Something's happened over here, sir," he exclaimed. "Did you go in yet?"

"No—is something gone? Has the watchman left?" I cried, forgetting my keys and hurrying across the corridor. Williams, following, panted out, "It's the new vase, sir. But it's not gone. Someone has opened the case and smashed it."

A momentary glance confirmed this. The hard baked shell had shattered on the tiles like an electric light bulb. It lay in widely separated fragments, perhaps beyond the repairer's skill. Some thief, surprised or awkward in his task, had dropped it escaping. I saw that it had disgorged a mass of withered fibrous stuff, sections of a dried vine, which, no longer pent in, had begun to expand. As we stood there a tendril dropped into place, a curled leaf sagged out to almost-forgotten dimensions, and the whole mass writhed gradually about, just as lobsters do when they lie on ice in a restaurant window. I poked it with a tentative finger, and found it to be more durable than its ash-like appearance suggested. At my touch a few large seeds rolled out on the floor.

Botany is not part of my work, though nearly everything else seems to be, and I had no idea of what the plant was or had been. Nor did I understand why it had been sealed up with such manifest care. My thoughts were moving chiefly about the attempted theft, but I picked up two or three shreds of the compressed material, with specimen seeds, and placed them in my coat pocket for later investigation.

When the clay fragments had been wrapped in cotton wool and sent upstairs to the workshop, I called the police in, but they could establish nothing. Only myself had been seen by the watchman, and none of the alarms had been disturbed. Specimens of fingerprints on the empty case were compared with those of the staff, in the hope that supernumerary marks would be found, but the result was exasperating. Mine, and those of Williams were all that were discovered. With considerable pomposity the detectives left, and I went out for a disconsolate breakfast. At that time I thought I would rather have lost a tooth than the Maya urn.

In the restaurant I got out my samples of vegetation and spread them before me. The seeds, of which I had taken three, were shaped like small brazil-nuts, perhaps as long as my thumb-nail, and bearing a high polish. I tried to break one open, but could not. They were intensely hard. I wondered if any fertility might linger in them, since neither they nor their leaves had become brittle in their clay sarcophagus. There have more than once been stories of wheat from primitive tombs being sprouted experimentally, and though I thought the idea extravagant, I decided to plant a couple.

I put them in a teacup full of dirt, which I set in the square of light falling through space for ninety million miles to illuminate my cellar room. It was not until the next day that I got around to it, and feeling vaguely absurd, I did not speak of the matter to anyone. The earth I stuck them in was moist, but they did not get any more water at all. I completely forgot them in my concern over the attempted robbery, and afterward slept at home for the better part of a week.

Monday I happened to be in the cellar again, and thinking of the teacup, went to my room to see if anything had happened. Something had: when I opened the door two delicate brown spirals, fully eight inches high, stood silhouetted in the window. I was not prepared for this phenomenal growth—I was not actually prepared for any growth at all. God knows what those plants were, or why their parent seeds had been kept. They should have been destroyed hundreds of years ago. They grew too fast, and they fed on things no other plant feeds on. Neither dirt nor water nor carrion had contributed to their unwholesome sprouting, but bare glass instead. . . . Three-quarters of the window-pane was gone, melted away precisely as if a blowtorch had been applied to it; and in the opening those hungry sprouts vibrated like small serpent heads. A chilly wind blew in from the March day: they seemed to breathe it avidly.

I destroyed those plants. Some deep instinct directed me to. If they could eat glass like a bubbling acid, they ought not to exist. It would be better if no one else should know of the strange fruit borne by my experiment. Something from the corner of hell had got life by it, and it must be erased. I carried the teacup on a shovel and put it in the furnace, watching the green vegetation curl into ashes. They stank abominably as I closed the metal door, satisfied as to their destruction. From the smell it might have been carrion which perished there, eaten into cleanliness by flame. And seeing them destroyed, my perplexity was dominated by relief.

The same odour, however, was noticeable in my room when I reentered it, prepared to stop up the window with cardboard. I did not carry out the project, but left the wind to blow in a while. The fragment of glass which remained was sticky along the edge, and because of what had occurred, I was not anxious to come into contact with the ravaging slime. I thought of the other vegetable fragments, which had been placed with the urn upstairs, and procured these immediately, adding them to the furnace. I was anxious to make certain that nothing of the plant survived. And then, having done these things, almost instinctively, as if a snake had slid into my path and I had clubbed it with the nearest stick until the fangs were hidden in its own dark gore, I began to reflect on what had just happened.

That night, when I used my room, the evil odour was gone. I repaired the window temporarily, marvelling at the damage those slender fronds had done, and taking great care not to touch the diseased-looking glass. It was excessively late when I lay down and wandered into sleep, the room becoming murky and indistinct at last, like something reflected in black uneasy waters, and vanishing before the intrusion of an unfamiliar dream-world.

At first I was aware of several various scenes, one of them associated with my childhood, when I had taken a dislike to the great field behind our house. We lived then some distance out of town, and since I was a city child, the vastness of the open countryside, especially at night, disturbed me beyond all reckoning. Only indoors did I feel at all secure, and sometimes when this oppression was strong on me, I hid in closets and small enclosed spaces. In the back of my childish mind was a frightening vision of the immense and roofless world, and I visualised myself as losing all anchorage on the solid earth, to be flung into the interminable chasms of night. From this sensation there was no refuge but locked doors and drawn curtains. My parents frequently scolded me for behaving this way, and I was more than once punished for my attempts to escape the genuine torment, which I never managed to convey to them.

With the curious plurality of dreams, while I was dreaming this I was also dreaming of the red furnace, tumultuous with flames which (it seemed to me) were being gradually extinguished by a heap of uncurling vegetation. The growth stuffed it up completely, just as it had the Maya urn, and vegetable fingers slipped through a red-hot door, thriving on the fire as they had thriven on bare glass; as if everything were food to them. . . . I woke at this, and for a while lay so befuddled with my composite imaginings that I even considered going to the furnace and making sure they were not true. Afterward, however, my head grew clear enough to know that this was nonsense, and I fell asleep once more.

This time my transition to the phantasmal universe was sharp. As if a real wakening had come upon me, I dreamed, vividly, that I stood beneath a dark sky, an sky which was immense and uniform, like the shadow-clustered roof of an unmeasurable room. A vague and subtle illumination descended upon my shoulders, though no moon was visible. Deep restless clouds appeared to diffuse the lunar glow, permitting only a suggestion of light to wander over the landscape. The air was stale and inadequate—I could scarcely breathe. Standing, as it seemed, upon firm ground (for the reality of my dream compels me to speak of it as if it were a genuine experience) I wondered at that sky. Since it was not broken by any visible star, the murky expanse above me seemed greater than anything I had ever before seen. The oceans of the air flowed before winds blowing out of every quarter; immense, earth-swallowing, they hungered to engulf the plain whereon I stood.

For it was a plain—a flat expanse with darkness crouching on it like a live thing; and darker than the sky, broken mountain-shapes standing along the western horizon. Again I must liken my surroundings to a naked vault whose sides and roof were measurable in miles, and on whose floor I was less than a rat in Pharaoh's tomb. The gulf and the plain stretched vaster distances than anything I had seen or imagined before.—If only there had been a single star, it would have seemed less huge and lonely.

Age reeked from that primal, night-bound steppe. Lying monstrous and uncharted, it could have swallowed and forgotten such expanses as Gobi or the Pacific floor. All the armies of history might have wandered out and lost themselves within it. As I stood (or dreamed I stood) there, I was troubled by a recurrence of my childish fear, which seemed a thing of today and not of lost decades. Something swept into me, confusing my sense of Time's orderly progression, and I was not even certain whether I was a man or a small boy who feared the night. The place was old not in centuries or millennia, but so much older that it had been drifted over with the sediment at the bottom of Time's well. It had known, I think, all the changes stone and earth can know. It had been spawned in flame, congealing like metal taken from a furnace; it had swelled with the pregnancy of mountains and split itself to bear them terrifically. It had rested for aeons with grain welling up beneath mild skies, it had dreamed in the wet spring and hidden its face in the bitter snow, lakes had flowed across it and vanished, and then its mountains had cast shorter shadows, its sweet turf had crumbled into sand, and that ultimate sand had become dust, lying deep and formless in unending fields. Finality had come upon it—there was no other change it might undergo. Sullen and featureless now, it had only recollections to brood on, and only the night to hear its whispered, inhuman secrets.

The mountains crouching on the western rim were almost lost in the edge of darkness. I could not tell their size or distance from me. I think they must once have been very huge, their peaks now broken away by the trampling of centuries. Something about them suggested an onrushing black wave, as yet great distances from the shore, but curling inexorably toward it, and my dim uneasiness increased. I looked up at the sky, which was still undergoing momentary change, and saw that it was filled with a myriad cloud fragments, all darkly driven on variable and conflicting paths. Then suddenly the moon swung clear, disgorged by the ravenous cirri. Clean, high, and brittle, a chiselled gem of light set against dusky enamel, it spun as the central maelstrom of heaven. A gulf of light remained where the clouds had been, and the corridors of outer space were disclosed, but there was still no star anywhere. I stared, and then, without knowing why, began to walk in the direction of the mountains.

These had assumed a third dimension, and were no longer ragged outlines, but solid, angular, and pyramidal masses having no modifying curve. A few great peaks and crevices gleamed skull-white in the moon. Indeed, the whole enormous plain, which continued to suggest a stage or a gaming-board, was deluged by those almost liquid rays, displaying illimitable miles of spongy sand extending dreary and uniform about me. In a half dozen places, all of them distant, some dark material which I judged to be vegetation lay on the ground in dim irregular splotches. One of these was between me and the strangely compelling mountain range. Presently I would encounter it and discover its nature.

I am writing all this as if it were something real, for again and again I slip into the conviction that it *was* real, and that by some incomprehensible process the delusions of sleep became as tangible to me as waking life. As an uncommonly skeptical and methodical investigator I am hardly able to account for this—mysticism has never ensnared me, and I completely mistrust the myriad superstitions and religions of our race. Yet through this sequence of incredible events my deep faith in science is shaken. Dreams, perhaps, are not wholly intangible, nor our accustomed world as unique as mankind believes. Vast fields of speculation crowd upon me, but I dare not and could not express what I begin to think . . .

After half an hour's walk, during which the mountains grew no closer, one of the dark patches loomed up somewhat to my left, and I altered my course to see what it was. The moon, however, was rapidly being engulfed by a precipice of clouds. Shadows a hundred miles long glided across the plain as that polished sphere sank into darkness. In a moment I was blundering along, and the scene a moment before so clearly displayed was swathed up in murk. Nevertheless, I continued to walk at a moderate gait, the utter smoothness of the illuminated ground being impressed on memory.

I must have covered a greater space than I realised, since a few minutes later something caught persistently at my ankles, and I realised that I had blundered into the area of debris or vegetation I had seen. Reaching down to disengage myself, I discovered a mass of stringy vines, which parted readily at the touch of my hand. There must have been fifteen or twenty yards of the stuff, and as I picked my way through it I wished that the sky would shed a less diffused light. After wandering around I got free, and kept on toward the vast forms, sensed more than seen, hung on the borderland of vision.

The plain and mountains were strange and yet familiar. Eddies of loneliness swirled over them; infinitely sad and infinitely remote memories rested upon them. Like one who recognises sombre, familiar and indolent harmonies in a piece of great music, I was made aware of some immense and majestic past lying behind them—a past more splendid than aught of human history, but long engulfed by secretive Time. Whatever that past was, I think it had been dead a thousand centuries, that the earliest outposts of human existence were new beside it. These thoughts arose of themselves as I toiled

through stifling dead air, seeking those dim jagged peaks and whatever they concealed. The mustiness of the air increased as it does
when we go far into a crypt or a mine, but I felt poignantly that I
must go on; that the secret of the place lying ahead was a thing worth
all conceivable effort to attain; that those mountains were guardians
of some boundless mystery of precious and eternal significance.

Then I paused and stared at them, becoming aware of a pallid
light streaming into the sky's abyss. Far but unmistakable it
gleamed—such a light as a city might give off from crowded brilliant thoroughfares—and the sight of it evoked a nameless emotion
in me. What was it? Lights from a secret land beyond those precipitate barriers! A city? A volcano?—The mountains seemed to draw
closer to one another, forming an impregnable shield. Like suspicious beasts they shifted and gazed malevolently across leagues of
moor. And the lights, whatever their origin, waxed in swelling
strength, till every peak was again a cube or a pyramid, this time
fraught with some enormous purport; and the air, stale and crushing, reeked with a familiar scent . . .

From there my dream was chaos, like reflections in a pool vexed
with stones. The stink increased, and it was the stink of *those burning plants. In the strong grip of nightmare I repeated their destruction
again and again, but like snakes about me they sought to drag me into
the raw consuming flames.*

When I awoke, the basement room was filled with miasmatic
vapour. Warm rain dripped through the flimsy cardboard I had put
in the window, seeming to revive the scent where the teacup had
stood. Such slimy exudations as had defiled the glass now ran diluted across the floor, and I shuddered to see a little channel eaten in
the cement. The cat Arky sat in a corner, trying to disentangle his
wet fur. Apparently he had entered the same way as the water, and
his elegant face was sour with distaste as he chewed at his shoulder.
Staring at him, I thought that I saw traces of the ichor smeared on
him. Had he rubbed against the edge of the window glass? With

something of fright I tried to examine him, but startled by my hasty movement, he fled under the bureau.

I felt that the cat was doomed. A substance which gnawed away glass and cement must inevitably have monstrous effects on flesh and sinew. Realising that he must not escape, I stuffed my pillow into the wet dismal opening of the window, and coaxed Arky out where it was light. There was slime on him.

From three o'clock till day I lay confused, trying to unravel my dream and wondering what to expect in the poisoned animal. The sky was pale with intimations of daybreak when Arky began to twitch and claw at his side. I leaned over him, horridly fascinated, and saw curious blisters swelling up. These presently disappeared, leaving sunken areas like decayed spots on fruit. It looked as if the ribs were collapsing beneath the surface of the skin. God, that cat was hideous! In another hour, his whole face was gone . . .

The contagion spread inch by inch, rotting the flesh away in pulpy blisters. Did you ever find anything beside the road, dead for a week? That is what he was like. I was repelled and frightened, but chiefly, I was concerned that no one should touch that damnable slime. I did not touch it, once. I know that. But I did break the rest of the pane away with a shovel, all of it; and I took the fragments to the furnace which had consumed the sprouts. Then I put a shovel full of ashes on the abomination which had been a cat, so that it would hold together long enough to carry.

Nauseated by my task, and with turbulent thoughts conflicting inside me, I rested awhile before going upstairs. There was a great deal of work on my desk, and when I felt able, I plunged into this. Some while elapsed before I was made aware of a persistent ache in the fingers of my left hand. There was an uncommon quality about it, and had I not been at all times extravagantly careful with the polluted window, my anxiety would have been acute. Since I knew beyond all question that I had not done so, I was less uneasy. Afterward, however, I glanced at the sore place, and perceived a certain white blister.

Mumbling in dull terror, I tried to convince myself that it was not so. Was sanity failing me? The unspeakable nature of Arky's death had rocked my brain, and I did not consider that the blister might have come elsewhere. Even less did it seem credible that *I* had been defiled. It was not credible—for a time—that my hand should blister with gnawing cancers.

I can appreciate your disbelief when I came to you. The contamination was then in the intervening stage, and there was no sign of what foulness boiled within my veins. I can understand your reluctance to amputate until I made it necessary. I forced you to do it, but it was not soon enough. For hours now I have not dared to look into a mirror—it is excessively painful for me to type, but the condition of my remaining hand is such that a pen would be impossible. *No one must see me afterward.* I was worried about this until I remembered the furnace. I have built a great fire within it, and shall by that means cleanse the world eternally of this blight from a source beyond comprehension. A thousand useless questions torment me, but speculation is the only thing to distract me from pain. Is the bond between the Maya urn and that stark mountain-bordered plain something hidden even from death?

I am made aware of linkages which are obscure and difficult to set down. This curious baffling procession of the human ape through a world designed neither for him nor for anything he knows; this hideous meaningless pageantry of stars and world and gulfs; this futile but exalted aspiration he contains for the tremulous flame of truth; all these things have acquired a unity in my vision, and anciently chiselled words are suddenly swept clean of the lichens which hid them.

Always, I have felt that some old and terrible secret lies behind the Maya cities. Those immense stone piles lying in the humid jungle stare backward through time to an unguessed origin, and the carven monsters which leer from a hundred walls hint damnably at something of unhuman significance. We do not understand a tenth of even what we have dug up from the graveyard of thousands of mouldy years. What curse drove a million people from their cities? Why did they build new cities afterward, and build them far away? I am beginning to suspect the reason for that abandonment. How much was anciently known of the thousand-mile plain, and of the lights behind those scowling peaks? (Was it indeed a city? A city—of what?) Vast antiquities unfolded themselves to the invading Spaniards—antiquities perhaps recorded in these codices whose destruction is so often lamented. Perhaps the men who saw them did right to burn them and to pray beside the flames. Some of the extant monuments bear dates millions of years old—God knows what reeling aeons were chronicled in the records that have perished.

Of the mysteries confronting me I have solved one at the least, though it is the least provocative. I stole the urn myself. Of this I am convinced. My fingerprints were thick about the broken case, and my inner consciousness shrieks out the vandal's name. A compulsion must have been upon me, a compulsion streaming from that malignant urn. How or why I do not know. And it was in the fulfilment of a kindred command that I planted those seeds. Probably the two incidents were really one, though whether my sleeping self intended to break the urn, or whether it would have done something else with it, cannot now be guessed. Perhaps my mission was only to release the seeds, by whatever means lay at hand. They had been sealed up a long time ago: but for my act they might have remained forever so.

The Mayan men have left their cities and monuments for a whole millennium; the halls of Chichen-Itza have long lain desolate. Birds have nested in the creviced monoliths and amongst the stones of fallen temples, indifferent to the faces of gods arrayed for war and to the recollection of man. Yet all this is an instant's space compared to the unmeasurable years which brood in the mountains of dream. It is their secret which torments me, it is their reality which I can neither deny nor be certain of. Surely, surely they were intangible shadows? . . . But now I can scarcely see the keyboard. A horrible thing has begun to happen to my eyes. Imposed upon the

images of this shabby, familiar room, the outlines of an equally familiar place grow strong. . . . It was the shadow-plant, and not the
real one. I was there, I was there. It was not a vision of madness,
but a reality. That reality is my doom.

This was my body, these were my hands. What body and hands
are now I cannot describe with sufficient loathing. Thank God for
the mist which dims my sight. Flesh which is no longer flesh but
corruption instead, cannot long support a reasoning brain. My
bones and sinews bloat into jelly; the signature of death is written
over me, and since death alone can cleanse forever, I shall meet and
welcome it. Only a moment is left, and now, while I am still able, I
must get down to the furnace.

*Florida, August 1937*

## The Swearing of an Oath

Said two conspirators who met, "When the king lolls bleeding over
his throne, all our broad valley shall be free. His nephew shall perish and we shall appoint in all the provinces new collectors for the
tax." And because they might die from some word said loud, each
gripped the hand of the other. "We shall establish the golden city of
our benevolence midway in the land, where it may be seen of
mountain men, of threshers, and of catchers of whatever the sea
chooses to give up. From it magnanimously our line shall rule, and
not one man shall remember hungry days. There will be granaries
filled with the gold of crops, and no one shall wear black at our
coronation. Other lands will send ambassadors humble and desirous of instruction in our ways, for with us, once the king is dead,
man shall be surely distinguished from the ape, and the earth shall
know a *new thing*."

They nodded and swore again by the light of a star which earlier was known in Troy, and later in Chicago.

*Spring 1939*

# The Questioner

Crowned with Sirius Night sat broodingly in a grove. Her lips were laden with secrets: with a song once uttered by Vikings at a camp-fire whose perishing would be the signal to harry Christian towns asleep nearby; with words a prince of India had said to his love when her mouth would let him speak; with groans unuttered but thought of by sick men and feverish; with words caught up from children's lips as they dreamed.

Of these things Night spoke not, but sat there receiving homage of the trees which in her honour wore garments they show not to men. And for awhile she thought little of Dawn who yesterday and for a thousand years had overthrown her, coming through a land hidden by the mountains; though in six hours he would step over them.

Then a poet who had loved the colour of her robes came questioning. "I would know most truthfully," he said, "from you who are guardian of ultimate truths, if they speak right who call you Queller of Unrest. A bird of yours shrieked it to me once, and I saw it written by moonlight on sand at a lake's margin, but since I have lived I mistrust. I would know if you will quench in time those fires consuming and reconsuming my heart; if you will feed them eventually ashes so that snarling of hunger they will die; if you will slay utterly several hours which lie bleeding within me; if to your populous city a man may come and be equal in grandeur with the Pharaohs, in wisdom with the two Florentines, in content with whosoever has possessed content."

Without looking at him she pointed her prodigious hand to a star no longer dwelt in, where graves had lain ruined and peaceful a thousand long years.

*Spring 1939*

## The Artizan's Reward

"Since each of us has gold, and twenty years to shape it," remarked the sculptor to his rival, "our king's reign will be remembered, and one of us."

He wished them to make a god out of the coin purveyed from a city lately conquered, for in that city were unendurably fine gods who perhaps only in sleeping had permitted its fall.

Of these craftsmen one polished his chisel eight years and went to Assyria to look at a certain frieze, and enquired into all subjects pertaining to the gods and their symbols.

He learned a little pondering the nine thousand volumes which in his land dealt with them. Some, it appeared, were possessed of twelve legs, and others of none at all. Some were female and some male, but most were more complicated. In a heathen land where the women braided flowers in their hair and no one worked, there was a god who had come riding a meteor as one rides a white-maned horse rapidly through the dusk. In a cold land there was a god with but one attribute. In a land of interlinking lakes whose people had never built a house but lived in skiffs and wore lilypads when it rained, the god was named Drought. In a dark land prisoned between two mountains bearing the same name, there was a god with a burning, inextinguishable beard. In yet another land all the gods had been broken across by a man with bright eyes, and for this his fellows worshipped him.

These things he found written, and afterward spent twelve years in hammering models out of lead.

But his rival lay on a hillside whose grass the sheep envied over low fences, and made up fables which he knew to be untrue about a star habitually blooming near one tree, or frightened pigeons at sunset where the river had sought to come ashore and even kept a garrison of reeds. Moreover, when the torches of the sunset and the stars and the young year were alike burnt out, he found them kindled anew in little jugs of wine as delightful on the lip as even a woman's lip.

The first sculptor wore a black gown and regularly went to bed, for he was very earnest in his wish to make an admirable statue.

The second wore a robe of any colour he fancied, even though full of holes.

And so time carried off twenty hampers of years each brimming with corroded or bright coins which people had put into them, and which were the more plentiful I need not say.

Then before him the king, no longer given to riding abroad as victor, called the two sculptors.

"I gave you gold to play with two decades long," he said, "and what will you give me back?"

A man in a black robe signalled his apprentices to wheel in a veiled god, and when the veil was removed, all looked. Neither head nor arms did the god have, and much of the rest was lead not yet covered with gold. And he asked another twenty years of the king.

Then the king asked him of the piebald robe, who was teasing the palace cat with a petunia-stalk.

He said, "I have wasted your gold and my days and have only this which I did last night when a dream woke me up."

From the second statue a second cloth was taken, and the god was as a god should be.

The company wept and the king lay for an hour on his face thinking of something he had done when only a boy and not really to be blamed.

The sculptor of the black robe went up to the god with a tape-measure.

Then as a reward the king gave his cat to the man, for the man had asked it of him, and appointed a priest to the statue.

And the bad statue was melted into a base for the other, though friends of the man who made it brought humbly a petition to the king.

For seven hundred years the figure endured at that court until its feet were worn away with kisses, and even now in eastern countries men exchange the coins into which, on the capture of the city, it was cast.

*Spring 1939*

## My First Cacomixtli

I bought the Cacomixtli as a going-away present. A going-away present for myself, to celebrate the departure of my Nazi roommate who was going to Vladivostok and studying German on the way over. I was so pleased he was going away that I walked down the street and bought the Cacomixtli. A man had it on a chain; it was creeping around his ears—not around them, but in their region; and it had pretty little eyes and a nose like an ear syringe—sort of soft and drippy. It was a little animal like a possum. He asked me to buy it. "Last night it tried to eat the baby," he wheedled. So I gave him three pesos and a half, because I didn't know how to bargain for cacomixtlis.

I didn't buy it to keep the rabbit company, though. I had a rabbit too; which had been given me by the Nazi because he feared parsley would be expensive in Vladivostok. There is a little store called El Conejo, the Rabbit, on the main square in Mexico City, where rabbits are compulsory. If you buy a hat, you get a rabbit. If you buy two hats you may have a great deal of rabbits. It limits one's wardrobe dreadfully. Well, he had bought a hat and given me the rabbit and I took it home and I had two patios and I put the rabbit in one—it had to dodge the cigarette butts my neighbors throw down in a sort of private Luftwaffe—and the cacomixtli in the other one which had an air raid shelter, and considered the problem of the houseboy.

The houseboy was a kid from a village out in the Tierra Caliente—I spent a night there once seeing a miracle play and sleeping in a haystack and he knew my address, so when my friend fired him, which happened a good deal, he got on the bus and came up to Mexico City and said he was going to stay with me. He rode on the merry-go-round most of the time at my expense. I told him he could help the cook, so he carried her bag to market and let her carry it back, and they sat out in the kitchen and looked at each other like Indians—they *were* Indians—and ate tortillas furtively behind newspapers. I never did catch them eating a meal. The cook ate hers behind a book on the housing situation in Mexico in 1550, which she had found in my bookcase and said she thought was very entertaining.

Well, I did the cacomixtli and the houseboy up together and sent them back to my friend on a bus as a kind of loan for his birthday present, and when they got there he was forgiven and the animal was put in an empty store which my friend had rented along with three houses one night when he was drunk. It slept in a bin marked 24¢ a kilo. Pretty soon it got out and came into his house and ate his pet chicken while it was asleep on my friend's pillow. It must have eaten it messily, perhaps it didn't eat quite all, because my friend was very angry, and the animal had to be caught and boxed up by an Italian who was living there. The cacomixtli scooted coyly along the rafters and was finally cornered asleep in a teakettle, and it bit the Italian rather snappishly when it woke up. And it was sent back to me.

By that time I had given the rabbit to a Mexican lady who bought it lots of good nourishing food, a good thing, for it wasn't thriving on cigarette butts, and then after about a month she announced it had died. I never cared to ask her how it had died. The Italian brought the animal with him and on account of what had happened to the chicken while it was asleep, I asked him to stay awhile. It lived in a room I hadn't any other furniture for, because the attacks on the patio had increased and in the daytime it slept, but at night it hurled itself in and out of the window and pulled the curtains down—with curtains people can't tell if you haven't any furniture—and hurled its box about savagely. Also it had the sanitary ideas of a camel. Once it got over the wall, and the Italian was morosely pleased. "You'll see, it will go and scare someone, and they'll tell the police and you'll be in trouble," he said. I said if it were a bear and went over the wall and ate a little girl all but her garters nobody would say anything because it was Mexico. While I sat there waiting for such shrieking as might be expected, it came hurtling back. Someone else had apparently done the scaring. The Italian didn't appear to care for the animal, even after it bit him, and one day there was a Dutch-Polish-American communist looking for some people to whom I had sublet the apartment during the winter, and she saw the animal. It appeared that she had always wanted a cacomixtli and he gave it to her, which made me feel rather badly, but he was my guest.

She took it home for her little girl who was a Mexican, and when I went around two weeks later it was running around the room happily, eating things it found on the floor. It had already eaten the head of a little plaster statue the mistress was quite fond of.

I heard nothing of the cacomixtli for quite some time except that someone said it was a *marta*. Then a lady who borrowed things from me said, "You remember?" and I said yes. "Well," she said, "the other night she woke up with a horrible pain in her toe, and she looked down and it was biting her. She spanked it and put it in its box, and went back to sleep. Then she heard a howl from her husband, and it was biting him, too, only not his feet."

It liked the Bohemian atmosphere there better than living with me.

## The Excursion

I met the lady osteopath in Huehuetzinco at a dance in honor of General de Gaulle. He was absent, but she had come. With the German consul. She had white hair and a lot of Irish patriotism probably because she wasn't Irish.

It was a lovely party including a lady who liked to push people off balconies, who pushed a lady she didn't appear to care for off a balcony without even spilling her drink. She spilled the other lady's however—indeed, she spilled the other lady. By the time her husband had got them apart the Law had arrived arid began with admirable decisiveness to take him to jail, which was difficult because the Law was smaller and the wife kept pulling the other way. The Irish lady criticized the Law to me, because I was handy, and then we danced and she criticized the English and the local water supply and several other things including my dancing. And I said yes, because I didn't want to spoil the party.

Well, the lady osteopath hasn't anything to do with this story, which is about a dear friend of hers whose name I can't remember who nearly killed me. The l. o. and I were in a museum a few days later criticizing pictures. We were on the borrowing and advice-taking terms of an early friendship and she suggested that I might like to go that evening to Vera Cruz with a dear friend of hers and fight off bandits without charge. The dear friend (whom she had just met yesterday) was going to meet her dear husband, and I could see the fortress and the mosquitoes and get back as best I could. "Of course she drives like a fool," said the l. o., a remark which I gayly dismissed. We went over to the hotel and found the lady with the husband, only we found her with someone else's husband. It was all very jolly—she would love to have me go with her, but she had just met her old friend, Mr. —— "I never can remember your name, dear!". . . and wouldn't be ready to leave until morning.

So she honked at me at 7 a.m. and I left a note for the cook, who had to walk five miles, not to bother to come that day, and we started for Vera Cruz. Without her old friend whom she seemed to have forgotten. The lady osteopath waved at us and said Vera Cruz wasn't worth going to anyhow.

As we drew out of the markets ringing Mexico City, my pilot set a modest pace of eighty-five miles an hour, crying "There's a boat for Yucatan at six tonight. If my husband doesn't come, let's try to make that." I said the ruins might be interesting, but that her husband would come. "He can't possibly make it before seven," she carolled, speeding up just enough to dent her fender on a man who wasn't quick. We both looked back, and she decided he must have limped all along.

She was asking me about a special use of the subjunctive when she turned the car over. Fortunately, there was nothing to hit but a ditch twenty feet deep and some pine trees, one of which came through the roof and nearly through me. We crawled out: I was sorry to see that she was still able to, and the motorcycle police caught up with us. Then lots of people came, some of every kind of people except for three women who were cutting brooms with their babies beyond the clump of pines. They moved a little farther off.

She took it naturally, and with an air of having done so before wrote a note to a man who would take care of everything. It said with admirable objectivity "The car has turned itself over." Then she went on to Vera Cruz with some tourists asking me to just wait for the wrecker, and leaving me a banana and tangerine after some little dispute. And in order not to waste the entire day I drew a picture of Clement Hernández of the Twenty-First Battalion of Rio Frio, a sad young soldier who had been driven up with several of his fellows to guard the wreck—the least portable thing one could imagine. He was sad, I discovered, because he hadn't seen it happen.

Then I ate my banana and tangerine without offering him any and walked over to the three women who were cutting brooms. One of them wore two straw hats, and a naked baby. The baby grinned at me lewdly and hit me with a broom. All the time people were stopping to photograph the blood and going away disappointedly. One man photographed the soldiers and his own automobile with a Michigan license plate and then came over and wanted to photograph the baby. His mother held out fearfully, but capitulated at the sight of twenty cents and handed over her child to execution. She was startled to get it back. As the man drove away I asked why she had objected, and she explained, "They say the female *gringos* see them and think they are cute and steal them and take them to their country—and God knows where that is.'

That evening, towed back to Mexico City by the wrecker, I tried to find the man who would take care of everything. He certainly took care to avoid me. It took me a week to trap him, during which I received a card by air-mail from Yucatan asking me to be sure no one took the spare tire. When I found him he said, "Has she gone and done that again?" And he was just out of the hospital, and showed me and the lady osteopath some large and interesting scars on his tummy, which had hair on it besides. She said he ought to know who he was driving with and that he would have been smarter to see an osteopath.

## A Glimpse of Euterpe

When he saw that Euterpe Alvarado had been invited, Edward nearly turned the crab-salad over. In the first place, she was certain to talk about "errors on page 42 in the Sánchez copy" and other matters about which his hostess was not very well posted. (She was not very well posted about anything, but she had a scandalous amount of money.) In the second place, he had screeched at Euterpe. It is not true that he had knocked her down. He had not thought of it at the moment. He only screeched at her in an awful row over a clutch of books she nested on at the library she directed, or, according to Edward, mis-directed. She said afterward that if he had been a German he would have knocked her down; which made him wish, for a very limited period, that he had been at least a close friend of Charles Lindbergh.

The widow Longshore, who had kept on wearing black because she looked rather well in it, watched Euterpe sidling into the room like something out of a fairy-tale—like one of the things that crawls out of a well in a fairy-tale and has to be dried off and disenchanted before anyone can abide it. Euterpe was short and frizzled on top, but she had one advantage. She was so dark one hardly noticed the moles.

"Dinner with you anthropologists is such an adventure!" the widow cried. "You are always inviting people with nose-plugs, or having stewed *n'gombi* as a surprise. Once I danced with an Ainu all evening, and his whiskers were always getting caught on my pearl brooch. Finally I had to give it to him because it is against their religion to cut their beards. I fancy that their devoutness brings them in a steady little income."

"Srta. Alvarado is a librarian—they say," he replied abstractly, while Euterpe sat down and thrust a rather large spring onion into her mouth. She saw him and crunched it as if it had been his spinal cord and she a terrier. He smile exaggeratedly at the lady beside her, though he had no idea who she was.

"Oh, I know her—" said his neighbor. "I see she's scowling at you. I suppose you had a row with her, too?"

"Sort of. She was trying to conceal *Winnebago Sister-in-law Nicknames* from me. I can't imagine why they invited her. Perhaps the cook addressed the envelopes."

"It's because she's the judge's cousin," explained the widow.

"I wish they'd send her off to Huehuetlalpallan with him tomorrow," Edward said dreamily. "She'd love it, if she could dispense justice. She'd just dispense *with* it. She'd probably appoint herself chief headsman."

"And then the tribesmen would carry her off and tie her to a tree and shoot her full of those rather inferior arrows they manufacture for tourists. And how she'd screech! That would attract more tourists," observed the lady, dexterously snatching her salad back from the maid.

Euterpe's attention was directed from Edward to her hostess, who was trying to escape a lecture on Andaman sculpture. "Do tell us about how you measured that backstrip again!" cried that hospitable soul. "And have some more Sauterne. Oh take the bottle, do."

Euterpe smirked. It seemed that by accident she had brought

along a copy of her only printed production, a pamphlet of seven years before, and she promptly gouged it out of her handbag and began reading figures to prove that what people had thought was the third edition of an unreadable book in Subtiaba was really the second edition in an inferior binding. The pamphlet was rather soiled along where she had creased it, and a corner fell off onto the plate of the gentleman who all alone amid that festive company knew about Andaman sculpture. She retrieved it with an indignant glare, though he had never stolen anything but a small cracked pot from a man who was out tending pigs. It was her librarian's instinct. Then the gentleman tried to talk about Andaman religion and she tried to talk about a book catalogue and the rest of the company took advantage of the situation to demolish their salads.

"I remember Euterpe last year at Christmas," said the widow Longshore. "And this Christmas there is the war. My, but Christmas can be nasty! It was on a train to Zacatecas. I was going up there to bury my poor Wilbur—he had caught his head in a wardrobe trunk, you know." Edward nodded, uncertain how much sympathy to offer, since it was not clear whether Wilbur was a Burmese cat or a former husband. "The train was full of people and bundles, and the ticket vendor's window got stuck—something like poor Wilbur—and couldn't be pried open until three minutes before the train left. I got on without a ticket, which was quite provident of me, since we lost the conductor at the next station where he got off to buy oranges. I found Euterpe on the train, too, avidly reading a book inside a copy of the *Ibero-Amerikanisches Archiv*. The book looked familiar, and I concluded it was an indecent novel, especially since she hid it. She was going to a librarian's convention."

Edward glanced down the table, where Euterpe was the center of animated attention. "Then you spread two layers on top of the first one, and it should get very hard," she was declaiming. "How to Glue a Book Together," Edward thought, wavering back to the widow.

"I can't imagine why *everybody* wanted to go to Zacatecas that night," she was saying. "Ordinarily, I can't imagine why *anybody ev-*

*er* wants to go to Zacatecas. Not even to bury Wilbur, though one couldn't just leave him in the wardrobe trunk. But the train was jammed. Across from us was the jammedest part of all; a fat man cinched up in an army belt with lots of medals and buttons stuck on the places he bulged. He had been wedged into the corner with his three little daughters packed about him (they kept coming unpacked), and boxes of candy and flowers and an anxious-looking wife trying to keep everything from slopping out into the aisle. The whole conglomeration looked like a laundry-bag after Wilbur had got into it. Every few minutes a child was getting her instep crushed or a banana was ground into the carpet. The fat man's wife finally tried to pacify everybody by playing Hungarian Dances on the portable radio. But Euterpe didn't seem to care for the radio. She said radios were a nuisance to serious-minded people. I said, gracious, how would I know? Then the anxious woman turned it off and sat there just re-packing the little girls every time they were about to get loose."

Edward wondered what Euterpe was saying to hold everyone spellbound at that moment.

"Next Euterpe began rummaging around in that handbag she has. She has forgotten her pamphlet, and couldn't find anything but her train ticket, but that pleased her rather unexpectedly. 'Look,' she said. 'They've got our seats!' I looked, and they had, and said well, and began to wonder when my daughter would catch that slippery Polack she went around with. But she said 'Well, they'll have to move. They're certainly presumptuous.' And she leaned over and showed the tickets to the fat man's wife, who jumped.

"Well, she made them all trek over to the other side of the car and they got re-wedged, and the tops of their candy-boxes got squashed in, and they kept their radio off, and their children off too, as much as possible, and then Euterpe settled down in their seats to read my newspaper, with mystifying comments on events I hadn't had an opportunity to read. One item caught her eye. 'Your husband runs the mine at La Quemada, doesn't he?' she said suddenly. 'My dear, how I envy you!' 'You never saw him in golf-clothes,' was my first thought, but I said 'Why should *you* envy *me*, darling?' wishing she'd let me just look at the landscape, though I was never fond of the cacti and underfed cows before. 'Oh, I know you'll meet the new Governor!' she breathed. Then I realized what the book was she had been trying to conceal. It was the Social Register."

Edward was touched, but bravely asked her to go on. Euterpe was certainly a success tonight, whatever she was telling the people at the foot of the table. "Well, that night went along very serenely except that Euterpe snores like a—"

"An alligator," Edward supplied. "One of them slept under our house in Florida once, and we had to pound on the floor with our shoes."

"You must have looked rather silly, all squatting around in a circle like savages in your stocking feet," she said.

"Savages don't wear stockings," he replied with dignity. "Besides there was no one to see us but the alligator."

"And he was asleep," the widow remembered. "And the next morning we pulled into Zacatecas."

Edward listened to Euterpe, who was speaking in a loud, triumphant tone, as if she had detected someone consulting the Encyclopedia behind her back, or otherwise abusing the library she held court in. "Cold cream," she said. "I use it on grape-leaves, and then put a towel on top and lie down on the ironing board for my posture." Now it was clear how she had held them from Andaman sculpture. She was talking about all the things she did for her complexion. Perhaps they were enchanted not by her recipes, but by her whimsy in bothering.

The widow toyed with a chop. "And there were people all over, playing horns. I rather think they were playing different things. And there were little girls with the baskets of flowers, in two lines with a carpet between them. They were all supposed to be the same size, but some of them were about two years old and some of them had been divorced: the citizenry had rounded up everything which could come at all under the heading of Little Girl. They were nymphs or something. And there was another little girl, about twenty-eight, dressed in a Typical Aztec Quaint Old Native Costume—that is, in a red sequin skirt with most of the sequins picked off, and with a white blouse and a green cap with a peacock feather in it, and some Japanese jewelry. Maybe it was a Cambodian wedding gown. Our car stopped right in front of this young lady, who was at the train-end of the carpet, and the fat man and his wife and daughters, all lugging bundles, staggered down the steps and nearly trampled her while she was making a speech. Then he stopped and set down the luggage in a puddle and bowed three times all at once. Euterpe was still dragging out a suitcase she had moved at great inconvenience the day before in order to evict the fat man, and had not seen the reception. 'What's that noise?' she asked me."

"What was it?" asked Edward.

"I had to bite my tongue," said the widow, biting instead a lamb chop which she had suspended in midair for some moments. "I suggested that she look out and see. It seemed they were welcoming the new governor of Zacatecas."

## Return by Sunset

*From a painting by Clark Ashton Smith*

Flooding up from abysses under abysses, streaming scarlet like gore from an enormous wound, the sun groped down into darkness. Its rays seceded from the great conical ruin on the valley-rim. Then for a little, vast flocks of birds sought haven amid the dirt-covered rubble. Clamorous with fear of the night, they piled and fluttered into shafts and crevices like swarming bees—and were gone. Not a feather then showed among the occasionally-carven stones which looked out across the valley. Night was there, still yet vibrant, like a pool which hides fish, like an age-darkened mirror which no longer shows faces.

There was no road to the littered cliff and had not been for a measureless time; for time enough to forget a civilization. Once a temple had stood there, but no more acolytes came to the broken shrine, no one remembered to pay homage to the gods. Of the walls remaining, not one was waist-high: much of the rock facing of the cone—whose centre was clay—had slid into ruin and been covered by vines: none of the square brick columns nearby supported a roof. A stone basin, large enough to lie in, and rimmed with half-obliterated carvings of some procession, alone remained intact, one edge buried—a sacrificial bowl, grown over with flowering gourds. The god had grown weary and departed. Whatever screams had once lulled him were now not even echoed on the wind; whatever blood and entrails had once gleamed before his eyes were now long superseded by the leaves and the rain and the snow. The ruin was old as the cliff it stood on, and like the cliff would last always. It could undergo no further change. A future as long as its past, disturbed by no slipping stone, lay before it—and already it was older than death. It would lie lonely in the rain for centuries; it would listen to the lamentations of the night-wind, who mourns that man should ever have been tricked into existence; it would stare by summer at the sun and dress itself by winter in the ice. Yet it would suffer no change by these. Unto the ultimate blackness, when all the small golden suns burnt out forever, the idols would lie and think stone thoughts, the tumbled walls would strive to remember what hands had built them a long while since.

When Dal saw it, the girl Leyenda was with him. They had crossed many valleys and delved into many forests escaping from her brothers; and weariness walked with them now. Up the long hill at evening they had seen the ruin, of a type familiar throughout the land, and hoping it might afford refuge, had climbed to it. When they saw that no chamber was complete, they sat on a low grey rock carved with half a face. How could they go on? Behind them was a route they dared not retrace; in front, the cliff fell straight away to obscure bottom-lands shielded with mist. They seemed to be on the crest of an onrushing wave.

How gently ruin had come to this place! Little yellow wild-flowers were sprinkled across its pavement; dirt and rubble lay where once rich-garmented priests alone could set foot. Yet war for once was not to blame—no battle but the wind had taken this high place, no victor but the frost had trod it.

Leyenda turned her face to her lover. "Must we go back?"

He lifted up a handful of her yellow hair and held it to his lips. "Tomorrow—tomorrow," he said.

She seemed satisfied with this. "I am glad that we can stay. Surely they will not come here."

He did not answer, but looked at her, and she bit her lip, saying: "I know, but that was twelve days ago."

"It was twelve days, and we have seen nothing since the water-hole; but who tracked down the creature with hands and fangs?" he asked. And she knew it was her elder brother who had done so.

They had a night at least. If there were no buildings, neither were there likely to be snakes or other dangers on this sterile height. The warm swamp country was left behind them, but Dal had a heavy cloak woven of green fibres: they could sleep wrapped in this. They chose a spot at the base of the ruin, a sunken place where some underground chamber had fallen in. Rest was more precious than escape.

The pale night darkened, and save for the fluttering once of a shadow dissatisfied with its perch, nothing disturbed them. The ground grew chilly toward morning, and Dal awoke and fell to pondering on their future course, and then a little later something called in a high voice and was answered from the valley, and the day drew near. He stood and saw the low eroded mountains, green and purple, many miles off, with such woodland and meadow country running to the cliff's base as he had suspected at night. It seemed a fair place—but was there any way to descend? He kicked off a stone, and thought he failed to hear it, but as he sought another, the noise of the first floated up vague and remote. Leyenda rose, untangling her hair, and said she was hungry.

With a stick he soon frightened three fat birds out of their nest on the cone, and lost sight of Leyenda as he pursued them. One, regarding him with little fear, led him a few yards and then disappeared suddenly in the hole it had been making for; but he killed the other two, tangling them in a snarl of blossoming briar. Their blood spattered and their floundering wings shook down a rain of petals. Then as he lifted out the sleek, nerveless bodies, necks adangle and gore on their patterned wings, Leyenda gave a little cry.

His heart was knifed with intuition, and he dropped the birds, but gripped the club he had killed them with. Leyenda was beyond the cone, which was flanked on the right by the cliff-edge and on the left by tumbled stone blocks, so he was compelled to scramble up over it to meet the danger from above. But when he could see her, she was alone, crouching on the ground, and exclaiming softly over something the size of a pear. Dal's shadow fell across her, and she started. For a moment he saw the image of his fear reflected in her eyes and suddenly pale lips. Then she laughed.

"How terrible you look up there with that big stick in your hand. Are you planning to have me for breakfast?" Then, solicitously— "Oh, you're all bloody. Are you hurt?"

He shook his head, but at that moment, in his eagerness to descend, stepped on a loose stone and sprawled toward her. His left ankle gave way, and was kindled to instant fiery pain. He slid a few feet, groaning despite himself. She sprang to him and stroked the injured part with frightened fingers, but seeing this pained him, left off. And then, not sure how much he was injured, and fearing to learn, Dal said it was a small thing and that he would rest a while before getting up. He told her of the birds lying where he had left them, and she in turn displayed her find. It was caked with dirt, but gleaming still—a bracelet, almost a shackle, of hammered metal. Copper or gold, but gnawed with verdigris, she had found it half-under a stone lintel while she was looking for blackberries.

"Isn't it lovely? I shall wear it," Leyenda said, putting it in his hand. "But I shall have to wash it first. And—" regarding him severely, "I'll have to wash you too unless you make yourself presentable. There is a sort of well—a shallow place with a stone rim—over there." She pointed to a clump of bushes greener than any of the others.

It was when he tried to rise that he realised his ankle was badly twisted, possibly even broken. She took the news with heavy face. They must stay here? Manifestly. Several days, probably. And any one of those days a figure, or three figures, kilted in scarlet and bearing axes that had bitten the vertebrae of many a beast might come silently up the long hill . . . None the less, they must stay. Perhaps they would be thought lost in the swamp, back where she had abandoned the small wooden god which alone of her posses-sions Leyenda had cherished and carried as long as she might. If they found the god, they would not believe she could have left it and gone, trusting only in her lover. Dal considered this matter and that; and finally Leyenda left him to pluck the birds, whose numer-ous nests on the ground and among the ruins assured them of plen-tiful food during their halt. And he, the man, with a little assistance, got atop the cone, from whose vantage point anyone lying on his stomach could see two miles down the hill. He thought of the lame man who guarded their village at night from the anomalous claws of the forest-dwellers.

It was good up there in the sun, which beat indifferently on man and brick and bush. The village they had fled, carrying only an idol and their love, was thickly beset by cypresses, from which little bleached serpents occasionally slid onto a man's shoulders. Here nothing was above him. Under the special tolerance of the sun, all jewels were mirrored in the landscape—emerald and amber in the grass, turquoise in the sky, and all the others in the thick-sown phlox, mounting and bannering the ruin. He lay and watched, and planned their descent into the strange country, and wondered what masks the priests of that land might wear.

During the afternoon Leyenda prepared a trap, whose cunning loops of twisted fibre made Dal feel numb-fingered, and proud of such a clever woman, he expressed his pride; and so they were con-tent until evening caught them. Then as on the previous day, the sun fled and the birds returned all in such a confusion of light and sound that it made them wonder. The sky was brighter than blood on a spear.

On the day following, after she had assisted Dal to his post, Leyenda spent an hour washing her bracelet in the mossy basin. After it had soaked for a while, the encrustations could be gouged from the design. Washing and polishing alternately with dried grass, she eventually was able to make out the picture. It had been hammered in with a small pointed instrument, and showed a figure lying in chains before an altar. She must have found a part of the ceremonial ornaments used by the keepers of the temple; and though all the old gods were discredited, Leyenda was uneasy. She knew her own god, the dog-faced image lying in the swamp two weeks' journey behind, would not like this uncovering of his predecessor. All the ruins, spiritual and temporal, of the old days were held suspect by the tribes, which sometimes wandered through them, but she wanted to keep her bracelet. Without conscious volition, Leyenda wedged her arm into it so tightly that she found it would not come off. She had not intended to do so—but there it was. Dal, fortunately for her peace of mind, thought all evil magic would have long since gone out of the bracelet.

Time passed, and Dal's ankle did not improve. For the first three days his eyes went back again and again to the region which they had left, and all its empty miles were a reassurance that their pursuers had faltered. He soon became so certain of this that he forgot to look eastward but turned instead to the west, where lay that fertile valley unreachably far beneath them, into which they hoped to descend. Increasingly at evening, as the sun grew big and spattered the cliff and the world below with various crimsons, he thought of what might lie in the future. Sometimes Leyenda was with him, but she did not care for the evening sky which so stirred his imagination. In a few short days it became to him as fire is to a chill old man: aided by the woman he would lie atop the mound with ruined wonders beneath him and stare through the golden lay-

ers as they became transmuted from light to gold and gold to
blood, and in the darkening heart of the descending orb it seemed
to Leyenda that he read things, for he would make no move to
leave his perch till darkness was full upon them. Then he would sit
up and stretch and limp down and he would be her lover with only
a glow of the sunset in his dark eyes.

This was the first of the things which Leyenda found disturbing. It was more than her vanity which protested at his finding so
great an interest outside herself. She wondered what the sunset told
him of the ruin; of the gods who had gone away. The place had
been a temple, and things had happened there; even the broken basin covered with gourds had once been slaughter's abode. She
pulled at her bracelet.

The moon came, and the bright nights. It shone upon the cliff
as it might upon a high tower—they were more conscious of the
altitude than by day. As it grew big Leyenda became restless and
sometimes left Dal sleeping—he was feverish in the evenings, and
slept heavily—while she went out in the air. One night while she
was walking with strange thoughts and plucking at her bracelet,
which still could not be loosed, she had a fright. Looking down the
long slope toward her eastern home, she thought she saw a moving
shape in the moon-steeped grasses half a mile distant. Her marrow
chilled. She tried to change her terror to disbelief, to tell herself it
was a mist, but then she saw it was *looking* at her. Screams paralysed
her throat, and she uttered no sound at all, but just stood there. In
another moment it moved or flickered out of sight, and she ran
gasping to Dal. Her brothers! Her brothers! How long before they
would climb the slope?

Dal was asleep, lying with face averted on his cloak. The sight
of him silenced her at the moment of calling out. What use to wak-
en him? She would go back and watch until no doubt was left. This
resolution surprised her--none the less she followed it out. She went
some distance, and seated herself behind a bush with flickering
leaves. From there every foot of the slope was visible--and naught

seemed amiss. What had she seen? One of the night-flying birds? In a little she had convinced herself it was so. The giddy moonrays poured as upon a distant arena; which, no matter what it harboured, could not affect her. She laughed, and was pleased that she had let her lover sleep. By dawn the unstirring sea of mist had ebbed, and there was a faint cold which made her creep back to Dal's side. He looked at her through a dream and said nothing.

When the moon was absent, another thing occurred. She lay in the shelter they had contrived, only a few inches of slate to shut out the stars thickening over the unattainable land. The tide of her thoughts wandered, and a dream took shape, of the sort which forms in a mind that has slipped its leash. She appeared somehow to see the stars beyond the roof—white crowding fragments of unstable light. Their numbers and intensity were uncommon, but more than that, like boiling particles they pushed and opposed and seethed and scattered in visible motion. Not in their habitual pace moved these dancers in ether, but with new speeds and in new relationships. They seemed to describe vast patterns that ought to have taken whole lifetimes to execute.

And they lit the ruins, and seemed to congregate above the tumbled conical altar, more brilliantly than all the moons of the year could do, and since they moved, their light came constantly from new angles; where darkness had been now was a star, two stars, or twenty, shunting from prodigious facets their own and their brothers' flames. And in the moments she stared at them, the altar seemed to change. Cracks became fewer, the moss retreated, the runnels of the rain were filled, the patient erosion of the wind undone, and the work of the snowflake defeated. Unexplained joys swelled in her as she perceived this, and with each crazy figure devised by the drunken stars a year seemed shed, a tedious year from the courtyard and the altar, and strangely, yet expectedly, from her likewise. She ran with joy to the altar and stood upon it, expecting, desiring, demanding . . . and then the stars retreated into mist, and about her the idols, tumbled grotesquely among the stones of their ruined house, stared with oblique or inverted eyes at the sky which had roofed their former grandeur.

Leyenda awoke a long time later. She did not tell Dal of her experience, but occupied herself picking berries all morning and afternoon till the closer bushes were stripped. She was nearly out of his sight along the cliff's edge before she had enough. The coloured sky gleamed like porcelain, the world of the previous night seemed unthinkably far, yet she was not easy. There was her bracelet for one thing; it seemed tighter than usual. She wondered why it would not come off. Repeated hammering with stones had done nothing aside from bruising her arm. It gripped her like an inexorable hand—the hand, she vaguely felt, of the past of this place of whose history nothing was known. She wondered who had lost the bauble—shackle—in that unrecorded yesterday. She wondered who had built this and the other ruins scattered over her land, mounted by the vine, invaded by the forest; and at the coming and receding over the centuries' shore of the tide of their inhabitants.

As she came back, Dal called down to her.

"I think we'd better have a fire at night."

Thinking she had misunderstood him, she tossed the long hair from her ear.

"We need a fire, I think. There are animals here."

A fire! Something to draw destruction on them! What if her brothers were still searching? She was very near now: he sat up and pointed to the north side of the cone. Where the bricks had slid away, something had dug a burrow in the clay side. The beast which made it must have been large and had large claws.

"Look at it," said Dal, "and find out what it was after. Perhaps roots we can eat ourselves."

She put her berries down and examined the planed side of the pyramid. There something the colour of ripe corn glittered from its clay matrix. For the second time the ruin had cast up treasure. A gold knife, long as her arm from wrist to elbow and scrolled over with words in a language which had no other monument, lay exposed. Conscious of the weight on her arm, she would not touch it.

They discussed the find uneasily, and decided she must put a great rock over it, and planned for a fire. When night came, they had a yellow blaze in the entrance to their makeshift hut. Fuel had been gathered and stored inside, and they were to keep alternate watch. Only the unknown land, and the unknown watchers therein, could see the flame . . . no one in the east, whence pursuit might yet come. And now they were confident Dal could walk in two days more.

The beast, if it came, was baffled by the stone, but something worse happened. From too much hobbling about, or from lack of sleep when guarding Leyenda, Dal complained of a fever, and before the second flame was kindled, was aflame himself. It had come so rapidly that the girl crouching beside him, touching his lips and cheeks, could not understand that he was ill. She sought to arouse him, and then when he turned away, sat up vigilant and perplexed while his sighs grew heavier. The indifferent flare popped and flickered and nearly escaped for lack of tending while she sat there. A sound aroused her finally, a pebble sliding, and she listened for the beast and watched the man and thrust twigs into the fire until dawn.

By noon of the following day she was going often to the well and soaking a strip from her cloak's edge in the tepid water to wipe his face. At intervals she brought him eggs, or the sweet gourds growing by the sacrificial bowl; but he paid no attention to them, or else strewed and crushed them with gesticulating arm. He shouted or muttered of animals which he had taken, appearing sometimes to think himself tracking a goat over frightful crags. Leyenda had his bow, Dal complained, and would not give it to him, so he could not kill the goat when there was a chance to do so. It stood and looked at him. Many times he said this, and finally she did bring the bow to him, but he only cast it aside with convulsive fingers; and she was puzzled and afraid. Then she thought of something more practical. Because he talked of a goat, some animal—or animal-shaped god—must be plaguing him. She would propitiate it, snare it with offerings, and then defeat it with a charm, and he would look at her calmly again.

Immediately she decided this—the shadows were spreading long on the ground—she built an altar; a tiny heap of reddish stones behind the hut, with red petals laid upon them; and then with a broken stick she obtained another ingredient—her own blood. The blood and the petals she stirred together, singing a chant whose words no one understood any more, and she crawled around this affair three times, calling herself goat. Then it was ready, and with a wintry heart she waited for something to come and feed.

She did not see the day wane.

Three hours she crouched.

Then, with her words of damnation unuttered, Leyenda rose and went back to the sick man. Inside, she stationed herself by the fire, and fed it, and fed her thoughts. With the image of forests passed, of paths traversed along muddy shores, of ravines unsteady with rock, of dogs and men avoided, of valleys and plains and slopes and hills and finally this last grim precipice beyond which there was no going, she remembered their flight. With what eagerness she had freed Dal, the death-destined prisoner of her brothers. How they had run in the first moments! And to what goal? She sensed somehow, but in an inarticulate way, that these ruined sunsets, like blood running across the decks of wicked defeated ships as they nosed down to doom, were not isolated and meaningless phenomena, but that they had all along presaged the now apparent tragedy. A tragedy so high and exquisite that mournfulness was not even to be thought of. Their fate was linked to the ruins; their coming and abiding had been destined. With them the old day had awakened. She had seen it in dream. She knew herself to be of it. How the centuries had flowed back beneath those intermeshing stars! As ignorant of man as was the earthquake or the typhoon had they revealed themselves to be—forming patterns unmeasurable by miles and years—patterns whose ultimate nature the race would not survive to comprehend. The audacious eye viewed them, but it was as if a housefly wrought in a warm dung-heap should nestle in a roof built for snows and winters. Though she sat by the fire and the sick man, she peered backward into pasts so dark that only a hint of something stirred in them; and forward in wonder and doubt at the end, when all villages should be as were the citadels of the old race; when nowhere on field or mountaintop would move aught but the pacing sun as its light revealed, caressed and forgot man's works in the course of declining day. Leyenda had not thought of this before. She would not ever have thought it in the village.

Calm as the light that flickered yellow in a little bowl in her father's house Leyenda grew. She wondered if her god had followed her. Diminished and spent was her woe. She had gone beyond protesting—she had reached an incomprehensible peace—caught, almost, some secret which fluttered in the dark beyond all fears. Beyond the night which lay all about earth, a fundamental source abode and dreamt in the desolations. Thence streamed the patterns which an hour ago had seemed agonising because she saw them dimly. Thence streamed all good and hateful things, and the power which shaped them knew them not apart, but somehow this was consoling. Her robbed goods were returned to her; her tears washed away. It was autumn in her heart, a golden-haired autumn which had forgotten the flower which was to perish, and nurtured the life-crowded root. What did she expect so joyously?—She turned with a face but lately contorted, and gazed ambiguously at Dal. She touched his incredible flesh with hands no longer restless for aught save the dust a thousand years deep on the ruin which was each day lighted curiously by an expiring sun.

Dal startled her with a request, made with closed eyes, for water. There was none. She had forgotten to bring any in. On the previous night it would have been twenty steps of terror to the well, but she roused herself, selected a bundle of dried stalks, twisted it tightly, and touched it to the fire. By its blaze she went out into the darkness. . . .

Awakening slowly, Dal seemed to recall a quest through unending corridors; through forests of black-trunked pines in whose upper gloom the birds flitted anonymously; through boulder-peopled ravines. His journey amid these things had been more strenuous even than that with Leyenda, and Leyenda did not share it. She had left him midway—though how or why he could not remember. Leyenda! He knew of course that it had been a dream occasioned by his fever, but still he grieved weakly. Then he turned and stared at the burnt sticks where the fire had been, and where she sat feeding it. The spot was cold, and she was gone indeed.

In a small voice he called her, with expectant eyes on the sunflooded door. A line of grasses, a few crazily embedded stone blocks, and the sky's blue were all that he could see, prone as he was. He waited. Was she gathering eggs? The dream of his lone journey remained disquietingly present. If she did not come, he would look for her. The half-remembered fever had kept him from using the ankle; it was swollen but only negligibly painful. He could make his way about with a stick—perhaps he could even climb the cone, from whose top such a wide range was visible. So, the wait becoming unendurable, and his cries availing naught, he stood up and found his strength was gone. Such weakness was incredible to him—his very hand, clutching the door-edge, was flaccid and powerless. Now he was thoroughly frightened, but he managed to stagger out calling her name. What devilish thing had happened in the intervals of his delirium? Had she gone out and fallen from the cliff? Had the thing which scratched at the cone-side . . . but he smothered the thought. Hunger told him of days that had elapsed unseen . . . sunless dawns and unstarred evenings.

Outdoors, he sensed a change in his surroundings, as if someone had assiduously *tidied* the ruin, set one block upon another, pulled away the creepers. His eye fell upon a brick pillar, and judged it to be higher than before, but this information can hardly be said to have reached his brain. Then, calling up a strength he did not have, propelling himself clumsily with a stick under his arm-pit, Dal searched.

He searched like the wind searching the night, the wind whose remembered cry was similar to his own; the wind which touched regretfully the grass of unsown fields, that fretted the wave of lake and sea; but not like the rain-weighted wind was his weeping.

Then by the gourd-vine he came upon a clue, and his heart was marble. It was the ruinous, thousand-year-old basin which had once served to hold the victims of the god. It had been righted, cleansed of moss, mended. And on its shallow curve reposed Leyenda's bracelet. Her hateful shackle of a bracelet. A while since it had clasped her soft arm. It would do so no more—nor would Dal. For the bauble was smeared with blood. He seized it, and drawing back his weak arm, threw it goldenly into space. Instantly he regretted that he had done so. A dark circle remained on the stone—blood clotted into the porous surface. He watched a while, then shaking with bewilderment—though in his heart he knew—lifted his eyes to the gold and gore of the sunset. There massive clouds, acres in extent, hid the sun but left an empty space. Across this window of the heavens undulated the expiring sun-rays. A nimbus shone there—a sign was blossoming out. Something was congregating out of the welter—being borne in on lapping waves from the farthermost spatial and temporal sea, growing stronger with each wave. With bloodshot hectic eyes and grinning teeth he sought to make it out. But it did not resolve itself.

So he stood there as the birds, clamouring to the nest never built for them, came in from wherever they had been; from the huts of men in green-shadowed forests; from the broken highways, from the changing streams and changing mountains; and from the land, broad and unattainable, beneath him.

*August 1938–June 1939.*
*Mexico and San Francisco*

# The Hat

After luncheon, which was never over until four, my nurse would come and take Federico and me to the nursery, which was in the back part of the house, and where I learned to be a little lady. My uncles would stay on smoking their cigars with the big red and gold labels which they sometimes gave us to wear on our fingers, and drinking French cognac from the supply in the cellar, which they said was getting harder to buy now the trains didn't come. They talked mostly about the trouble a mad man named Sr. Madero had caused in Mexico. Federico and I were not allowed to stay, but we did not care, for as soon as the big Indian woman who was our nurse had shut the door, we sprang out of bed and looked down into the courtyard, which was paved with sunlight. If the maids were washing, we had to wait, but as soon as they went to look after their babies, or to hang the clothes on the roof, we tore down the stair and across the courtyard. There I would take the key off the nail where it hung beside the green door, turn it in the lock, and look into the back street. Then when there was a lull in the shooting, we would sneak out.

No one ever seemed to discover the door unlocked, or if he did, no one wished to bring on a general scolding of the servants. Nor did anyone ever check up on the food we stole, though we took canned vegetables and other valuable things. I suppose the servants all suspected each other, and all had guilty consciences.

The gun duels in the hot sun were soothing, like the sound of fireworks on a feast-night in front of a little country church, or rugs being beaten by the servants. We never could be sure where they were fighting—sometimes the Villistas would be in a cellar and the Federalists in another, so that everyone but us would avoid that street. Sometimes the Carrancistas would be shooting at both of them from a garden, or a flat house-top. No one seemed any more anxious to finish the shooting than ourselves.

If we could reach one of the cellars and talk with our friends, we would do so. Then we would trade with them for bullets and military insignia. We liked the copper barrels and the soft lead points of the bullets, and cut faces on them with a knife. They made nice ten-pins, and Federico and I had large collections hidden under the bath-tub where the maids never swept. We would take out the cans of fresh garden peas imported from San Antonio, or the little bags of coffee, and trade with the soldiers until they did not dare give us more bullets. We never cared which cellars we traded with; they were always changing as different revolutionary generals captured the town, and sometimes we found the same friend on opposite sides in the course of a few days.

I always got what I wanted from the soldiers, being a beautiful little girl with long black curls, and if they did not want to trade buckles and bullets for the fresh garden pease from San Antonio, I would cry a little, and then put my arms around their necks the way I did with my uncles, though I did not like to do this, since I knew they were only ugly Indians.

Sometimes there was a battle going on, and our friends did not know we were coming to trade for bullets, and we could not get close enough to tell them. When this happened, we would hide in door-ways and count the number of bullets fired, and try to guess what kind they were, at which we were very expert. "Diez y siete, 'z y ocho, 'z y nueve, veinte" I would shout, while Federico lagged one or two behind. Then we would argue and call each other Liar, and some-times both of us would lose count. Then when the Carrancistas had retreated back over the geraniums and the Villistas had scurried over the wall, we would go and knock on the gate, like little ladies and gentlemen, as we had been taught to knock. And the soldiers would let us in, and admire my lace panties from Paris, as we tried to make them tell us how many bullets they had fired. Somehow they never seemed to count them as well as we did.

Their uniforms were dirty and they did not button them properly, the way the *rurales* did in my uncles' photograph album of the Centennial celebration and Don Porfirio Díaz. This was because they were revolutionaries and dirty people from the desert around us, who had not wanted to learn geography with their governesses. Only one of them had nice clothes and seemed to wash his face every day as he ought to. This was Alberto, owner of the Hat.

When I saw that Hat, I knew it was more beautiful than any of the bullets or rifles even. It was about a meter wide, and made of pale blue felt, with lovely things embroidered on the underside of the brim. There was Our Lady of Zapopan, and green hummingbirds drinking out of pink lilies, and a heart with an arrow through it. When I saw it the first time, I offered Alberto a whole kilo of coffee which I had almost been caught stealing. Alberto was lying on his blanket in the corner of a box-car in the railway station, which his friends the Carrancistas had captured the week before. He must have been about seventeen, and I thought he was as pretty as my cousin Concepción until I discussed the matter with Federico and we decided he was an ugly Indian. Still, his teeth were nicely brushed when he laughed at me and my kilo of coffee, and I was more puzzled by his appearance than hurt by his laughter. And since I wanted the Hat very much, I hung around him and let Federico trade for all the bullets that day.

Alberto had a white horse, too—as beautiful as the Hat. He cleaned and combed and curried the horse all the time, whenever he was not galloping off into the desert toward Chihuahua. I heard some of the soldiers say that Alberto brought them their orders, which as why he came and went. They seemed to think his horse was more beautiful than his hat with the silver and pink and green embroidery.

The soldiers held the railway station a week, and ate twenty-four cases of eggs which they found in one of the box-cars. Then they had nothing to eat, and Federico and I might ask whatever we pleased for the cans and packages we brought. This was a little after Christmas, and when I discovered how willing they were to trade, I persuaded Federico to help me steal a fruit-cake which had been left over. We always ate fruit-cake and turkey and had a sweet Christ-

mas like the Americanos and Franceses who were such good friends
of my uncles. Federico and I carried the fruit-cake down to the station in a lavender hatbox I had been given for Christmas. It was
heavy to carry along the hot vacant streets, and when we reached
the place where the shooting was, and had to run across to the back
of the station, I almost fell down. I was scared the Villistas would
kill me and take my fruit-cake away, but Federico dragged me and I
dragged the hatbox, and we were there once more, guessing how
many bullets had been fired.

The soldiers were all anxious to see what we had brought, but I
sat on my hatbox and said only my doll, and they looked sad and
went back to their posts under the box-cars and behind the locomo-
tive. I know what I wanted for that fruit-cake, and why I had
brought it in the lavender hatbox.

Alberto was due that afternoon, and I stationed Federico where
he could watch the road to Chihuahua while I rested. It was only a
few minutes later than he called out, "Here comes Alberto! Here
comes Alberto!" in a voice which carried across to the Villistas in
the houses facing the station. A soldier jumped up and slapped Federico, and he began to cry, but I did not care, for Alberto was galloping toward us, and his white horse was like the pictures in my
Perrault's Fairy Tales, and we wore his blue embroidered hat.

Then the Villistas were shooting, and we were shooting back,
and I had counted diez y ocho, and Federico had stopped crying so
as to count better than me, and Alberto was nearly in front of the
station when he fell off his horse and the horse kept on galloping
with a red spot on its white side. Then Alberto just lay with his
cheek on the cobblestones, which were too hot to go barefoot on,
even if we had been allowed to.

I forgot my fruit-cake and ran out into the bullets before anyone
could stop me, Federico following. The bullets stopped suddenly,
and we went tiptoeing up to Alberto. He lay still in the sun, and did
not seem to be wounded anywhere. I had to go closer and closer,
although I was breathing as if had run a long way, and my insides

were cold as ice cream. I heard Federico whimper. Then we saw Alberto's face suddenly.

An explosive bullet, the sort we collected, had entered the back of his head, and he really had no face anymore. There was only red and white. And around where his face had been was the blue felt brim, the embroidered Virgin of Zapopan, the green humming-birds and the pink lilies of the beautiful hat, now mine.

## Cousin Anna

Cousin Anna. when she was not correcting geography papers, dabbled in literary form, as variegated as the furnishings of her living-room. Sculptured prose was among her triumphs. This was ordinary narrative prose broken up and arranged something like poetry, "only I don't use any capitals," she would explain. It was all very obscure, and had to do with reflective or descriptive clauses, thus:

> Belle,
>> daughter of a miner
> had been taken
>> by the aged wood-cutter
>>> Alphonse
> to live
>> among the whispering romantic beauty
> of the northern forest.

When this arrangement was read aloud her audiences were sometimes unable to detect the nuances of rhythm, but she reassured them "It's good for your style, anyway."

Cousin Anna rented a house built in 1913 by the edge of a handsome neighborhood, and kept house for an aged, unwell father and a brother who was not young. She had done this for two decades; teaching school to help out on the rent, resolutely ignoring opportunities in order to help Pa and Clinton. For a long time she believed that somehow she might escape her tyrannous duties, but the years crowded along without changing things, except that her chin grew less firm and her complexion murky. The last chance of her reprieve was gone with her mother's death; and by that time Anna had ceased pretending. It was her duty to be a good daughter and sister. She was aware that the neighbors thought her a good daughter and sister. Pa might last a long time in spite of his heart, and Clinton had been more thoughtful when he was young than most brothers. Only at times did she regret her decision—indeed, there had never been an actual decision, but only an acceptance of the drift of fate. That fate was to wash dishes twice very day for twenty-three years.

She had been twenty, and rather more pretty, with full lips and cheeks that dimpled gracefully, when Pa was ordered to spend the balance of his life in vegetation. The disease which might have killed him then spent years in subtler work, and the old man lying upon a shabby couch was a fact as long accepted as the couch itself. He passed the time talking to his wife until she became ill and died quite suddenly in the night: after that he listened to the radio, which—since it was above him on a shelf at the end of the couch—he could not dial. At first he had had a crystal set with strange-looking ear-phones, and then the children had bought him a huge black loudspeaker. He said they were a good son and daughter to give him so much of their time.

Every night, even if she was tired, Anna recounted her experiences. Clinton did not always stop when he passed through the room to ascend stairs no longer open to Pa, but he would speak with a smile and a word or two of jest that made it seem to Pa as if he weren't really ill and near the end of his life. Clinton was not praised as much as Anna by the sympathetic neighbors, but his qualities were appreciated. Somehow people expected Anna to be an old maid, and even joked about it. Clinton's bachelorhood evoked comment at times. People liked his amiable, once-handsome face with its watery blue-grey eyes and wide lips. Anna had once been pretty, her brother was still pleasant looking. Clinton had always been slight, but when thirty passed he became as substantial as Anna. He was reminiscent of a child even in young middle-age; and did odd things for the proprietor of a feed-store. The crooked wool tapestry above Pa's couch was his product, as were the home-framed watercolours of white ships against cement clouds. Upstairs there was a bureau drawer full of these pictures. Some of them had been kept since Pa was up and about, although when Clinton showed them—a rare occurrence—he implied that they were casual discoveries among old papers. Many were marine subjects, and in these the rigging was always wrong. There were some two-dimensional castles on hills, and at the bottom strata very many drawings in pencil of a young man's head. He did now show these to anyone, and Anna had been surprised to find them one day in searching for an old bottle of cough-syrup. She took them out of the disorderly drawer and scanned four or five before recognizing the subject. "Why, it's the Albertson boy that Clinton went around with when he was in college!" She recalled that her brother had greatly esteemed the older boy, and had been depressed at his marriage. Since the wife was a close friend of hers, Anna had thought that unkind. She asked him in annoyance if he was jealous. Afterward, sensing that her brother would never marry, she regretted saying that. Clinton should have had a wife and family: he was so fond of the home atmosphere, and nearly as domestic as she. Anna was a little puzzled by his bachelorhood, but taking it as a gesture of filial devotion, respected him for it.

There had been times, in a space of twenty years, when everything about her seemed heavy and stifling, and she would be unable to sleep at night. At these times, dully eyeing the photographs of five married cousins now prosperous and secure and eating too much, with good children attending good schools, she felt annoyed at Pa, lying on a shabby couch and growing thin and feeble. It was too bad to waste a life, because you didn't get another chance . . . She glared at the murky darkness and the photographs, and scolded herself for sham heroics—but felt them half-justified. Sometimes this aimless protest gave way to embarrassing thoughts—reflections, which though imparted to none, appeared unmaidenly. Anna was no

fool: she did not consider herself a nymphomaniac, but lying alone on a hot cotton spread in the August night made her restless with thoughts. At moments she would stroke the pillow in a futile impulse.

At nineteen a man had called on her and during their acquaint-
anceship kissed her several times when her parents were absent
from the living room. He was slightly over twenty-two, and never
kept his hair straight. Later he went to New York and did something with electrical goods. Once he became amorous on the sofa
where Pa lay afterward, and made distinct Advances. She remembered that his dark hair had been mussed, and that his necktie—
white with black spots—had needed straightening. After he kissed
her (she had protested decorously) he seemed quite pink and out of
breath, and sat with an embarrassed smile to survey her. For a moment everything ceased as he realized that all he required was en-
couragement. It was a most extraordinary realization. Not because
she really wished him to cease, not because her conscience was a
heavy weight in the scale, but out of the reaction of habit and training—and nothing more sincere—she did not provide that encour-
agement. There was no visible incentive to virtue: her parents were
out and her impulses mixed but frighteningly strong in the presence
of the man who sat looking at her. His body was so near and
warm; his mouth so agreeable.

She assumed a guileless look as if she didn't understand, and
began to speak rather loudly. He was a complete gentleman, embarrassed at his own behavior, and they resumed the conversation.
Later, Anna was not certain she had gained anything very satisfactory by hearing about Tennyson's use of alliteration. Then as she
considered her near-seduction in retrospect, a rush of thought
swept her to opposite convictions. Men were strange: she might
suddenly have found his flesh repellent or meaningless. She thought
of such things at night, but it was always with hesitancy that she
touched a man's cheek or hand or shoulder; always with an inner
fear it might become alien and unpleasant.

Yet she wondered how life might have been if she had not mis-
led him that afternoon. . . . Certainly the man was honourable, if
impulsive. Anna speculated cold-bloodedly on the probable results
of her seduction. He would have married her in hasty guilt; and he

was amiable and good-looking. They would have gone to New York and escaped Pa's endless sickliness. She might have wantonly abandoned Clinton and the cousins on the wall to live with this man in another and more desirable city.

The shabby couch and the pink-faced lover can through her head till sleep was washed away, but in the day time she became a good daughter and taught urchins to help pay the rent. Time, which is often cruel, has kindly aspects because it makes things seem to lose importance. Anna did not wither in her loneliness, nor was she morbid. Her cheeks stayed plump, if not strictly rosy, and she appeared to be contented with her literary devisings; much as was Clinton with his badly-composed watercolours. At twenty-eight she resumed the composition of nature poetry, and had a quatrain about geese printed in the women's page of a rural magazine. This success was repeated at intervals, and by thirty-one she had enough for a collected book, not including the unpublished amatory verse based on Teasdale. She was saving to finance publication in permanent form. Nearly all he members of her literary club had books for which they had paid. These were reviewed in the *Honolulu Star-Bulletin* and elsewhere. Standards in the club were ostensibly aesthetic, although Edgar A. Guest was looked upon with upon with smiles, and the membership was largely feminine.

She had belonged to the club for eight years when the first masculine being, timid and plump, appeared. He sat next to Anna, and they had a long conversation during the lecture. Since he was dark and young and something like her young man, Anna became so engrossed in him that Miss Millay had been condemned as incomprehensible and Mr. Masefield as superficial before she listened to the speaker.

Afterward, she was introduced to him, while peiople were congratulating the lecturer and asking her opinion of Walt Whitman. He was a Student of the Piano; and rather subdued, with a trick of brightening when addressed, as if he felt favored by any attention. They met several times at the migratory club, and once he chirped an epigram with delighted wrigglings of eyebrow and shoulder.

Anna thought he always looked as if he had just had a bath, and he smelled of clean linen. She felt vaguely maternal toward him, and they got along quite nicely. After a little, it was reported that he called on her and played Beethoven in the original, as well as some of his own compositions: *Sunset on the Hills,* and *The River Merges with the Sea.* There were also rumours, later, of a joint composition in the modern vein. Anna was certainly versatile.

Mrs. Phipps, who had been sought after in her thirties as well as twenties, and liked to stride late into a parlour tapping a riding-crop against her fine polished boot, met Anna at the club, and thought her a rather pitiful fool. The woman's got a martyr-complex, she reflected on learning her story from random chatter. "Her real pleasure is knowing that people call her a Good Daughter. She'd be miserable if she couldn't sacrifice herself." Nevertheless, when it was discovered that they lived only four blocks apart, Mrs. Phipps was not unneighborly.

On a Sunday in October she ascended Anna's tiny steps and pushed a doorbell embedded in stucco. It looked like an eye surveying her from the side of the house. There were scuffling sounds within, and the abrupt cessation of what seemed to be piano scales. Then Anna appeared and led her through the door (Mrs. Phipps thought) with unnecessary determination, as if she hadn't intended to come in.

The young man was there; he had risen from the piano bench and was bowing and nodding amiably. Pa croaked from the davenport, and Mrs. Phipps was deposited in a chair amid sounds of welcome. "I hear you've written a symphony," she began.

Anna nodded excited confirmation. "Lawrence and I wrote it together." It seemed to give her pleasure to link their names. She launched into an explanation as the visitor stared in polite interest.

"I can't play a note," she began, "but when I had the idea for this symphony I felt compelled to get it written down. I tried to pick up a little music, but I just didn't have time. I'd like to, some-day: it's so intriguing."

"Wrote most of it in the evenings—used to stay up till eleven o'clock," interjected Pa from the recesses of the couch.

"Yes, Lawrence studies all day, and of course I don't have any time until dinner is over. It took us three months to write it, and we were working every night."

"I suppose you told him what you wanted, and he wrote it down?" asked Mrs. Phipps.

Anna laughed with a touch of falsity. "Well, it was partly that way. I'd show him how it should go, and sometimes he'd make suggestions about changing it." Her fingers scampered up an imaginary keyboard in the air before her. "Lawrence has studied harmony, and when he'd tell me a thing was wrong, we'd change it. I was always willing to learn."

"Played it for his uncle, once," suggested Pa. Supine upon the couch, he was like an old tree, feeble and blighted.

"Oh, yes," Anna recalled. "His uncle has studied for years, and we showed it to him—that was before it was finished. He received it very kindly, and made a criticism of two which we adopted. When we told him we'd written a streamline symphony he seemed rather surprised, but afterward he said it was *very novel.*"

Lawrence, hunched vaguely in the stuffed chair, dangled his hands from plump knees and stared into his thick glasses. Anna did all the talking; he was never a conversationalist. She gave him an approving smile and continued her happy monologue. There was an attitude of detachment above her as she spoke: the complacency of a creator whose work is wholly done. She spoke for him, as if his personality had merged with hers. It was their mutual triumph—in a moment he should play it for them, and everyone would admire. This brief prelude of words was a slightly intoxicating pleasure—a pleasure of which nothing could rob her.

Mrs. Phipps got in a sentence as Anna hesitated in the choice from her rich experiences. "Do play it for me now: my curiosity has got the better of my manners!"

Anna was willing and gratified. As Lawrence edged onto the

stool, she bent over him to open the music. For a moment she was seized by a tormenting emotion. There was something familiar in the male body, close and breathing—something which she recalled but partially. His clean, carefully-pressed grey suit and virgin shirt were crumpled as he leaned forward and fingered the high keys. A faint warmth radiated from him. This warmth bore a scent beyond analysis—a fresh, masculine fragrance which touched something dormant in the woman. Abruptly, she longed to touch his smooth, rounded jaw. The incompetent Lawrence had in him all the dominance of man. His shoulders and back were strong and desirable. . . .

A little frightened and confused she opened the blurred pages and retired. These impulses must be stifled as she had stifled many others during twenty years. "A woman of my age!" she reproved inwardly, and hoped that Lawrence hadn't noticed.

He wrinkled up his face and adjusted the rimless glasses. There were ascending and descending chords on the music . . . little black spots in methodical rows, and he translated them with facile fingers. The introductory bars sounded very much like exercises to Mrs. Phipps, but she assumed a look of admiring wonder, and hoped for more understandable passages. This desire was not fulfilled—it grew more complicated and meaningless, until Lawrence had become a machine racing the notes with pallid hands.

"Some of it's very difficult," Anna vouchsafed absently. She was not really listening, but felt compelled to speak and distract her futile thoughts. Indeed, it sounded difficult. There were four movements—Anna had read that the classic symphony must have four movements; and while she wished determinedly unconventional subject-matter, she thought it nice to use an ancient pattern. She did not appear to respect her own work, for every now and then she made comments on its progress. This was only from her lips— the perplexities of her mind were not mastered. If Lawrence was annoyed, he gave no indication. Coping with the music required all his attention.

Then it was finished. Briefly silent, in case there might be more (some music is deceptive) Mrs. Phipps voiced commendation. "My! how do you do it, Anna? I couldn't write anything like that. As a matter of fact, I couldn't write anything at all."

Pleased and out of breath, Lawrence deserted the piano and requested a cigarette. The members of the club were bohemian: they even had cocktails whenever they were at Mrs. Phipps'. "We put that las theme in because we thought it sounded Chinese," he remarked. "It's all explained in the prologue."

Looking at the music, Mrs. Phipps saw that it was indeed explained in a prose-poem by Anna, typed inside the front cover. "Have you offered it to a publisher yet?" she enquired.

"No, but we have it copyrighted."

The moment of triumph was over, and somehow unsatisfactory. All were quiet as Pa shifted restlessly. He turned his head and looked at them with a feverish, burnt-out stare. When they were gone Anna could turn on his radio. Somehow, everyone glanced outside. A curious light was on the crowded walls, and Clinton's tapestry became an ugly blue. Bare trees showed through the bay window, and late refuse of autumn swirled past. Everybody spoke but Anna. Lawrence said, "I've really got to go," and Mrs. Phipps said, "Is it five *already?*" and Pa said, "Getting wintry out."

Then there was much hunting of coats and struggling into them, and a muffler which had been mislaid. While Anna searched, Lawrence decided to accompany Mrs. Phipps as far as his street-car line. The sky was like faintly dulling lead as he swung open the door, admitting a strong wind tinged with cold. The new-found muffler, bright with plaid, required adjusting.

"Gracious, I hope I won't freeze," exclaimed Mrs. Phipps. "It was so nice of you, Anna."

The hostess rallied. "Do come back soon. Don't forget I'm having the club Thursday."

When they were half way down the littered walk, Lawrence glanced back and saw her lingering at the door.

## Fine Bindings

I had not been in San Francisco or years, but in 1930 my study of the De Anza exploration route, and especially of the odd Indian tribe which he found below Santa Barbara, took me to the library of the Grandsons of the Golden West. Amid its expensive metal files of grimy old miners' papers, and mahogany-framed handbills of circuses of the '50's, I found the slender collection of leaves, loosely stitched together, which was the scribe's report, and which put an end to my search.

After four days of note-taking and photostatting of early settlers' maps, I found myself ready to change my literary fare. The waddling little librarian, whose attentiveness seemed due more to mistrust than to courtesy, suggested that I go over to the Donnermilch bookstore if I really wanted something different to read on the train back; and so I wandered into that prosperous establishment.

In the window as I entered I caught sight of a charming over-done binding in red calf, gilt, of a book of gardening and thought how absurd to imagine such a book would even be exposed to the inclemencies of anything more than an orchid garden with a tight glass roof. Then I became aware of a sign, FIND BINDINGS, CLEARANCE SALE, and ascended the interior stair beyond the Best-Sellers, with the intention of viewing them.

The collection of fine bindings without regard to their content is one of the mild perversions which bibliophilia has spawned, and though I have been touched by it, I have always thought up some historical interest in the type of binding purchased, so as not to be mistaken for a mere magpie like certain other collectors. Indeed, I have many times had operations performed so as to combine some lovely old tooled morocco inlay ("Life of Edgar Gilchrist," privately printed, 1882) with some book of real merit and comparable dimensions. And so I half intended to do the day I saw the little books.

On a sort of billiard-table of staunch dimensions lay a fortune in unrecognizably ornamented pieces of animal hide. Goats had perished without ever suspecting the halcyon hue which would be wrought out of their epidermises by African tanners; porkers had gone down to death's dusty doom without ever having suspected that one day they would aid posterity in the defense of Escyclus [*sic*]. And a huge library of varicolored works, having no single theme in common but Mr. Veblen's conspicuous and very agreeable waste, sprawled before me. I dipped into it.

Since there were at least two hours before luncheon and train-time, I turned over one or rows [*sic*] in detail. Then I noticed the little books.

There were perhaps a dozen of them, done with charming ama-teurishness and exceeding care. I rather think the material was a fine calves'-skin, dyed grey and lavender for the most part. The titles were lettered in to just the right degree of crookedness, and I picked one volume up to examine it. Inside, the paper proved to be a hand-made type used mostly by artists for watercolors, I think, and the text was not printed but written by hand, in the same lav-ender tint. They ranged perhaps forty little pages to each book, and seemed to contain little stories written by or for a young boy. The one I held began "The Treasure in the Lodge".

I glanced through the banal story and at the end noticed an in-scription: "For my dear Eddie, the little story which he wrote and which we bound together for Christmas in our little binder. 1907"

This seemed charming enough, and I visualized a boy of per-haps eight or ten learning an old and dignified craft in company with his mother, in a workshop of a quarter century ago. Probably the other little books were of the same age and source—it was in-deed evident that the same hands were at work. On opening others, I found the same sentimental inscription, sometimes intensified, with the dates 1908, 1911, 1912 (two books) and so on. And I be-gan to calculate the age of Eddie when the last was made, only three years ago. If he were eight in 1907, in 1928 he was twenty-nine. And still the collaborations with his mother, for so she proved to be, by other inscriptions. There was no break during the war, as

I found by arranging the books in sequence, and the themes continued to be fairly romantic and jejune.

I wondered whether Eddie were still alive and how the books had ceased to be written, or indeed, how they had been sold. A family with a private bindery of that quality was not likely to have sold them except under the dire pressure, "This strange and trying year of 1930" as the papers said. The Great Depression was setting in, and M. Ilyin's "Primer of the New Russia" had been widely circulated. Probably the Depression, I surmised.

The salesman took my doubts away. "Pretty little books, aren't they?" I agreed: "I suppose they wouldn't have come to a bookstore ordinarily, but been inherited by the family" was my reply. The salesman smiled, "I doubt if there is going to be much family in this case. The owner was quite willing to sell them, and we were glad to have the bindings though I doubt if the text will be of much interest to anyone." "On the contrary," I said, "the text seems very curious. Was he still reading the Rover Boys at twenty-nine?"

The salesman settled himself on an elbow, after dusting the corner of the table and gave his report. "Mrs. Phillips kept the house on Nob Hill, one of those silly brownstone camels herded piece by piece around the horn, after she divorced her husband in 1906. Edgar was born during the divorce trial, and she seemed contented with the exchange. As he grew up, she managed to keep him pretty close to her: he knew the plot of the Nibelungenlied before he was ten, and played Siegfried in the garden, I am told. They had a little bindery and even a little printing press, but he found setting type was too much trouble and they gave it away to a Catholic Girls' School on Sutter Street. Anything which would take him away from the house, however, was another story. His mother kept him out of the Boy Scouts insidiously, and began to suggest that he had a weak heart when he wanted to go to summer camps. She was perfectly willing to have the summer camp come see him, but not for him to go away. There were often boys from the neighborhood visiting him, but they fell away as he reached adolescence, bored, I suppose, by her conspiratorial little suggestions that they must treat Edgar delicately. He had a tutor, finally, in his high school years and wrote quite convincingly to his relatives of his "poor health", and of his mother's constant solicitude 'really very touching'. And they went on making these little books, and the household began to turn into something like Mr. Eliot's patient etherized upon a table.

"If Mrs. Phillips has not been so careful to keep young girls out of her employ, out of consideration for Edgar, I suppose, they might still be making the little books. She has taken up Theosophy in Los Angeles now—of course she is living." He noted my surprise. "About three ago they got a houseboy instead of a maid to keep the rambling old solid-oak house clean—one of those exotic ideas of the fin de siècle group who had to be European, I suppose. He was Portuguese, and about a year younger than Edgar, though ten years older in his ways. Black hair, rather operatic in his gestures. I think he drank pretty heavily. He used to come in here and sell books which he said Mrs. Phillips wanted to get rid of, and his prices were so low that I could only suspect he had stolen them. Rich people don't give anything way, I've found. And so one day when she came in herself for a gift for someone in the hospital, I remarked on the frequency of the Portuguese visits. As I suspected, the books were stolen, but she was distraught. Instead of firing him, she said vaguely 'Oh dear, I'll have to handle Eddie carefully; he won't *listen* to me about that boy.' And the Portuguese continued to come.

"The next I heard, Mrs. Phillips had gone to Los Angeles, and the Portuguese had a suit and overcoat of English woollens, tailored to his very good proportions. I sized them up when he came in with this lot of little books, this time with a note from Eddie.

"'Please take these things off my hands,' it read, 'and give me any old thing in exchange, except New Russia's Primer. Jorge will pick it out.' And Jorge chose one of these albums from the Art Department."

He indicated a pile of books on the nearer table. They were of that mildly disguised type of erotic opus "The Body Beautiful" (two

volumes), "One Hundred Artistic Poses with Live Models" etc.—
Which one had Jorge chosen? Oh, smiled the salesman, with a wary
eye but for other and more active customers, "The Body Beautiful
(Male)."

## The Sombreron

*By B. Ortiz de Montellano*
Translated by Robert Barlow

THE CHARACTERS
The Sombreron's Mask
The Sombreron
The Woman
The Father
The Son
A Dog
The Spirit Which Is Inside the Earth

The Sombreron is a mysterious character of Maya Quiche myth,
with supernatural erotic powers. In this theatrical venture he repre-
sents the virtues of fire. In the fragmentary legend, he is character-
ized solely by the use of an enormous woven straw hat (sombreron)
with which, along with other elements (a Mexican mask and the
slippery body of snakes which abound in tropical groves) he created
his mortal figure for the stage.

   The Spirit Which Is Inside the Earth might be Ah-Mucen Cab, of
Maya myth; a name meaning "He Who Is Hidden Underground."
In this farce he is arbitrarily represented by a face made from a thin
balloon which gives it elastic movement, and a lone green glassy eye
surrounded by tree-roots like an enormous land octopus.

   The other characters, peasants of the southeast coast of Mexico,
present no problems in their characterization.

   The dialogue is serious and clipped. The action should be slow,
with marked pauses and silences.

PROLOGUE

*(The Sombreron's mask, representing the Devil, appears between the stage-curtains, without anybody holding it up. Behind the mask the speaker will be found.)*

*The Mask:* Ladies and gentlemen: In order to appear before you properly I have cancelled my engagements with the witches and wizards. I prefer, however, to find in your faces surprise and not fear. I'll tell you: yesterday I had the pleasure of burning the last library, with all its eleven thousand Bibles and all the books of the demonologists, my calumniators. It's more difficult all the time to detect my presence, and as a consequence harder to mock me! Science and custom evolve, and Dr. Faust and La Celestina no longer need me, but I keep on living, and now I use a mask—you will observe it—I disguise myself, I do hocus-pocus, sleight-of-hand that no one notices. Anyhow, my business dealings were always cleaner than my intentions; I invented the bill of exchange and received souls with a rigorous inventory, even though they often deceived me. Now that everything is done with contracts and receipts, I've taken to juggling; I've turned from an honest man into a thief; I work by night and only the doctors keep their eye on me. However, I know that I am as deathless as death, and the instincts have always belonged to me.

Before I present you with the personages of this dark farce, since I am interested above all in those who know more through accident than age, I should like to give you some advice, if you will permit me: believe in dreams, in the efforts of poets and wise men, workers in the mines of my noisy silence, believe in wizards' laws more than in men's; and though what I say sounds wrong and unreasonable to your ears, believe in the gods as you believe in money, in the Social Contract and speed. Believe in me also, and in my many masks; because there are days and nights in the life of every man and every woman, when I rule with the same innocence with which a child always imposes its will, or with the wise sculptured stare with which the hypnotizer rules the person who, like myself, does not believe in him.

Have I insisted enough in this infantile attitude of faith to prepare you to accept the illogical happenings which you will shortly observe? Perhaps this may be the fabric of my discourse and the reason for which you will have to excuse my intrusion into your world.

## SCENE ONE

*(Exterior of a peasant hut in a wooded place among ravines. It is growing dark. The woman is kneading dough on the grinding-stone near the fire, while the son sharpens his hunting knife.)*

*Woman:* Don't you think you'd better get through sharpening your knife? It's dark now, and not safe to be outside.

*Son:* In another moment, mother, before the tiger's eyes shine, it will be ready.

*Woman:* . . . and your father hasn't come. Night will overtake him on the road.

*Son:* He must be taking in the odor of the fireflies. He'll come soon. *(The dog enters barking furiously, and perhaps fearfully.)* And now what's the matter?

*Woman:* Shadow-fright, or the full moon.

*Son:* Couldn't the Sombreron be somewhere near?

*Woman:* Be still, don't say it even if you think it is; if that One should come, your mother is in danger.

*Son:* That is why my knife and I are with you.

*Woman:* It is not that, my son; it's not that. You don't know what might happen to me! *(The dog howls uneasily.)*

*Son:* Why, what danger are you in?

*Woman:* I cannot tell you. *(The timbers of the house creak softly. The cloth of the wind rips.)*

*Son:* Did you hear, mother? Did you? *(With his knife raised, he peers into the darkness of the wood.)* I'm going to look for this Follower, to see what he wants.

*Woman:* *(Restraining him quickly.)* No, son! It's time for supper; we had better go inside.

*Son:* But if it is the Sombreron, I must wait for him.

*Woman:* No, no, I don't want you to suffer for me. Let's shut ourselves in, your father can't be long. *(The same noises. The dog runs away.)*

*Son:* Then I will not leave you . . . . *(They enter the house. A darkening silence falls. Great shadows, as if of a bird's wing cross the stage. Sound of rattles. At a bound the Sombreron lands on the stage, hunched and sinuous. His voice is deep and broken like that of boiling water.)*

*Sombreron:* In the imperceptible hollow of the woman's shadow I shall rest! Next to the red flame, the tiger tongue licking the cold! I shall rest, watching, for the green stones are two, like men's eyes, and between them a slender cross rises! . . . My body divides the shadows to keep awake, and in my eyes there is no hollow for ashes. *(Curls around the fire in a circle.)* Phew! shall rest, calcifier of stones, on the roots of all trees and the poison of all yellow serpents! *(Dragging himself toward the door of the hut, in a low and sibilant voice.)* Woman, voice of the dark well, bowl-breasted, my hands shall be the leaves of your dream and my eyes the eyes of your awakening! *(Darkness. Strange lights pass across the stage. The silhouette of the Sombreron, glowing, shines in the night. The curtain falls briefly: the night has passed. Little by little the dawn lights up the stage again.)*

*Father:* *(He returns at daybreak to his house. He detects the Sombreron's presence, and cautiously draws near until he touches him with his foot.)* Who are you? . . . What are you looking for in my house— viper or demon? . . . Answer, don't make me angry: what are you doing here? . . . Eh, silent one, reptile! Trunk without sap! Sloughing-off of the night! *(Strikes the motionless body of the Sombreron with his hatchet.)* Then you shall die, strip of vile and poisonous rag . . . Ah, knives shatter on your gummy body, and my anger is useless! . . . I'll throw you in the ravine, I'll shred you on the rocks, viper or demon! *(Lifts him and throws him violently, but a cloud comes down from the air and catches the Sombreron and carries him away. Rapid red lights make the scene shaky.)* Cursed devil! Cursed Sombreron, Lord of the Hill! . . . Again you escape my hand! Again . . .

*Woman:* Pelucho! Pelucho! I was waiting for you. I'm so glad you're here. Do you know what's happened to us? *(Crying.)* Oh, what shall I do?

*Father: (In fear and rage.)* Did you see him ? Tell me . . . Did you see him?

*Woman:* Yes . . . from only seeing him there were two . . . fallen from my breast.

*Father:* Here now! Where are those children?

*Woman:* Here in the house: I'll go bring them. *(Opens the door. Two live doves fly out. Try to keep them from staying onstage.)* Look at them, there go my little doves! Oh . . . oh, my children have gone now! Now I shall not see them again!

*Father:* But what are you crying for? I'd have had to kill them anyway, because I don't want any of the Sombreron's children.

*Woman:* Yes but they were mine . . . And now?

*Father: (After a silence.)* Evil signs pursue us . . . The earth rejects us . . . We must leave chis place.

*Woman:* That's so, Pelucho; let us go away from this place.

*Father: (In the form of a prayer.)* Those who know not, poor in vision and understanding, ah! they say naught. He who knoweth, joyously goeth in quest of the Flying Tiger. And then he returneth with him.

*Son: (Coming out of the hut.)* Father!

*Father:* Is it you, my on?

*Son:* It is I, father.

*Father:* Are you noble, my son?

*Son:* I am, father.

*Father:* What are your companions doing, my son?

*Son:* Father, they are in the woods looking for the tiger. "There is no tiger," they said.

*Father:* And at that moment, the tiger was prowling in front of them.

## SCENE TWO

*(A camp of broken branches. Afternoon light. The Mother and Son en-*
*ter. The dog frisks about.)*

*Woman:* (Carries a bundle of faggots to the foreground and sits
on it.) We have worked enough today! Let's rest.

*Son:* Yes, mother; sit down a while. I'll finish the work.

*Woman:* All right, son, don't be long. *(Pause.)* This place is nice,
and so is or new house! With so many trees!

*Son:* I like it too, and I'm happy away from the danger we were
in back there. *(Pause.)* Ugh, look how many toads!

*Woman:* There are many of them here . . . for the snakes.

*Son:* As the story says . . .

*Woman:* Yes . . . the youth Tamazul turned into a toad in order
to carry a message to the grandmother, and since he did not run
fast enough, the snake swallowed him to carry him faster . . .

*Son:* And since the snake didn't run very fast either, he let himself be swallowed by the eagle, who carried them flying to where
the grandmother was.—I bring you a message, said the eagle, and
coughed up the snake.—I bring you a message, said the snake, and
coughed up the toad. And inside the toad came the message from
Tamazul.

*Woman:* That's why snakes eat toads and eagles eat snakes.
*(Pause. A rustling in the bushes. The dog goes off.)*

*Son:* Mother, I think he hears something. I'm going to go and
see what it is.

*Woman:* Be careful, son, it's getting dark. *(The son goes offstage.*
*Pause. The light thins. The dog comes back, and with a sad air, comes up*
*to the woman.)* And you, what's troubling you? . . . Why do you
hang your ears? *(The dog howls desperately. The light becomes dimmer.)*
What can you be seeing? . . . the snake in the tree? . . . *(The dog*
*howls and runs away.)* And Pelucho hasn't come . . . Nor the boy . . .
*(Looks into the edge of the wood.)* Nothing . . . you can see nothing.
*(Sits down again. Slow sound of rattles and of splitting boughs.)* The

branches are breaking . . . *(Sudden light and the Sombreron leaps on-stage. The woman screams and faints.)*

*Sombreron: (In a dark voice, which billows out like smoke.)* Woman, tender ear of corn in the heart of my roadways! Like the new maize-ears wounded by the lightning of the hatchet . . . A necklace to your neck, I pursue you! Remember . . . they were not gods, because they did not tell what they loved, and you fear me because you do not listen to me . . . The word walks like lightning in the snake's mouth . . . So it was told to the deer and the birds. *(Coming near, until he touches the woman's body.)* My warmth turns the bodies of those who went away into worms. Gives life to your children . . . Slants in the lightning furrow and the sky's heart. You shall be a breath of water between my hands, for my eyes, for my mouth . . . thirsty . . . *(The woodcutters are heard returning. In the distance, the song which marks their steps, a song of the ancient Maya, grows louder. Hunched over, the Sombreron moves away.)* Enemies of the earth! Choppers down of Mother Ceiba and the red Zapote-tree! Enemies of my lair of eternal leaves! Eh, Ja! Jay! Through the roots of all stones my sap shall push . . . at the feet of all trees my word shall spring forth, green and poisonous weeds. It is useless to look for the gem in the well. It is useless to find me. *(The Sombreron disappears into the hollow of a tree. Night falls, and a set of fireflies distracts the bad thoughts of the spectator. In the uncertain light of the fireflies— which can be arranged by simple electrical means—appear the shadows of the returning father and son.)*

*Son: (Seeing the Sombreron's shadow.)* Get out of here, devourer! I am not afraid of your claws, nor of your teeth. My knife knows how to pierce vipers in the corner.

*Father:* Is it you, my son?

*Son:* It is I, father.

*Father:* Are you noble, my son ?

*Son:* I am, father.

*Father:* What are your companions doing, my son?

*Son:* Father, they are in the woods looking for the tiger. "There is no tiger," they said.

*Father:* And at that moment, the tiger was prowling in front of them.

SCENE THREE

*(The stage is divided into two parts horizontally. The lower part should be the larger. Above, the wood, the tops of the trees lost above the line of vision. In the middle a large tree with a large hole. In the setting of the lower part the roots of the forest trees continue. We are going under ground, and the scene presents us with the cross section of the Sombreron's hiding place. The Spirit Which Is Inside the Earth, with his green eye and his many arms, tree-roots in motion, is with the Sombreron. The bottom part of the stage is illuminated by a live green light, the other remaining dark until the Father and Son appear, lighting it up with the yellow light of a hatchet.)*

*Sombreron: (Mending the wings of a bat.)* Don't get into any more trouble with the lovely Owl, brow of the shadows, who carries a scythe in his beak. *(The bat repeats this word constantly:* quilitz, quilitz.*)* I can't always be mending your wings with my magic glues, young bat. *(The changed tone of Sombreron's expressions should be no surprise, when we know that even such mysterious beings become human in moments of intimacy.)* And now you can fly to your caves . . . We shall see each other tomorrow when you bring the wind's whistle in your blow-gun. *(The bat escapes through the hollow tree still saying:* Quilitz . . . quilitz . . . *which may mean: Many thanks.)* Grandfather! *(To the Spirit Which Is Inside the Earth.)* The scene-pots are dry . . . the guanabana roots are fading and the fruit has lost its odor . . . the black-nippled sweet-potato and the jicama and the pitahaya and the red zapote need freshening from your hand. What are you doing, grandfather, that you should forget your slavery and your kingdom?

*Spirit: (Old man's voice.)* I am old, and the winter is not long enough to rest in.

*Sombreron:* But the bees still adorn your brow and your hair is rain.

*Spirit:* Just as your hands hold the measurement of women's names, and the flint's heat, the Western Stone's heat.

*Sombreron:* Have no care! I shall help you, grandfather . . . We shall invent fruits of my season.

*Spirit:* When all the birds and all the butterflies dry out in the gourd . . . when all the bones I do not have turn into lime . . . then. *(The upper part of the stage grows light. First the Son enters. The Father follows him, carrying an enormous tree-trunk on his shoulders.)*

*Son:* I found his footprints here, near this leafy tree.

*Father:* This time he shall not escape. We are in his hiding place.

*Son: (Soft bat-flights and owl-songs are heard.)* Do you hear the flight of the bat and the scream of the owl?

*Father:* Yes, they graze right past me.

*Son:* Here it is, father. The hole I made to see him is hidden behind the leaves. Here it is!

*Father:* Help me then. *(They push with the tree trunk until they force it through to the back of the second scene.)*

*Sombreron: (Suddenly lighted up.)* Who knocks on my door?

*Spirit:* It is the man, with the hallucinations born of his power.

*Father:* Did you sharpen the points of the flints well?

*Son:* Yes, and I sink them deep into the trunk, like leaves of knives.

*Father:* Then help me to crush the body of the Sombreron thoroughly. Push more on that side . . . like that . . . now inside . . . so it will fall heavily.

*Sombreron:* Ja, Jay! Grandfather Ah-Mucen-Cab, Man wishes to discover everything: what lies behind the sky's gourd and what is scattered and burning in the earth's heart . . . Let him watch his morrow and his yesterday, because the white corn is his corn, and the yellow-backed bean is his bean!

*Spirit:* Keep your rage behind your thought, and obey me. When the timeless trunk of Man falls, give an immortal cry so that they shall think you dead.

Now, to convince them, have the ants bear bits of your body on their shoulders, nails and hairs. *(The Sombreron fetches a long row of giant ants, tied by a cord: the ants will be almost as large as men.)*

*Sombreron:* And the earth about me shall tremble!

*Father:* Get your knife ready, son, and guard my back—the enchanter is going to die. Dig the ground until the hole is bigger. That's enough. . . . The trunk is slipping now . . . There it goes. *(The trunk falls like a battering-ram. Deep underground noises and the cry of The Sombreron.) (Pause.)*

*Father:* His death is certain . . . but this great silence. Son, put your ear to the ground and see what you can find out.

*Son:* Nothing, more than the silence. He must be dead now. *(Through the hollow of the tree the giant ants come out, bearing bits of the Sombreron.)*

*Father:* Be certain, son, be certain. *(Jubilant.)* The Sombreron is dead!

*Son:* Look: the ants are carrying off his body.

*Father:* What are your companions doing, my son?

*Son:* Father, they are in the woods looking for the tiger. "There is no tiger," they said.

*Father:* And at that moment, the tiger was prowling in front of them.

*(A curtain of smoke hides the stage. At once, darting out of the smoke, the Sombreron's mask grins silently.)*

## CURTAIN

# FRAGMENTARY STORIES

## Collapsing Cosmoses

*With H. P. Lovecraft [Portions in brackets written by Lovecraft]*

[Dam Bor glued each of his six eyes to the lenses of the cosmo-scope. His nasal tentacles were orange with fear, and his antennae buzzed hoarsely as he dictated his report to the operator behind him. "It has come!" he cried. "That blur in the ether can be nothing less than a fleet from outside the space-time continuum we know. Nothing like this has ever appeared before. It must be an enemy. Give the alarm to the Inter-Cosmic Chamber of Commerce. There's no time to lose—at this rate they'll be upon us in less than six centuries. Hak Ni must have a chance to get the fleet in action at once."

[I glanced up from the *Windy City Grab-Bag,* which had be-guiled my inactive peace-time days in the Super-Galactic Patrol. The handsome young vegetable, with whom I had shared my bowl of caterpillar custard since earliest infancy, and with whom I had been thrown out of every joint in the intra-dimensional city of Kas-tor-Ya,] had really a worried look upon his lavender face. After he had given the alarm we jumped on our ether-bikes and hastened across to the outer planet on which the Chamber held its sessions.

[Within the Great Council Chamber, which measured twenty-eight square feet (with quite a high ceiling), were gathered dele-gates from all the thirty-seven galaxies of our immediate universe. Oll Stof, President of the Chamber and representative of the Milli-ner's Soviet, raised his eyeless snout with dignity] and prepared to address the assembled multitude. He was a highly developed proto-zoan organism from Nov-Kas, and spoke by emitting alternate waves of heat and cold.

["Gentlemen," he radiated, "a terrible peril has come upon us, which I feel I must bring to your attention."

Everybody applauded riotously, as a wave of excitement rippled through the variegated audience; those who were handless slithering their tentacles together.

He continued: "Hak Ni, crawl upon the dais!"

There was a thunderous silence, during which a faint prompting was heard] from the dizzy summit of the platform. [Hak Ni, the yellow-furred and valorous commander of our ranks through numerous instalments, ascended to the towering peak inches above the floor.

"My friends—" he began, with an eloquent scraping of his posterior limbs, "these treasured walls and pillars shall not mourn on my account . . ." At this point, one of his numerous relatives cheered. "Well do I remember when . . ."

Oll Stof interrupted him.] "You have anticipated my thoughts and orders. Go forth and win for dear old Inter-Cosmic."

[Two paragraphs later found us soaring out past innumerable stars toward where a faint blur half a million light-years long marked the presence of the hated enemy, whom we had not seen. What monsters of malformed grotesqueness seethed out there among the moons of infinity, we really didn't know, but there was a malign menace in the glow that steadily increased until it spanned the entire heavens. Very soon we made out separate objects in the blur. Before all my horror-stricken vision-areas there spread an endless array of scissors-shaped space-ships of totally unfamiliar form.

Then from the direction of the enemy there came a terrifying sound, which I soon recognised as a hail and a challenge. An answering thrill crept through me as I met with uplifted antennae this threat of battle with a monstrous intrusion upon our fair system from unknown outside abysses.]

At the sound, [which was something like that of a rusty sewing-machine, only more horrible,] Hak Ni too raised his snout in defiance and radiated a masterful order to the captains of the fleet. Instantly the huge space-ships swung into battle formation, with only a hundred or two of them many light-years out of line.

(Unfinished)    (1935)

# The Last Prophecy

If the hill had risen above the Rhine or the Loire it would have borne a castle. It was lofty and wooded, commanding miles of countryside—a perfect place for fortification. Through the slow-changing middle ages Teutonic lords would have ruled from it, finding occasionally a coin or a broken jar from previous Roman encampments: before ever the Romans came, unknown and unarmed tribes would have struggled for its possession since the arrival of man in those regions. So long has every strategic site in Europe been steeped in blood. Rising not in Europe but in Northern California, on the Blake River, it had known only the Indians, who did not care to own it, and in the past two centuries a trickle of campers on holidays. Persons to whom a panorama of trees and hills endlessly by varied in shape and colour, ending everywhere in bright blue green haze of distance, rendered the hike worth while, walked the eight miles from the edge of Blakeville to its summit, but in all its history not 1000 persons had climbed it. This is conceivable only in a country of geometrically shaped states.

Although it had been named Mount Culebra by the 1774 exploring party which first mentioned it, the name was in a transition state, after being translated as Rattlesnake Mt.

Robert Jarvis had climbed it as much as anyone. There was no gymnasium in the small town to which he had returned from college, and so as to provide the exercise his clerical world never gave him, on Sunday mornings he would change into rough clothes, pocket the lunches his churchgoing landlady, had left in wax paper on the kitchen table, and set strenuously off. He was a hearty young man, a little vain about his muscles, and climbing simply to keep in trim, but the Breughel-like vistas framed now and again by the foliage on his ascent were not altogether wasted on him. The long rays of the sun over the lowlands and inlets and mounds that were in reality hills, the change from moment to moment in the quality of the light refracted by the mist, which at 4 o'clock was always beginning to come in from the ocean, the gathering forces of mystery first in the shadowing among the leaves and in the little dark thickets, and then among the larger trees and in whole glades until it came forth furtively and claimed the forest, the colour of the dusk when a moon below the horizon filtered up long rays like a fire in some abyss, the unfamiliar aspect of everything as he returned home by night, these sank into Jarvis without his being away and the banal books he read, the syndicate verse in the newspapers, took on from his experiences tones of richness it did not deserve.

He was pleased when he heard they were going to build a CCC camp on the summit of Rattlesnake Mt.: this would give him a definite destination on his walks. There was a trail ending in a sort of camp about half way up the less energetic had made this by driving their cars as far as possible. Now this was pushed ahead with additional ruts by the olive coloured trucks bearing lumber for the camp. and the addition of clay began. After it had been under way about two weeks, Jarvis visited the construction. He came at it through a back way, and emerging into the clearing they had made, perceived the yellow fragrant framework of a a barracks and a mess hall. Three men nearest him were digging a pit.

"How're you doing?" he asked. One looked up.

"Here's one of them Japanese spies already," he grinned to the others, "wanting to learn how our guns are placed."

This banter did not offend Jarvis, but he thought it odd. The place would be a good one for cannons at that, if there were anything to defend. "You better hang out a few signs," he retorted, "if you're setting this off as a military zone."

"Sure. Don't be in any hurry—remember this is a CCC project. Don't you read the Republican papers? Come back in a thousand years and we'll have it done."

Jarvis came back sooner, though he remembered the remark. By the autumn rains several buildings had been constructed and were inhabited. Some of the men were working on a bridle path to lead to Blakesville. He was told about this on his next visit and decided to follow it on his return. He stayed and talked about horses to one of the men in charge; learning that a riding academy was being moved down from Elliot in the spring. They discussed aspects of jumping until it was quite late; and then, although offered a bunk in view of the hour, he left and strode rather hastily away from the clearing.

The paths lead to unfamiliar points, and after a few minutes he glanced back to orient himself. He was surprised at the strangeness and glamour which a row of yellow lights provided. The small glaring bulbs, a mecca for insects, shone out upon bushes which at this hour were accustomed only to starlight. Now, although other parts of the forest showed cold and indistinct beneath the pallid dome of immensity, the crest of the hill was captured by man. Jarvis' heart gave a sudden twinge, as if he were about to remember something unhappy. He did not know whether it was at the persistence of men which sought to climb every height, or the smallness of the lights in the old darkness. He was not used to such feelings. None the less, the lights might have been there already for 1000 years. . . . He started, remembering the phrase the man with the shovel had used.

[. . .]

# [Untitled Story]

Pressing to the wall, though it was slimy enough, and populous with slugs, I watched the man. He had come in through a little gate hanging askew; in the shadow it had spoken rustily; and was now advancing by a course to avoid the moonlight. Though I couldn't have told him so, this was hardly necessary, what with the bush I stood behind, the obscurity of the place, and the fact he was necessarily [a] stranger to me. I had not been three days in the city.

He was a short man, and he carried a bulging parcel on the left shoulder. I thought it very unbusiness-like of him to be in that place, and sunrise three hours off, so I waited to see what he would do: whether he was merely delivering something—though as far as I could see the occupants of that place needed nothing. The meads and grasses, all of them disgustingly like seaweed, waited him too, and the whole place stopped decaying to peer at the man who had come too soon in their midst.

He put his package down, abruptly, by a tree which was making slow efforts to escape over the walls. In another fifty years it would be able to touch the street outside, at least. Then he began searching the headstones, or such as remained in that abandoned place. Without a light he figured out their legends very laboriously. Then giving these up, there was no choice but to come into the moonlight, and glancing up, as if to implore the planets, he scuttled to the tomb in the central plot.

It was a large monument, with two angels, or what I took to be angels, disputing over a vase. Once it had cost a great deal, and the birds had been fond of it for years. My visitor goggled at it a moment, leaning back with a great mouth anthropoid open, sizing it up, and trying to recognise it. Then he retrieved his bundle from the ____ surrounding the tree, and dumped it by the low and useless fence surrounding the monument. I wondered if it was meant to keep things out or in. Then I cursed as a slug, without warning, and not the warmest thing in that clammy place, reached tentatively for my hand. I said *"Bgah!!"*

Once I had stood so long by a gate watching the stars that a tom cat, out on some private negotiation, took me for part of the landscape, and after rearing and looking through the slats, bounded away to my very feet. Then he saw his mistake and was overcome. So was this man in the graveyard.

Once I'd said *"Bgah"*, there was no more conversation. He snatched up his bundle, found it an impediment, ran a complicated course through the headstones, tripping once, and was over the wall before I'd caught on.

# [Incomplete Story]

The old woman sucked in her withered lip and stared at the walls of Yarall-Yotl. It was thirty feet high, and was said to go far underground. Every angle which had once been in the grey stone was rounded, softened. A tiny lichen, which she knew to be red in the daylight, made the stones feel like the outside of a peach. But Yarral-Yotl was not soft. It had withstood a hundred assaults when the night was not quiet but jarred by screams and curses, and not dark but golden with scurrying torches. It was arrogant with its victories. For thirty generations the peasants of Baagl, the old woman's people, had grumbled and cursed the line of Yarall, squat conqueror out of a rugged eastern land, a broken hell of canyon and cliff, and the line of Yotl, the daughter of a southern lord. The old woman had cursed them, generation by generation, for she knew their geneaology with precision. Yarall-Yotl was constantly provoking wars—religious wars—with her neighbours. She was a stick in a hornet's nest, but her walks never sheltered the peasantry when great southern captains came riding up in fury at the infamy of her professions. The circle was the emblem on her standard: the circle which implied the lunar parentage of god; but the other barons with which implied the bore the leaf and the spider of orthodox belief. The prophesyings of Yarall-Yotl were another source of conflict.

The old woman was not thinking of these things. She was wondering how to get in. After night, unless these was a moon, the guards were forbidden to admit anyone. This had been the custom 323 years, since Lady Tutliuma had been murdered so curiously. However, it was a law often broken and the guards were fond of mushrooms. They respected her astounding ability to find them— she could smell them before they had burst through the ground.

She cocked her head at the sound of laughter from a gate twenty feet away. Someone was choking over his own wit. That augured well—at least they would not trip her up or pilfer from her basket.

She hobbled toward the guards, coming at them through the open space and with more noise than necessary.

"Good evening, Sirs," she panted asthmatically.

There were two of them, a dark heavy man called Domson who had consulted her secretly for herbs to overcome his shameful lack of virility, and a supercilious man with high cheekbones. Domson stopped laughing and seized his spear.

"Go back to the village. I can't let you in."

"I'm sure I wouldn't ask you to forget your duty to our noble lord and let me in even if I should ask you. It was just that I had these fine swamp-mushrooms spoiling my daughter brought home so many of them, and I thought you might like them."

Inasmuch as the climb from her hut outside the village was four miles, this generosity seemed improbable.

"Mushrooms?" said Domson.

"They're probably toadstools," suggested his companion.

The old lady recognised him as a young priest, one of the sect which lived under Yarall Yotl's protection. She chewed her lip.

"These are likewise those I set aside for the offering," she said.

## Hunter's Trophy

I cursed the dog for losing himself and me, since by that time the sound of my companions had died completely away. At first there had been a confusion of voices followed by crashing underbrush as they roused some covey. I'd not expected to be gone for more than a half hour. But Discobolus eluded me. From his first mystifying yelp I had been hard put to restrain him, and no sooner did I look the other way than he was off—lean body twisting through the brush with a speed none of us could equal. He had found a good many birds during the afternoon, and seemed losing interest when he heard or scented whatever it was drove him crazy. As I ran after him, struggling against the bushes, and one time jabbing my hand rather badly, his back moved up to a peculiar key, and in a moment it was only this back I had to follow, since the dog was running in tunnels through the grass.

It was all downhill, where the woods lead gradually into a bowl of swamp-grass, puddled with shallow water just then from a July rain. The ground was highly insecure, and my final glimpse of Discobolus showed him flinging himself from spongy isle to isle, smeared with mud but too eager in pursuit of his game to run round the edge. I had no choice—the grass clumps bowed down too far into the gulping swamp for me to use them, and the moments it took to get back to firmer footing lost me Discobolus.

I did not realize it of course but kept on, even though I did not know this territory. Whatever had got into the dog would make him hard to control, and in my half-amused annoyance I somehow forgot that I might just as easily lose myself as find him. . . .

The chase wound up a hill thick with bushes, a further delay which added to my annoyance. Sweat ran into my eyes and stuck my hair flat as if I had been under water, yet the more I hurried the fainter became that entranced and interminable yelp, till at last I knew he was gone. No chance now of catching him. With this realisation came a second and more unexpected one—for in addition to losing the dog, I had lost my companions. I stood still and called, in every direction, but save for the natural sounds of the forest, no response came to my ears. I had got thoroughly lost. There was no way to retrace the hundred-times varied route I had taken, and with no perceptible improvement of mood, I began a calmer, but aimless walk. The farmhouse where all of us stayed lay, I judged, somewhere to the west, and I hoped to reach it eventually by walking that direction. My watch said two fifteen: at four I called a halt.

Then I sat on a stone and wondered where my dog was. There was a tree behind me, part of a half-circular wall curving in upon the unexpected glade in which I had wandered, and for a moment their orderly spacing impressed me as almost deliberate—the work of some Johnny Appleseed who chose to play at making orderly a never-seen forest spot. All were oaks, incompletely surrounding a saucer-shaped declivity. The open side of this natural auditorium lay sloping in the first of a series of wide irregular steps—green close by, and successively brown, purple and grey as they moved to the western horizon. The sun lay low above the farthest hinterland, and shot its rays at a peculiar angle among my trees, so that long spoke-like shadows radiated outward.

Resting a while, I sat in these pleasant surroundings, a tired stupor excluding all but the most contemplative thoughts from my brain. It was curious that no farms could be seen in the extensive and largely treeless area which I commanded. Neither square of cultivation nor roof of any building broke the treeless dawn. A road, however, was discernible just at the edge of sight, whether paved or unpaved I could not tell. Some faint traces of golden dust hanging over it gave reason to think it was not. Apparently some vehicle had just gone by, so I was not altogether out of the world. Perhaps I had come on some private estate whose owner's whim was not to put it to any use . . .

I was conscious of its being late from the bustling departure of a bee which had clambered in and out of a nearby flowering bush since I first came [. . .]

## The Fugitives

Those of us who escaped made camp only when a mad weariness put an end to flight. We stood about the camp-fire and faces peered from the black to watch some who danced. Crimson leaped from the flames and twined among the watchers, but more kindly than fire. Perhaps there were twenty of us, yet we seemed fewer because of the silence. No one left the hot uneven circle of firelight, but many had stopped in the song: knowing other verses, yet they would not sing.

A young man danced, hot with fire and blood; and his sinewed torso was a thousand shapes of god and devil as he postured. Transcendent in the ecstasy of rude steps, he knelt one moment servilely; the next had flung himself up and to the side, like one who eludes a slaying arrow. All this time were deep voices, from the darkness; and the noise of music from simple instruments. The youth had ceased his agile pantomime when I turned from that close-gathered circle, and looked toward the plain.

A thousand feet away earth and heather were still and somewhat cold; they heeded no dancing, or the fires of men. The grass was thick, and sweet with tiny green blossoms, moving a little in the wind. It was not so dark but that a vast plain showed—a plain whose horizon was a black blot—an old plain. There were no trees in that expanse, whose stillness was akin to the oceans' if one went but a little way from his fellows; there were no paths. Yet far out was outlined an enormous ruin, shattered and no longer bearing a name, though it must once have had a name. This was huddled lonesome in the moonlight, like all man's things; which cannot seem other than frail in that cruel illumination; and it was nearly two miles distant. We had seen it when we made our camp, passing in the naked world among serene mountains. Now one of us had gone to it; because it is tiring to flee for twelve weeks, and yet fear that unwonted steps are about. Now, of a sudden, I had a wish to see this pile of which no rumor had been in all the records of the Tower; and I would see it that night, but it was dark and chill ahead, and a lone man sees things in the darkness if he is given to thinking of death. I called to my friend where he sat among those singing. He came to me, wondering, and when I told him of the desire that was near to a compulsion, seemed to wish that I should not go, or if I would, to go by dawn and return in time for eating. Yet when I said that some finger stirred me, he understood.

We stepped into the night, finding the wind chill but exhilarating, and began to stride over the ground. I had cut ten-inch-thick bones and bitten the heads from little beasts to cook. Thus armed, and young, with young men's muscles, we had survived the long flight. Oroom, my friend, conversed with me as we strode, feeling something of relief in abandoning our companions. I asked if he did think we could ever find a Tower anywhere, and he said that as I knew, no other Tower had sent messages for many hundred years. But I made out to be hopeful, suggesting that we might find a whole world, and people, across this plain. Then our spirits were a little raised, and walking became poetry, as it gave new blood to the heart like some ballad of triumphant wars. I was pleased, and my friend, to hasten in the phantom starlight. It shaped thoughts of which I cannot tell: I felt that it was good to be thus, and yet I would ever think of the doomed place we fled, and of the small planets watching, and of the ruins which no longer had a name; so that my pleasure was half dolour. My friend was also touched by this emotion, so that for a little we were silent, and then together began speaking of food and the small things of life. I hoped that a night-bird would cry, but only the grasses had a song, and their song was too old to like or understand. Somehow, our speech crept ever to the stars, and death, for these are linked in a secret way. Though stars are wonderfully mysterious, the necklaces of gods, they are also dead men's bones astrewn to frighten men who are not bold. Do not kneel to them, for they are eager to slay.

A distance with a friend is short, and presently we crept alongside the ruin like roaches at food on a table. The pillars wore only a tattered roof: the mass of it had fallen in, and blocks too large to climb were strewn below. Three vast columns stood complete, but others were jagged and broken off, with all the edges rubbed smooth with years. Earth had klnown a thousand winters, and the sea moved in its bed since this place was whole, and its emptiness was no new thing. Is man great or weak because he passes before those things which he has made? Its masons had been earth and wind a span of centuries, yet three pillars stood, and there was a little roof. Moonlight altered and moved with the chords, showing time's destruction; and suddenly we felt that fires and dancing were a reassurance.

[. . .]

*October 1, 1936*

# The Burrow

Written for H. P. Lovecraft's birthday: Aug. 1937

Dear Howard:

Although by common standards the tale is unsavoury, yet it has but a single aim, and that aim is to divert you. Often products of my dabbler's pen seem to have accomplished this which was, after all, the cause of their existence; and now, I am merely being honest in advance about this fact. If the story is worthless, then I have merely wasted a considerable amount of paper, for which I ask forgiveness.

R H B

The horror in the fields and the earth is greater than the horror in cities, however nauseously decayed those are, or submerged in the accumulation of reeking centuries. An untouched forest can spawn of itself such noxious things as a dozen generations of slum-dwellers do not create. For the loathsome things of cities are physical: disease and misery and black hopelessness roam along wet alleys, but these things are less terrible than the cosmic terror which seizes on our minds when nature is violated by her own act. Ghostly and repellent things are natural in man, whose decaying race has gone into cities to die, but the forest should not produce monstrosities.

## Argument

Clayton Singer, a poor white of north Florida, having got a child by his daughter, drives her out, accusing another. In the swamp, she discovers the burrow, and is mated to the burrowers, after her child is born dead. She has another child, slays it, and flees to Julian Marks, a sportsman who has been kind to her.

## [Outline]

I:    Mrs. Paul: the store
II:   Clayton: his family: Emily: abuse of Em: hunting agreement
III:  Mrs. Paul, on neighborhood traits, the Singers in particular
IV:  The wounded deer: Clayton's reticence: Julian to home puzzled
V:   Julian asks after Em, is put off. An odd skeleton—Clayton's reticence
VI:  (Lapse of time) Em comes to Julian. Her story. Her vanishing. Destruction of Singer shanty and vanishing of Singers. His speculations.

## The Burrow

### I

In certain portions of the South things have been bad for a long time. The War did not do it, nor Reconstruction. What has taken place there—the physical decay and spiritual inversion of normal stock—was guided by the very nature of the land. No person can be blamed—and no specific circumstance. Certain families have always been segregated by swamps and pine-woods. They were alone in the beginning, and that had something to do with it. People too much apart from the rest of life are very likely to go odd, just as neglected plants grow back to weeds, or produce malformed blossoms on wizened stalks. At any rate, these families and their dirty shacks rising all alone by the swamp and pine-woods are no new thing. They seem now, having stood for half a century, always rotting and yet never falling, to be a growth of the dangerously fertile land, like the grey, shining-leaved swamp-oaks about the houses.

To a northern eye, the landscape is exotic, for instead of the familiar trees—maple, walnut, and elm, one finds the lean pine hung with parasitic moss; the palm, and in hot damp glades, the cypress, whose dead-looking trunk slides up grey and naked into the woven forest roof. These, of course, are rooted in a mud too unstable for the foundations of careless shanties, but they form a jungle background for such miserable erections, and among them snakes and alligators sleep evilly.

In the spring of 1931 Julian Marks, a young teacher from the state college, and something of a sportsman, desired a place for the months of April and May, so that he might hunt whatever quail, rabbits, or infrequent deer the neighborhood afforded. He learned from a friend of the incongruous house—furnished with a private lighting system—built as a hunting lodge by a retired merchant, thirty-eight miles from the city. This place was not much in use, and the owner desired an occupant who was willing to discourage thievery in return for an absence of rent. It was essential that the house be occupied, but its isolation made tenants difficult to find. Since Julian wished to spend his vacation away from everything of the city, an arrangement was made whereby he should have the place.

There was a sort of community four miles away; at least, mail came there on Tuesdays and Fridays, and the natives could buy necessities such as plug-tobacco, green liquor, and flour. A repellently obese woman was postmistress and store keeper, and since Julian had been decided in his amenities, he made a point of seeing her and buying some few goods, so soon as he was moved in. His luggage being sparse, it did not take long to oil and inspect the guns, and go over the house, which was large. There were canned goods in the kitchen, and tins of milk left in the zinc-lined ice box by his predecessors, gone only a few hours. He noted the requirements, and locking the door, set off on a walk of four miles to call on the presiding harridan, but ostensibly to buy fresh bread. Failing in the latter, he did spend the required time in gossip with Mrs. Paul, whose benign leers were singularly disturbing.

When Julian swung back the patched screen and entered her rough-planked store, she was leaning heavily on a counter, scrawling in a ledger with the stub of a pencil clenched in her puffy hand. She looked up, grinning professionally, and pushed herself into the vertical, inserting the pencil in her hair, and rubbing greasy palms on an equally greasy apron. There were signs about the place. Uneven letters on a background of grey cardboard announced NO CREDIT PLEASE DONT ASK FOR IT.

"Good morning, Sir, what would you like?" she enquired, through obviously removable teeth. These fitted only approximately, and since she kept them together her speech, filtering them, seemed odd. She came very near lisping.

Mrs. Paul dyed her hair, since it was normally a dirty yellow too streaked for bleaching into the dignity of white; but she was unpunctual about this, as she was untidy in keeping clean aprons, and the coarse strands bunched up in back where like old corn-silk. Her red eyes behind the crooked glasses-frames were damp from working at the book: she saw only a part of things. In an effort now to inspect Julian without seeming to stare, she peered uncertainly at his dark figure.

She was unable to place him, and wondered who he was. Not one of the men from the logging-camp—his clothes were too neat. She was aware of her own appearance and pushed at the dingy hair by her left ear, squirmed obscurely inside the cotton dress.

He asked for bread (which she produced in a torn wrapper, apologizing) and planted a conversational lead. "The pantry was pretty low when I got in." She lifted her face up to look under the lenses, dexterously thumping the bread into a sack. "Oh, you must be the gentleman who's took the big house. Pleased to meet you." And she exposed the insecure teeth, just as if they were meeting under the gaze of a hostess.

"Why yes, I am: you're Mrs. Paul, aren't you?"

"Yeth." She beamed the word coyly, as if it held a private, slightly amusing secret; and then clamped her lips decisively.

"Mr. X spoke of you," he observed. At this, she waddled toward him, proffering the bread somewhat as one might thrust a weapon into an enemy, and spread herself amply on the counter, ready for a nice talk. Her red fishy hands, her calloused elbows and shaking forearms all seemed made of suet, and she had large shapeless breasts stuffed down her dress-front.

"Oh, we *like* him. He's such a nice man. I suppose you're going to stay in his place till he comes back?"

No, Julian replied—only for a time. Mr. X wasn't coming until fall.

She continued to sound praise of Mr. X (without citing any especial instance of his charm) until Julian was certain that she didn't mean any of it. Experimentally, he dropped a hint of derogation, and she snatched at the bait.

"Of course, I don't mean to be saying anything against him, but he is kind of superior about us who works—maybe that's because he's got so much money, but I always feel that *a man ought to work or he's no good.*"

After that, they got along nicely. When he had stayed for the length of time demanded by sociability, learned about Mrs. Paul's unfortunate sister in Chicago, and the troubles of tending a store where charge-accounts were a hazard; and that Mrs. Paul was a Christian Scientist (who excused her approaching death from over-eating and diabetes), Julian asked if someone could show him where hunting was best.

"There's Clayton Singer. He lives back of the swamp, about two miles from you, but you'll have to go around. He's guide for Mr. Merrill sometimes. He'd help you. It's six miles by the road, but you won't have any bad places to get through. Nobody's ever put a road through the swamp. It's called Jordan's swamp."

## II

Clayton was discovered washing at a pump standing twenty feet from the privy. He made a great deal of noise with the creaking handle, and did not see the approaching stranger. Several of the children, like himself, lean and dirty, eyed Julian timidly, retreating into the house as he entered the roughly-defined clearing. The house itself, dark and collapsing, was outrageously filthy. Garbage littered the decaying steps, a hound with large fly-plagued sores lay indolently before the rusted screen door, and grey barren sand poured up to the edge of the rickety porch, scuffed over in a dozen places. After a moment, their mother joined them at a smudged window holding one pane of warped glass. Their actions were furtive, like those of animals unused to man, and their cautious inspection from indoors was tinged with fear.

But if they were unnaturally retiring, Clayton was not. He turned and faced the caller in belligerent silence. Julian greeted him and spoke.

"You're Mr. Singer, I think: they told me at the store that you knew these woods pretty well: I wonder if you'd show me the ropes. I'm down at Merrill's for a couple of months."

Clayton advanced, eyeing him. He answered slowly, perhaps thinking Julian some inquisitive man of law, come in search of evidence on his motley lawlessness. "Why, sure, I guess so: but it'll cost you something: I get $1.50 from Merrill, by the day."

Although Clayton shaved when he was going to Mrs. Paul's, his angular jaw was rough with short bristles. Water and sweat glistened on his dark face; his upper body was naked, and the ribbon-frayed shirt hung over the pump. He spat between decayed teeth, and panted slightly from the exertion of pumping. Usually he spoke through a battered pipe, which never seemed to burn, though now he had removed this with insolent deference. The man's whole attitude was odd: clearly he wished a job—or at least, the money, but his lids were tightened beneath suspicious brows. He spoke with a tense bravado or defiance, almost boorishly, as if ready-lipped with lies in answer to whatever questions he feared. Certainly, he did seem expectant of questioning—and resentful in advance.

Julian was puzzled to know what the man expected. Thievery and bootlegging he was doubtless guilty of; but these were commonplaces in such a district—had the man some more sinister guilt plaguing him? It was not Julian's concern, whatever it might be, and since he really wished a guide, he tried to conciliate the sullen prospect.

He succeeded in this, and it was arranged that they should go out for quail at six in the morning. He paid Clayton, as a clincher for the bargain, and asked if they were to hunt in the swamp. At this, Clayton considered, pulling audibly on his disreputable pipe, answering, "There's no hunting there, and hasn't been for a couple of years."

"Game killed off? How?"

"There was a storm from hill to breakfast in '26, and lightning struck all over the place. There was dead animals till you could smell 'em clear out here. I went in afterwards, and saw them myself. I guess those that wasn't killed all pulled out."

Curious about this episode, Julian would have remained on the subject, but a lanky flat-chested girl of twelve came timidly down from the porch and addressed her father. "Mom wants you to ask the man if he'd like her to do washing." Apparently there had been espionage. Clayton turned and glared at her. "Get the hell out of here when I got business." Julian spoke hastily, "I'll see you afterward about that. I think I have something for her," and the girl sidled away, showing neither surprise nor resentment.

The young man was annoyed by Singer's attitude toward the girl, but realizing the half barbaric relationships prevailing in such lost corners of the South, he did not say anything. In the Singer family, as in a dozen others scattered ten miles around, wife and children were submissive parasites, tolerated only insofar as they were useful to him. Mrs. Singer had grown shyer than a beetle under a log, as her flight to hiding showed. Em was not yet terrified into self-effacement, while the younger children were either abysmally afraid of their father, or callous with quiet defiance. What Julian found strangest was everyone's acceptance of these relationships, as if no other way could possibly exist. Resignation seemed to his incredulous young mind the ultimate vice.

What Emily, the lean ignorant child of that abominable father, saw beyond Jordan's swamp will remain uncertain. The story she told cannot be true. She came that evening like a starved and tormented animal, to Julian where he sat polishing his rifle. It was close to night, and his gaze lifting from the obscure, dim-gleaming metal, turned in surprise to the girl.

"Oh, please—" she moaned, and left the words uncompleted, whether from weariness or fright he did not know. "Oh, please—"

She continued trembling even when they were in the kitchen, and the door locked at her behest. The child was unable to speak connectedly, but evaded Julian's troubled questions with curious whimpering sounds. Obviously, a great fear held her, though she did not seem afraid of him. Her actions were planless, she edged into a large wooden chair, and sat upon it for a time, with something odd in her eyes. Her dress was unbelievably torn and soiled— a rag encrusted with the dirt of weeks, and mud was caked in the stringy black hair. She ate greedily of the cold oatmeal left from breakfast, despite his protests. Upon perceiving her hunger, he searched out other food, which she took, though she finished the oatmeal first.

Julian was baffled. The condition of her clothes, this wild hunger, showed that Em had been wandering an unknown length of time, somewhere in the woods. How long, though, could she have been lost? Nothing of such an event had reached Mrs. Paul: he had been there on the previous day. Yet the girl had certainly been lost for a long while. What had she lived on, and where had she slept? Could that beast Clayton have ignored her absence, as if she were a strayed animal? Lack of interest in his brood amounted almost to callousness, but Julian was unable to credit this suspicion, which was only shaped like a dim recollection of an unpleasant thing.

The fear in Em's eyes: that was a thing as cold as the gulf in which the universes hang, and yet somehow afire with strange wisdom. It was not a mortal terror, however extended such a terror might become through war or torture or the knowledge of death: it was a new thing born of some new and uncomprehended experience. When she turned at his continued words, and looked at him, her grimy face—too thin for a child's, too immature for a woman's—fell back before the intensity of that dark gaze. The winking of her lids rendered only more terrible the intermittent fear. Julian did not like her gaze, or the drawn, quiet lips, slightly crusted with food and dirt. It was too calm to permit any belief of madness. Whatever her experience, its purport had gone far past that. Privation and excesses of fatigue were in that face and in that trembling body, but Em was sane. Julian felt a vague terror at her sanity . . .

"Good God, Em: what's happened? Can't you tell me?" His voice, directed at the quiet figure, vibrated aimlessly. He might have been alone. Words have a goal: they are futile and somehow grotesque when spoken aloud to an empty room. "What is it you're afraid of? You're safe, now: I've locked the door, and the windows. And there's this . . ." He pointed to the gun, flung hastily aside when they had entered.

She did not answer, though after a moment she turned her eyes to him again, and looked fixedly into his face. Sensitive to the quick contagion of fear, he was possessed by an uneasy doubt. Were they alone? What moved in the dark house, or beyond the windows? Day had vanished, and the ensuing dusk might harbour anything. Fear building upon fear, Julian caught himself listening for sounds above the child's uneven pant, and watching for motions not hers or his. The animal equipment which man retains latently seemed abruptly keen: aware and ready . . . Ready? For what thing was he ready?

Julian only shook his head a little, but within, he fought the senses roused by Em's manifest terror. A lost child, dirty and ragged, was giving him too much of a start; and what had likely come from a glimpsed bear, or merely from exposure to the marshes and woods, was serving as base for towering wild fantasies! Dulness is not unpleasant: the mind that is not attuned to dulcet chords of pleasure is likewise free of fear's cacophony. Reasoning with himself as a logical man must now and then reason, if in evasion, Julian drove back the dark bungling steps of horror which had begun to sound within him like the tread of coffin-laden figures on a rotten stair.

Em spoke, paying no heed to his exhorting. She spoke quite rapidly, as if rehearsing words to appease her father or some other dreaded authority. Possibly her tired voice merely took over the reeling torrent of thought—possibly, whatever lay behind that gaze was too fierce to be held back. She did not, however, address Julian, or take any heed of him.

When papa saw I had to go, I was scared. He had been shouting at me, and he hit me on the mouth four times because I cried and said I didn't want to go. I said I loved him and mother, but I didn't. Sometimes I loved mother, but I never loved him. He kept on shouting like he was drunk and we didn't have no tables or chairs 'cepting the boxes so's I c'd get away from him, and mother came in scared too and asked what I done he was so mad about. He shouted at her too, and maybe he was going to hit her because she moved away. He shouted "None of your fucking business: I gotta right to punish these goddamn bastards; they're mine, ain't they?" And he went over and squinted up his eyes, looking down at her till she kind of smiled. I didn't like her to smile that way even if she was scared. I didn't like it, somehow it made me curl all up inside, but I guess I would have smiled too. And he said "Goddamn it, I gotta right to make this little bitch get out." He meant me. Mother said, low, "Don't call her a bitch, she ain't, and that's wrong to say." He jerked his head like he was going to spit on her, and said "She is a bitch, and you're a goddamn bitch yourself."

Em paused, and moving her lips in a vague twitch, resumed the toneless narrative.

"I didn't like to hear him call my mother a bitch, and I guess I tried to hit him. I wouldn't have but I was so scared. He grabbed my arm and held it so it hurt, and said, 'There, by Jesus, that settles it.' And he told me to get out and he didn't care if I went and lived with a nigger, or died and rotted out in Jordan's swamp that's out behind our house. Mother was crying too, and begging him to let me alone and asking what was it I'd done. 'It's not her,' she kept saying, 'it's just that you've had too much likker. Just let her alone, or whip her like you always done. You'll be sorry tomorrow if you make her stay out tonight.' Then he laughed a funny kind of laugh, like he was watching a snake and a frog, and said it wasn't only tonight. Then she said, 'Oh, God, Clayton, you ain't going to send her out there?' And he said yes. I didn't know what she meant, but papa did. She twisted her face and said, 'Oh God, they've made a new opening,' and then he did hit her, and said 'Goddamn it, keep your Goddam mouth shut. The bitch is gonna have a child.' But he didn't say it was his, and I was ashamed, even if he made me do it."

Em hesitated, her thoughts arranging themselves into a pattern, the lines of which she resumed. Her fists were bones spaded off with hollows, and she clenched them. Julian stood by the table listening. When she broke off, he was afraid that silence again bound her, but it was not so. She continued, her gaze going somewhere beyond the yellow plaster and the gleaming kitchen fixtures, which matched a tan linoleum. He traced the floor design abstractly: three curves, and a large curve, set off by a dot, which led again . . . But it was only his eyes that did this as he listened.

It was a tale of considerable length and he wondered at times how even Em could speak so long in her condition. Her normal strength, torn down by exposure and ill-nourishment, was replaced by a tense fire of nervousness. Although she trembled like a bowstring old and brittle and ready to snap, her toneless words flowed on.

She had gone into the woods, whether in flight, or under compulsion he did not gather. Apparently he rather made no further resistance on learn[ing] Em's condition. Likely, the child did not intend to go far—she had been in Jordan's swamp when the men were getting out cypress logs, and she knew how vast an area was claimed by struggling intermeshed vegetation above the quaking ground. From the squalid house, more offensive in its decay than a rotten tree because it was less natural, she had known but a single

aspect of the jungle outline. When she had gone on a previous day
to the clearing where logs were dragged after precarious felling, she
had seen another phase—it was then no longer a tangle of untouched cypresses, but the source of lumber for an avid mill. The
ancient trees, whose shafts had thrust themselves into the light and
struggled with their limbs as with their burrowing roots, had met
an adversary with metal teeth. Men brought the saw into the silent
battlefield, and the trees were stricken foe and erstwhile foe. The
violent battle of the trees makes no sound, but its turbulence is no
less than that of other battles. The keenest struggle is not always
that which is heard or seen. Em had perceived, as she stood by the
sweating workers, that their part was incidental to the forest strife.
The trees had contended for soil and light before there was any
man: man's harryings would end that long contention. Cut and fell
them he might, and sacrifice their bodies to the greedy mill, but afterward growth was theirs again. Even as a tree is an older thing
than a man, and its separate years of life twice the number of his, so
is the jungle older. The elements are wine to it, heat fecundates the
buried roots, and slender new things are sent up by exploring parent trees: the rain is a delirium of joy, and the wind a welcome
thing, as each man knows who has seen trees in the wind. The forest is older, as becomes a dominant form of life, and fire and lightning, which are greater than human tools, cannot destroy it. A
young tree may fall before steel weapons, but a hundred others lie
dormant in the soil, roused by its death into contention for the spot
it occupied. No more than wind does the jungle take heed of in-
truding man, and for no great space will it grieve his vanishment.

Em felt something of this when she fled into the edge of the
advacing pines. They were stiff and with an alien dignity, and bare
for three-quarters of their height. Only the high branches, near the
sky, had burst forth in clusters of green lances. It was ill-advised
that Em should try to hide her wet eyes and fearful, contorted face
in such a trackless place, but for three-quarters of an hour she ran
aimlessly, tripping over roots, and scrambling on in awkward flight,

so great was her shame and humiliation before the stinging gaze of her father. His malicious stare, only half sane, was intolerable to remember: she knew that his action was cruelly unjustified, and wept fresh sticky tears in a paroxysm of impotent hate as she realized her position. If something in his physical domination had not made her flanks and shoulders contract in repugnance, she had a wild wish to defy him: scream in his lean face and beat against his oblique will like a thing seeking escape from a trap. Though [what] he had done was by his will only, his nearness made her seethe with humiliation, and she knew that no defiance would have been possible. There was no refuge but flight, and since no person had ever given heed to the wretched child, it did not occur to Em to look for help at a neighbor. There was in any event no home closer than Julian's, and one night at least of wandering was destined.

Em realized this when the channels of tears were exhausted and her blood a hot wave that beat drum-like within her. At that time she was not lost, despite the aimless nature of her course. She had been all through these pine and clumps of dwarf oaks, many times with her sister. Sometimes they had let Richard follow them, and then frightened him by disappearing. He always ran around like a boy in the damp, and cried something terrible till they would show themselves, she recalled, realizing in a flash the peculiar horror of abandonment. Maybe she was as big a coward as Richard when she was alone out there. Considering this, Em sat down upon a dead tree, black with charcoal from the August fires, and let her swirling pulses quiet. In a while, she did not shudder except when she thought of her father.

Em did not know the woods as Clayton did. For thirty-five years he had lived in a succession of hovels surrounded by swamp and forest; and through hunting and bootlegging he came to a deep familiarity with every sand-rut, deer path, and alligator wallow throughout a wide area. His grandfather had been a Seminole,— renegade descendant of that miscellaneous tribe—who did not care for cities because of certain deeds for which he was responsible,

back in the early 80's. At the side of this crafty old man Clayton
hunted and killed and explored strange swamps alive with Druidic
boles, till he knew the topography as well as any animal. Particularly, he knew Jordan's swamp.

If his rat-faced wife, eternally fidgeting with damp red hands at
her cotton, beltless dress, knew what interest Clayton had in Jordan's swamp, she kept it in her dark, tormented mind. Likely he
had a still, Mrs. Paul believed, and spread her belief rather widely.
He said that it was hunting took him there so often. It couldn't be a
woman, because the Singer house alone had been made so close to
the swamp.

[...]

*January 30, 1937*

# The Daughters of Darkness

## I

She was a young Indian woman, taller than most of them, and
more delicately built. When she saw me approaching, she stopped
and waited by the road. I wondered if she wanted to sell me idols—
the barefoot villagers about Cuzco manufactured them in quantities; always keeping a basketful hung on one arm as if they were hot
chestnuts, to sell to the tourists. But this girl wore shoes, Oxfords,
which were the most un-Indian trait of all. The deep scarlet poncho
drawn about her was like a flame against the endless green of the
valley slopes.

Given a choice between what was not starvation, but was certainly discomfort, as a student of engineering in Chicago; and wal-
lowing prosperity offset by boredom in the household by my
Peruvian uncle (a man devoted to the history of his land and the
collecting of ten thousand pots and jugs from the groves of its early
inhabitants) I had chosen the latter course, redeemed my only coat
and watch from the other "Uncle", who seemed about to require

them for good, picked up my books, and began to practice my Spanish irregular verbs. The bargain was that I should superintend his household and properties for a period of three years while he filled a very decorative office created for him by the latest resolution, to which he had contributed funds. Faced with numerous absences from his semi-baronial home, and with some feeling of responsibility for his exemplary but unprosperous nephew, he had solved both problems at once. A week after arriving, I had begun to explore the mountain roads leading from the backwater of conglomerate wreckage which was Cuzco. On one of these trips I met the woman.

The road behind her twisted around a steep sided hill given all over with uniform plants. There was no end to such hills—they jutted and swerved and pressed and sloped into one another for miles, for hundreds of miles, and most of them were the half-seen fists of the higher Andes clenched in chill hatred against the bonds of the mist. She said to me, not in the tribal tongue, "I am sorry—it is so stupid of me—but can you tell me where we are?"

It amused me that an Indian, brought up in the streetless wild, should ask a green American for directions. "This is a new approach," I thought, saying, "A little north-east of Cuzco." She gave me the obscure grin of her race. "And where is the northern highway?" Here I was baffled. What highway? "All I know is a road, like this which you must have passed a while back," I said. "Was that it?" "No, the highway with the resting-fort," she said, troubled.

I hesitated a moment, not sure I had identified the words correctly—my boyhood Spanish was not very limber. And I noticed that she spoke a rather curious dialect which I attributed to the influence of her native Quichuan. "There is no highway," I stated, unfolding my map. She advanced a step, peered at it with a flash of cat-like interest, and then withdrew. She replied carefully and formally.

"It has been some years since I was here. Has the viceroy allowed it to decay?"

The word viceroy was incredibly quaint. Did the hundred-year independence of Peru fail to percolate through to the aboriginal folk with their lives as steady as stones? She watched me and said rapidly, "The Presidente must have allowed it to decay. Thank you. I shall go another way." And turning her back she walked rapidly in the direction from which she had come. More than a little curious, I watched her and to allow a graceful interval to elapse before following her, I turned my attention to the skies, which—as is usual at such heights—were cloudless and mirror-like. Some bird darted across the edge of my vision. I thought momently it might have been an aeroplane, but hearing no sound, decided not.

When I went on, and came to the foot of the steep hill, although the length of a treeless valley was revealed to me, there was no trace of the woman.

## II

At dinner, which began at nine o'clock, my uncle diverted the conversation from the business matters we had discussed on previous evenings, and told me something of the history of the house. This was a many-roomed edifice of two stories built about a courtyard, and stood on the edge of Cuzco in pretentious and draughty decay. In the days of Don Fernando Avilés y Garcia, illiterate but ferocious partisan of Pizarro, scourge of the Indians, so massive and extensive a building was needful, not only to establish his line as eminent but to shut out the incessant wrath of the conquered—a wrath which they carried like obsidian knives secret[ed] under their ponchos. Each blow of the whip on Indian flesh, each new chain welded on ankles that had wandered the hills, sent a ripple of widening resentment through the brooding swarms, and a torturing in ...... was known in [_____] by nightfall. Don Fernando, whose wealth derived from the sacking of the fourth most important temple in Cuzco, whose brutal humor it had been to set fire to the hair of the sacred mummies from [_____] arranged as torches at a feast of a dozen meats and twice that many wines, had more reason than a desire to impress his companions and successors when he designed those walls, observed my uncle. The disgraceful affair which had caused our ancestor to remain in Cuzco, instead of going to the new coastal city of Lima, then being built, was well known; but less well known was the fact that his house was built on the site of the temple he had looted. It was even possible that the stone-lined pit which held my uncle's fine sherries was a part of the destroyed building which had survived unchanged.

Mention of his sherries led him to pour me another glass of the sunset-tawny beverage, for which I would have given any mummy, even my grandmother's, and at the same time set me wondering at the richness of spoils which could endow twelve generations and still provide such high prosperity as we were enjoying. The flower-woven lace of the table, the ponderous silver plates burnished by the fire near which we sat, the chests and sideboards ranged massively in the gloom, the unobtrusive servants whose skill in preparing and serving meals made up for their lack of American punctuality. Don Fernando may have been the bane of his antiquity-fancying descendant, but he had done lavishly by him otherwise! The constant sipping of my sherry and the constant filling of the glass by my uncle—both things unnoticed by me—had put me in a mood of benediction, and if I had dreamed that night of the goateed Andalusian desecrator I should have smiled on him. As it happens, I dreamed of something else, which will appear later in this account.

"Did you find any new ruins for me on your walk up the valley?" my uncle asked.

"No—I thought you had them all catalogued," I chuckled. Then I remembered the Indian girl. "But either there's something wrong about my guide book, or I met a flirtatious Indian wench." And I told him about the road. His brows snapped up, and he gave a kind of surprised squeak. "They have long memories. She was in the right place, but the wrong time. There was a road there some time ago—400 years ago, approximately—but I've never been able to find it. It was part of the Inca highway system which I regret to say our legislators have never duplicated. Runners used to relay messages from Ecuador clear down into the Argentines." He paused, dreaming of lone figures companioned by the wind along crests and valleys where no houses had ever been, through darkness the gods feared, over anonymous chasms and at the base of stone heights like huddled mummies with heads askew and idiotically agape.

After a time he spoke. "If she'd been about sixty years old, I might know something about her. It was rather odd," he went on, "last spring we had terrific rains up in the hills, and everything that wasn't above ground filled up overnight. My cellar was a mess, and the boys practically had to dive in under to rescue the brandies, and all the cobwebs that I'd been nurturing for years went in one swoop. I was more pained over that than over the patching we had to do afterward. It takes a lot to budge this old stonework—there have been five earthquakes in the past year, and not a stone displaced, but the water must have shifted the pressure of dirt behind the walls, because the first thing I saw when they called me was the top row of the east wall dumped in quite neatly. Fortunately, only a couple of cases of sauterne were under it—they made enough of a mess, as we could see when the place dried up.

"What we found was worth a great deal more to me. Behind the damaged wall was another, earlier one that had been sealed up a long while—perhaps since the Conquest. It was fitted together of larger stones, and the part that showed had the corner of a design engraved on it. You can imagine how long I waited to tear off the rest of the outer wall."

"When we finally got it out, it was about the size of that," he said, waving toward a yard-square mirror which brightened the prevalent gloom beyond the fire's scope. "I've sent it to Lima, so I can't show it to you. It was sandstone, as thick as a ham, and about the same colour, with the background cut away to leave the figure and inscription in relief. It was a skull-headed god sitting on a bench, staring forward with its knees spread wide and elbows resting on them, and it held in its left hand at shoulder height an unornamented disc. Crowding against this was the inscription—a sort of cartouche of three or four symbols which meant nothing to me. The right arm was drawn across the bosom. There was a general symmetry, except for the variation in arm-positions, about the figure's position, and the sandalled feet were twisted sidewise with heels touching, in order to make them fit the square. Well, that's as much as I can say about its appearance, except that it seemed to be female—I'm not too sure—but impressions it produced are less describable. Perhaps it was the absence of eyes, which seemed to have been burned out through eons of staring on the night and the sleet of suns blown across it—perhaps it was the death's head set gruesomely on the thick-limbed torso, which was as sensuous as so conventionalised an art can create. It was in no recognisable style of carving, but seemed to antedate them all. I felt like a man who has gone fishing for sea-bass and caught the tentacle, but the tentacle only, of some creature under the surf, and dragged it up severed on the beach while the monster remains unknown. There are so many pasts to this land, and the links between them are so doubtful.

"Well, I hadn't had the thing a day when the woman came. She was short and dark and dirty, and stood on her bare feet like a pyramid. She had the usual pancake hat and shawl, with a boy hanging from the belt embedded in her expansive middle—and she came up to me grinning as confident as an old whore. It was in the library; I was picking out some books to take with me, and I still don't know how she let herself in, or where she ever got the courage to. She seemed quite at home parked on my carpet, although it was very likely the first time she'd ever been on any floor but clay or stone.

"'There is a stone with a picture on it,' she said unhesitatingly. Thinking she was offering me a specimen, I said I would like to see it.

"'You see it plenty,' she leered. 'I do not sell; I buy.'

"To discover a companion collector in this grimy old llama was a little unbelievable. 'Did Rosa tell you about it?'

"She shook her head, and with dogged directness opened the sack at her belt. It was full of gold pieces. 'You have many stones. Sell me this one.'

"The idea occurring to me that she might know something about it through those secret rivulets of legend the Church has never been able to dam up, I hesitated to refuse outright. The stone remains in the cellar wall. I would take her to it, and at least find out why she wanted it, [. . .]

# POETRY

## Poems 1934–1939

### Strife

The crimson blood-flecked orchid
Lifts its eyeless head, unsated from the feast
Of mangled flesh, and rears soft tentacles
Like wiry traps wherein to slay
The fair-haired man who nears its lair unknowing.
An hundred creepers, hairy-barbed,
Steal forth unto their prey; and rasp
His naked flesh. With scarce more terror than surprise
He strikes a double-bladed sword
Upon the clutching tentacles, and wounds
The red and noisome arm that spurts
Fresh blood upon his tunic. Nor is the creature
Vanquished, though its severed limbs
Lies awkwardly askew.
Again it clutches, brokenly, and finds
A grasp about its prey. The furry creepers
Twist and bind him while he strives
To hack the pulpy horror from its hold
And failing, tear with maddened haste
His sanguine body from the plant.
And as the dying man expires, blood
Both greenish-brown and human
Mingle on the ground.

*[April 1934]*

## To W——

Dark evil night of ecstasy
When first I know the honeyed sin
And burning, foul delights of thee!
The pallor of the myriad stars
In jeweled constellations dim
And coldly intricate shone cut
Above our restless couch to limn
The questing and unheedful forms.
The richness of thy laughing mouth!
Astain with mad and purple wine
That spilled upon the eager flesh
I sought in sinfulness with mine.

*May 5, 1935*

## Bouts Rimés

*With H. P. Lovecraft*

### Beyond Zimbabwe

The drums of the jungle in ecstasy boom,
And summon the chosen to torture and doom;
The quivering throngs wait expectant and sad,
While the shrieks of the priest echo drunkenly mad.
Round the altars are tributes of barley and cream,
And the acolytes stagger in opiate dream.
It is thus that the Shadow grows mighty and whole,
As it feeds on the body and sucks at the soul.

### The White Elephant

Dim in the past from primal chaos rose
That form with mottled cloak and scaly hose
Who bade the lesser ghouls to earn their bread,
Perform dread rites, and echo what he said.

They bred the leprous tree and poison flower
And pressed dim aeons into one black hour.
Wherefore we pray, as pious pagans must,
To the white beast he shaped from fungous dust.

*[23 May 1934]*

## Dream-Battle

The world is dark, dark all about
And far atop the distant walls
Red torches flare, while here, without
The citadel, or mortal falls
Before a monstrous metal leech.
There lumber forth the endless ranks
Machines of iron tentacles that reach
The topless ramparts—banks
Of twisting rods and cruel claws
Enshaped in some forgotten mould.
And clambering, the iron maws
Are flesh-encrammed, while fogs enfold
The flaming Armageddon dim
As monsters top the ramparts' rim.

*May 23–26, 1935*

## [Untitled]

Into the clear and jewelled heart of day
   I turn, whose life has been a darkened room
   Of shadow born, and wedded to a gloom
Triumphant over joy and hope; when gay
And sun-filled, came your heedless voice—
   Calling, not to me, but calling, "Love
   And life are tapestries rich above
Compare: these joys are offered you for choice."

But I have known the ancient darkness long
   And tired shadows make their own a mind
   That is in shadow ever steeped. To find
Where mournfulness has reigned, your fragile song
   Perhaps to me is something of delight—
   Perhaps, gives only hatred of the night.

## [Untitled]

The crucibles of war; and pomp and might
   Of lords in Egypt, Rome, and Crete have brewed
   A motley brass. Life's ingots are renewed;
Long-idle, rust-gnawed swords are polish'd bright
    For fighting strife, and armies have been born
Of wreckage, for a new, more worthy fight.
Uncomprehending witness, does the sight
   Mean naught to you of mounting rays of morn?

The slaves have cast their shackles in the pot,
   And women, love, and warriors' diadems
   From sneering kings, and with them bloody gems
And serfdom's ancient hatreds, like as not.
    And above the battlefield rise heights unscanned:
    The threshold of man's majesty at hand.

## [Untitled]

The morning ocean, glimmering with mist
Of blue-white cloud and spreading diamond foam,
Weaves intricate and melting jeweled webs
That loop where coloured fishes dart and roam.

It bores a reach of shells and yellow sand
As swirling nets of greenness fall away—
Pale Mermen leap and roll within the waves,
And caper in their hidden, secret play.

*July 15, 1935*

## Dark Echo

That thin high wail—Like the summons of doom
A moon-builded web, and as frail as the moon-beams, as pale
As the loom

## [Untitled]

A lover I had in the starry night
As fair as the budding day.
His flesh was an ecstasy pallid and white
And his curls were sweet-mown hay.

Together we sought, in a passionate quest
That which all lovers seek.
Assuaged by its glory we lay back to rest
With flesh by the finding made weak.

## The Papyrus of Nyarlathotep

In ancient years before our glories were forgot
when yet the land was young and vast, and wondrous to see
lived a man called Nyarlathotep.
Strange and terrible he was
and wise in mystic ways.
The people of the land found oddness in his silent calm
for in his eyes were cold and dark like that of secret Yugot.
Thus for many years he dwelt and then was made into a death
that came from whence no man of Egypt knew.
Yet he perished not, nor shriveled,
for cunning herbs were put into his body,
so Corruption touched him not. Within the ancient silences his
    body lay
in curious vestments of the tomb.
    *It is thus he shall be found*
    *Or hath he been found? for time is timeless*

*and eternity is circled by its breadth.*
And from his cavern tomb
all carved in secret hieroglyphs and symbols of the ancient lore
Azathoth woke the One who waiting lay
and from among the dead in majesty
and silence came the Messenger
to go amidst the fearing mortals.
    In tattered garments red
as a vintage made of serpent's blood
he spread the word. And man and beast
made homage to the Messenger
whom none dared fear or question; stricken dumb when absent
    fellows
sought to learn his words.

## Sonnet

White flakes drifting in the night concealed land
And when we rose that dawn the wind-plucked branch was stilled
And black as ancient bones. The thick snow filled
Protected crevices. Dark firs on every hand
Were hung with crusty ice that sent a million rays
Of rainbow hue to our sun dazzled eyes,
And the calm pure snow was a printed maze
Of bird tracks underneath the morning skies.

We watched the slow sun's red ascent, a molten coin—
I think that morning you were very near to me
Yet somehow there was nothing I might say
No binding lover's spell to join
For as I sought to bind you with some key
Dawn's banners were des_____ged in day.

*February 11, 1936*

## Sonnet IV

As on a languorous summer day comes peace
Through the vague humming of the emerald fly
And the bland indifference of cloud and sky,
From the weariness of life, of ___ give release.
Heritage of the sweet, rich scent of spring
Is yours, but rejuvened; as the golden breast
Of August yields up more repose and rest
Than April, with her fertile promised blossoming.

To me, thy youthful beauty is as sweet
As mellowed sunlit fruit, that I may taste
Unhurried, restful, shorn of fear and haste
Since eager passion kneels before the feet
Of acquiescent love; and I behold,
Untouching, all the splendour of your gold.

*March 25[, 1936]*

## Sonnet V

Regarding your bright loveliness I stood
Beside the morning sea. About you curled
The opal mist of down-grey waters swirled
To weave your naked form a silken hood,
As laughing (heedless of the majesty
Of unhued earth and sky) you danced
Amid the pressing waves as they advanced
And overthrew their legions momently.

On godly beauty, and in mortal strength
Your flesh was insubstantial as a pale
Bright flame, where eagerness must fail
And leafing on, the ancient sea at length
Your briefness showed, and sorrowing I knew
When morning went, she had forgotten you.

*[April 21, 1936]*

## Sonnet VI

*To G. J.*

They too knew love, whose hearts are pressed to dust;
Whose shapes (forgotten now the glint of hair,
The flesh of ecstasy that was so fair)
Are merged with ruinous wood and coffin-rust
From jealous life they stole what joys were best
As lovers do; the worth of love they merge
Against the judgment of maturity, and swayed
No whit by sanity, pursued their guest.

And thus their evanescent lips were wed,
As ours hove near, and life and flesh were real
With all the lines of love, that they might feel
Love's joys: but in a while the joy was dead
In their own vanishing—Nor any wept
Above them long, when once they slept.

*[May 1, 1936]*

## Sonnet VII

*To G. J.*

I have been put into a sadness by the tale
Of lovers, whose cherishing was great as ours,
Yet is no more remembered, though the flowers,
The wind-washed sky, the gorgeous fail
Of sunset are as sweet as when they move
About their fragile love a fleshly guise
And looked upon work with eager eyes:
I have been grieved by this nostalgic love.

Yet every grief must bow before the night
Nor may we sorrow for the diamond star
Whose grandeur winds, and vanished afar.

It's death betrayed by momentary light.
That is had been triumphant; or that they
Knew love is that may be sought of day.

*[May 1, 1936]*

## VIII

By no pursuit may joy be trapped—
Faint, yielding pleasures are most sweet;
The scented winds that breathe upon our flesh
Bearing fragile gifts of ecstasy.

It is a honeyed pain to kiss your lips
To hold your flesh in bonds
Of passionate relinquishing embrace
Yet I do not ask this.

Enough of pleasure to have known your love.
Enough, the memory of an old joy.
I ask no alms: but that you shall be near,
As one who in autumn roads, being chilled
By the faint orb, remembers the lost sun.

*May 16, 1936*

## Song

Joy does not yield
To those who would bind her.
Searching afield
Never shall find her

Her flesh is the sunlight
On spun clouds at noon;
Her spirit, the night
Surrounding the moon.

Joy will conceal her
If you pursue.
Naught will reveal her;
Seek not to woo.

Late is the hour
When her pace impends—
By the lone flower
Her brooding face bends.

As the sun goes
From gardens long dead
Joy shows
Her obedient head.

*May 1936*

## [Untitled]

Well I know the starless night awaiting
    Yet should I spurn the pleasant gold of day
    Because I may not always hoard it? Say;
Must we then defer for e'er our mating?
To wait, and wait again, in formless fear
    No goal can reach. Fear not the bubbling cup
    Of life's delight, but turn it, wholly, up—
The heady draught imbibe, this blossoming year.

For I have seen the joyous bloom that clings
    To April boughs, and I have seen no field
    Whose fertileness is hesitant yield
To spring the homage that is always Spring's
    So frail the breeze that sets these petals falling.
    Hush with thy lips my anxious calling
That love and youth are slaves of death is not
To me of consequence. Your lips are hot.

*[May 25, 1936]*

## Sonnet

Forbidden the languid rapture of your lips,
Lone and regretful, I shall dwell where sighs
The enigmatic sea. Denied your eyes
My life shall dim where gleaming water slips
Like my own heart; to a mournful secret deep
Where lost in a vaster thing it wanes
To nothingness, yet by this fading gains
The great oblivion, and lulling sleep.

There death shall come, or life come afresh
Yet which it shall be, the consequence is small;
For I within my weary heart recall
The radiant bright beauty of your flesh:
The snares that love and fate conspire to weld
Of [words missing, ending with *?beheld*.]

## [Untitled]

I would weave my happiness into a song
   And with melodious words, from Lethe stay
   The crystal boat of joy; or hide away
The coin of love, which tarry never long
Within our coffers. I would like a chain
   About the soft dear throat of Eros; bind
   Him here within the summer garden—find
A spell confining joy and love and pain.

But pens speak slower than lips would sing
   And the word is very subtle which evokes
   Emotion sweet but transient. He who cloaks
His love in words has done a wondrous thing:
Though passion bloom today or yesterday
No song his hurtful, silent flight can stay.

## [Untitled]

Love came, and abode his time
Reluctantly.
The beat of his departing wing,
Golden in the sunset,
Wounded me:
Better, he had not come.

## R. E. H.

*Died June 11, 1936*

Conan, the warrior king, lies stricken dead
    Beneath a sky of cryptic stars; the lute
    That was his laughter stilled, and sadly mute
Upon the chilling earth his youthful head.
There sounds for him no more the clamorous fray,
    But dirges now, where once the trumpet loud:
    About him press old memories for shroud,
And ended is the conflict of the day.

Death spilled the blood of him who loved the fight
    As men love mistresses, and fought it well—
    His fair young flesh is marble where he fell
With broken sword that vanquished all but Night;
    And as of mythic kings our words must speak
    Of Conan now, who roves where dreamers seek.

*July 4, 1936*

## St. John's Churchyard

Endless the darkly-printed tombstones rise;
Dim evening sunlight pours about them now,
Golden and pale, on path and grave and bough,
And furtively they stare with listless eyes,
Remembering ages lost beneath the years.

\*     \*     \*

All silent now, with strife and love and tears,
Like scattered leaves through which the autumn sighs.
Lesser than leaves a century can grow
As tale and memory blend before the gaze;
No longer lost, these half-forgotten days . . .

Perhaps the shadows stir, perhaps they show
Outcast by life and death, the lonely form,
Exiled, of Poe; the man of night and storm.

*[August 8, 1936]*

## Dirge for the Artist

Most poetry concludes, with gloomy sighs,
    That what have seemed as lutes are squealing toys
    By cowards wrought to end death's nearing noise;
That Truth is but that man unwilling dies.
Fame, Honour, Love, and all the various crew
    Consoling us are like an elder's lies
    To soothe a child when night is in the skies;
Man is but born his coming death to rue.

Futility my theme, and how 'tis vain
    To nurture beauty's seed in hue or rhyme,
    Since soon or late each bloom is nipped by Time
Who never stays for long his wintry rain.
    The hour-glass measures life: a pox be on it!
    It scarce gives time to write a decent sonnet!

*Fall 1936*

## Alcestis

I.

Why have you brought me back to this dear land
Where I once dwelt such ash-dead years ago,

To stand anew within these rooms I know,
My husband's house, where I obeyed his hand?
I died for him, since he desired to see
For more decades the morning sun ascend . . .
Was it his mouth on mine which made me lend
The hours of life intended once for me?

I followed Death—his face was not so grim—
By that lean road where no inquirer goes
Lest business force him there, and I suppose
I can return, though life has faded dim.
Submissive still, to this familiar net
I yield myself, reluctant to forget.

II.

Yes, it was peace that I had found so dear,
A settled pool by night-winds undisturbed.
The drink was free, no greedy soul was curbed,
And there I drank and slept and did not hear
Nor wish to hear Admetus sigh forlorn.
The note was cancelled, long destroyed in flame,
The ashes swept: I soon forgot the name
Inscribed thereon, though he was kind to mourn.

And now I stand and see the violet
Sprout by the brook, and wonder what it's for—
Inspecting life as through a furtive door,
Hating a little this resurrected debt,
Renewing now the half-remembered strife,
Having to life, and offer myself as wife.

*[Fall 1936]*

# N. Y.

Town of Gargantua! sprawling hills give way
　　To factories, begrimed with years of mournful smoke
　　Which morning's blur of icy mist-fields cloak
But ill: They stand monotonous by day.
For league on empty league there is no end
　　To sightless wall and chimney; aching feet
　　Of smudge-faced workmen crowd the littered street.
Above, the hueless depths of heaven bend.

Kaleidoscopes of car and subway hold
　　In brief assemblage men of every mart
　　Like withered leaves in autumn wind astart
In aimless flight from harbingers of cold.
　　The indifferent splendours of the dawn peal forth
　　Behind a row of factories in the north.

*November 1936*

# [Untitled]

In aimless whirl two thousand million years
　　The Earth has spun beside that gilded ball
　　Her deathless sun. The final star-hung wall
Of night is far, but endlessly it nears.
Autumnal days beneath a waning sun
　　Half-lost in vapor hued with luminous gold
　　Are like a recollected dream. The fold
Of leaf is symbol of a summer done.

The winds are restless in a gleaming sky
　　Too pale and chill, like image-catching steel—
　　No truth this world's swift-changing cloaks conceal.
Serenely, mountainous white clouds go by:
　　The autumn's languid end, the ending day
　　Are weary witnesses of vast decay.

*November 1936*

## [Untitled]

Like figures scattered on a noiseless clock
    The stars are symbols flung against the night
    To mark eternal hours; forlorn and bright
Their patterns shift, and only eyes of rock
Have seen their fragile web with webbing lock:
    The stolid seas alone behold the sight
    Of failing sun and universe's blight
In years of dust. No beast has lived to mock.

In this great scheme, where year and century
    Are like forgotten moths that died in flames
    Extinguished long ago, the dulcet names
Of Love and traitor Hope are frail to see
    Though written in bright embers: embers die,
    And stars; and Death's a hard one to defy.

*December 25, 1936*

## Altamira

"Toros!" A childish cry, and overhead
    The settled shadows drew apart to mark
    A long procession, veiled in windless dark
Before the pyramids were dreamed. These dead
And secret caves served once as stinking lair
    For things not ape nor man; usurped by stones
    Of creatures new beneath the stars. Dry bones
Lie deep and mixed; no sound disturbs the air.

The flaring torches show with shifting light
    A painted beast, whose ribs pierced through by spears
    Flamed agony a score of thousand years.
The dust of fires extinguished in the night,
    The virile daubs by hands forever gone,
    The walls cry out their memories of the dawn.

*December 27, 1936*

## Cycle from a Dead Year

### I.

Now on this ledge by tortured feet worn deep
Where some shall walk until the fall of night,
My steps advance, unendingly in sight
Of those two chasms, Wakening and Sleep.
Some old precede, some youthful forms pursue;
A shifting crowd wherein I speak to none
Though all are kinsmen here beneath a sun
Which swells each day to see the throng accrue.

I know the law set down by gods of hate
Which sends me stumbling toward the shrine called Pain
And cease evading it. By whip and chain
Subdued at length, I recognize my fate.
Yet this perplexes . . . *children yet undreamt*
*Must go this way in shame and bafflement.*

*1936*

### II.

A gorgeous fruit can grow from boughs of pain,
And suffering's potent opiate is art,
That vault wherein we hide some sorest part
Of our distress, though much with us remain.
Your long lean lips whereof I have no taste
Invade my heart assuming single sway:
Like some trapped thing which eats its flesh away
I scourge myself, lest keener whips be faced.

Some human wound has borne each lovely thing,
Each chiseled dream immensely set in stone.
Penelope, when she was long alone,
Wove peacock silks; yet did I seek to sing
And thus from sorrow loveliness construe,
I'd still recall, still deeply covet you.

*1937*

### III.

With no hot wine nor opium defiled,
It is the ocean wind your lips have sought,
Blowing from sands whereon no scar is wrought,
Their kiss as frank as that some waking child
Might give. Borne out upon a flowering crest
Of joy to where the dim and chartless brink
Of fever looms, my soul is mad to drink
From the unravished blossoms of your breast.

There upon that garden I would lie,
Your bosom's rondure—life of your very life,
Insatiate to capture in our strife
All of your being, and let my own self die.
Yet each embrace but ripples me away,
Telling such loot may not be kept by day.

*1937*

### IV.

Washed ashore upon these satiate sands
By tides of lust which loomed to swiftly wane
Into their parent sea, I gaze again
On this snatched coin, so thin between my hands.
Your mouth returning in the pallid light
As climbing hours spurned stars beneath their feet,
Your eager flesh, laid bare and aching sweet,
Seem fragile pelf when viewed by saner light.

My heart—too deaf to comprehend the strain
Of Eros's song—succumbed to brief desire.
Another's lips made my mad lips aspire
To wrest from yours what they dared not obtain
From love I loved and could not well possess!
Your flesh was farthest in my close caress.

*1937*

# H. P. L.

**March 1937**

There is engrained in us the twisted myth
Which, using as symbol the change from worm to wings
Or slain year's birth ensuing eager springs,
Makes parables to silence weeping with.
Since it distracts the empty hand of grief,
I set the scentless blossom in my soil
And seek to mend with slow uneager toil
The ravaged plot, the broken stem and leaf,

And know I shall not fail, though wandering far
To see the gulf which bounds my yesterday.
Since Sorrow's word must hastily be drowned . . .
They prate of Somewhere, call you highly crowned
With Christian wreaths throughout eternal day.
You, who are crowned with Death's tremendous star!

*March 1937*

**March 1938**

And now a year recedes into the wash
Of aimless centuries, and now my eyes
Perceive the pattern of their fall and rise,
Yet memories are the heart's incessant lash
Like rain upon the cloudy ocean hurled.
All past and future hours emerge as one—
Twin stars which swing about a perished sun
In some far reach of night beyond the world.

What thing makes gulls defy the pushing breeze
Or iris bloom, what knife of silver flame
Was bright in you, a year can scarcely tame.
It flares up yet beyond the shipless seas.

But I upon this beach, perplexed by night,
Dare not advance bereft of your keen sight.

*March 1938*

## [Untitled]

The ocean vast from myriad darts of rain,
The seeds of atoms sprouting into stars,
The cells of flesh, its ecstasies and pain,
These things are one, masked by its avatars.
That comets whirl, that sinew clings to bone,
That seedlings swell, that insects spawn and die,
Is fore-ordained—the patterned evening sky
Is brother to the patterned river-stone.

Prolific life spills out of chance's cup
Across this lawn of green and golden fields,
The fountainous grain matures and thereon yields
To mouths of drought, but other crops well up.
In this design all cosmic patterns blend,
Involved and gorgeous, void of ultimate end.

*1938*

## [Untitled]

The night of iron, the day of foam is made,
And though brief worlds in briefer ages spin
Round hot-eyed suns, their anthracitic kin
Dead stars of the abyss, will see displayed
In time Death's signal . . . all sieged lands
Whose armies break, must scar the cherished wall
With final wound, and signify its fall
With some black banner held in reluctant hands.

Though various dust shall of his flesh be spun
And eddied off when this dear jewel Earth
Is once more hid with kindred star and sun

In rayless vaults, the gods with maddened mirth
Have wrought them Man, to laugh and dream by day,
Ignorant of night, till it sweep all away.

*1938*

## H. P. L.

The dimensionless sun, an hour since white with flame
    Withdraws its beams from glades grown dusky green,
    Silence walks from fastholds scarcely seen
By birds or eyes of furtive woodland game.
The phlox afire beneath this blossoming sky
    Is stirred by wandering winds in sudden hush
    Van Gogh set down with gaudy narrative brush
Such hues and patterns sifted through his eye.

As yesterday, the pines are tall and dark
    And meaningless against the yellow glare,
    As yesterday, the eyes of twilight stare
Confirming naught, the sunlight's tired spark
    Departs; and eastward move the glooms
    Where Sprague Memorial dominates the tombs.

I took a room in Providence at the Y
    Since Mrs. Gamwell wished to be alone:
    A decent place, though somewhat lacking tone,
And had my breakfast—prunes and toasted rye,
In dripping butter steeped, and paid the dime
    Knowing you liked the fare and would not come
    Again, and that your active flesh was some
Way off, and still for what remains of Time.

I saw such things as you had liked to see—
    The evening sunset radiant from the hill—
    Sorting your papers before the dust was still.
Since you could not, the task remained for me.

Going to the washroom with toothbrush, towel, and cup,
A Goddamn fairy tried to pick me up.

On such a night the high majestic moon
    Seems less removed, as wreathed in flimsy robes
    Her body bares among the stellar globes
Each minted bright as some engraved dubloon.
The evening shares the delicate pretense
    Of kindliness which nature has assumed,
    As captive woman, claiming passion doomed,
To torment more, from adamance relents.

They thus deceive; the blossoms and the stars,
    Beguiling us into a perfumed snare;
    And if chance aspects force the mouth to swear
The galaxy as more than aimless spars
    Adrift; to join by night such graceful play
    Is not amiss, since it departs by day.

*March 1939*

## H. P. L. (March 15, 1940)

I shall write until the wind is done scraping the air
That my brain is two brains,
And one is dead,
But the other is alive in the
Clutched clay fist,
A frog with painted muscles.

I shall write of death with selected words,
Of the lilies killed with the shadow
Of the four sides of death
Still lacking your initials;
Of the flooding voice running over stone tears.
The rose I took is in a box
Or dropped out of the book I gave Catherine,

Whether Mrs. Gamwell has kept the house
I don't know;
The road being greyer even than your inn,
I have pulled my horse's head from it,
Forever.

## March

With sombre pen the icy rain
Has drawn a scrawling line to stain
Spring's document, begun so plain.

The woman Wind, with love congealed
To hatred, walks the blighted field
Divested of its half-grown yield.

Impartial through the world the sleet
Treads blossoms down beneath his feet;
While from a window moist with heat—

Content in a security
No falser than belongs to me—
My warm cat bends his neck to see,

And seeing, soon will drowse again,
Heedless of the blossoms slain
To halt the hunger of the rain.

*Spring 1938*

## [Untitled]

From a soft bank I looked into the sky,
    Where stars of pallid majesty were hung
In frightening chasms incommunicably high.
    Beneath their frozen gleaming heart was wrung
As once again I knew that love must die.

## [Untitled]

That night the birds had ceased their painful cries
And each thin breeze was whisperily stilled.
Forgotten was the white moon: and the sighs
Of glowing ardor in the dark fulfilled.
I lay there as the silence covered me
Content to rest with old desires pale
As all nocturnal blossoming must be
While gusty breezes voiced again their wail.

## [Untitled]

I shall be gay this night as any fly
That ricochets from wall to wall bedecked
With turquoise shell, gone mad from catching sight
Of all the beckoning window-eyes of light;
I shall do every mad thing I elect—
Spinning with words and wine I shall be sly
And show you off, at pains to make all see
By our discourse how you belong to me.

As most becomes yourself, you shall be clad
In clothes so rich that they display no mark
Of costliness; spark after golden spark
Like a burnt firework, night shall go to rest. . . .
These are the wings I stretch and call my own,
And break forever on Reality's stone.

*1938*

## Reproach

My life was a silken pool, by evening, starred
And each sunset witness to the orb's decline—
A mirror by no pallid ripple marred
Till your evasive lips were briefly mine.

\*　\*　\*

Then tortured was the image-bearing lake
By love's evasive fingers set a-foaming
And each vain cloud beheld its likeness break
To ripples, on the troubled water roaming.

## The Unresisting

Like a small round world revolving separate in the antarctic night of
　　the stars,
My room looks from a besieged hill
At a sky blind with winter.
Snow flakes down from the robe of the hurrying day.

The elemental kings, not fierce, for they have all eternity to ex-
　　tend their domain,
Not greedy or anxious, for they own many worlds, even vast
　　Neptune is their satrapy,
Have sealed the dawn forever beneath the East,
The green seed in the ice,
And driven the heron to the warm equatorial swamps.
Yet I do not hate them for this—their dark overlordship is almost
　　welcome.
Their voices are rich with the woe of ice-girt shores never again
　　to break prismatically,
Are vast with the narratives of worlds decayed.

I shall not close my window against the mounting snow
Or shelter my heart from the sleet's cold insistent spear:
Long, long since I have sworn my fealty to these.

*Fall 1938*

## Shub-Ad

Even as I wandered the tropic jungle of fever
There were men digging beside A-bar-gi's grave.
Even as I breathed the strange blossom's heart,
Spades flashed and turned.

They warm my cooling cheek with roses
As I lay on the bier,
They circled my throat with necklaces,
And gave me the bull-head harp
Whose strings had lulled many lovers.
Then all the court lay down and tasted death
In a poison the priests gave them,
And the city was frightened by the prophecy of floods,
For I was the last of many great queens.

An obliterating tide walked over my tomb,
And then I lay still five thousand years—
I thought to wake
Only to see decaying suns hurled down
Like ruined fruit from the boughs of time;
To hear only the knelless tide
Break black upon an altered shore—
But a fumbling hand
Opened the starlight on my fragment of a skull,
And all my looted gems lie clean and ticketed now
In a glass prison,

They have re-strung the beads,
But the speech of the harp is lost.

*Fall 1938*

## Who Will Not Know

Never does the rose withhold her lifted lip
    From him who would salute her, never the waves
Avert their crystal arms from beach and ship.
    The cool star knows not shame though all the slaves
Of life yearn up, nor does the mare enjoin
    Solitude, when on the spring turf knocks
Her lord's wild hoof; yet rich with fairer coin
    Than all of these, you hang it with hateful locks

Never denying that furtive Beauty sits
    A friend at your table, that fair as gems to view
      Are your sea-hued eyes, yet I must confess
With lips not free of wound, when one admits
    The sun has dimmed to pewter in his blue,
      Loss of the brightest candle matters less.

*Fall 1938*

II.

In me a wing, unmendable and torn
    Strives at the air, deprived of further flight
    By accidental storm . . . the jagged light
Of your grey eyes, as of a cloud at morn
By rainy breezes through spent heavens borne
    Past forests where no fire yearns up at night;
    The hue of your golden cheek—a trophy bright
Left by the hasty harvest in the corn.

What craftsman in what drunken humour planned
    This gorgeous futile van more frail than glass
      And dropped it on the ground where cold seeds lie
Sealed in by winter's white impenetrable hand?
    Must all its clamorous motion fade and pass
      For want of the swollen grapes it sees on high?

*Winter 1939*

## To Bacchus

### I.

Land of the beverage ecstatic
Youth who art stranger to pain,
Dreamer with lips aromatic
And dark with the vintage's stain,
Where is the arborous places
Hidden from starlight and noon
Fertile with fevered embraces
Yielded by nymphs as they swoon,
Built they your altar primeval, unbroken, and destined to last unto
    doom?

### II.

Was it in field unremembered
Where blossoms desired of the bee
Near the hot Nile were engendered
Far from the rumor of sea,
Where some young dark-breasted maiden
Postured to sistrum and lute
Under a portico laden
With paintings of flowers and fruit,
Where the monarchial river in slumber flowed past the flares in
    the gloom?

*Winter 1939*

## [Untitled]

She sought the hut wherein the gods abode,
His snarling face a splendor in the murk
As was the sacred lightning when it strode
With streaming clouds from hills where horrors lurk,
Her urgent need outspurring prudent fear
She crawled along the crushed and stinking straw,

And loved his feet, and afterward dared peer
A little upward, toward the shape of awe.

Guessing thereon, no more than did the stars
So strange to look at, would he stoop and smite.
She dared to weep: amid her bosom's jars
And jostlings gabbled of some plight
Novel to her, though to the god of wood
Preoccupied, one drop within the flood.

*Winter 1939*

## [Untitled]

Our regal city, which for one long day glows fair
Is built a mile above the thousand-shadowed lair
Of earthquake, who unrestful scans amid his dark
A record with one anticipated mark.

This is the foetid cavern she broods in—
Let us slay Grief and string the violin
With her dark hair, discard her sombre eyes
And of her skull a sounding drum devise;
Make rattles of the teeth about her tongue,
And music of her bones, who never sung.

*Winter 1939*

## Winter Mood

Unreckoned, the frozen tears of night
Which flake into this northern sea,
Or the small suns kindled on the height
Of the mapless mount, eternity.

Unreckoned, the drift of shattered days
Which congregate along Time's shore,
Or the tracks of man, which swiftly glaze
Sunk in the marshes black and hoar.

*Winter 1939*

## Burlesque

Before a gilt and bloated cardboard dome
    Like a temple reared to soothe some Eastern queen
Whose lords become the maggots' honeycomb,
    Sleek harlots, smiling tawdrily to screen
Whatever they think, in swooning rites pretend
    The love no longer theirs. A trumpet's voice
False and ecstatic, screams at the cowering night
    That only desire is worthy of our choice.

But even as stagnant dark compels the crazed
    Too-much-enamored sun to leave the snare
Of some white lip from slime and mould upraised
    In tropic gardens, impossible and fair
The blind and fallow curtains fall and blend
While jaded eyes perceive at length the end.

*Winter 1939*


## Frustration

Within my garden, urging spring
To rise before her custom, yawning,
I pried the pebbles from the ground
And heaped them in a tidy mound;
The broken glass I threw away
So flowers upon a later day
Would show the sky superior hues
To those rich browns and greens and blues.

"Here phlox may bloom, and here a walk
Of brick shall be"—so ran my talk.
No compromise with scattered seed,
No pattern broken for a weed.
But where my marshalled garden ended
I saw the vaster fields untended.

Beyond my roses stars grew wild,
Heaven's garden was not aisled;
The meteor untrellised, gay
Through swarming chaos made its way.

*Spring 1939*

## To a Companion

Freed from the crowding mist, your face is bright
    At last, this hour, though dark forevermore,
Calm as a bird on water, calm as night
    The massive gaze my hours have labored for.
Rich in meanings never a wooden saint
    With angled robe bestowed on worshipper,
An arm held underneath a head grown faint,
    The mending knife the sick dare not defer.

Too long in search of other coin, I've spurned
    The gold austerely crested, you could lend.
        The days accrue: though harsh at noon, the sun
Enriched the fig concealed in shadow. Earned
    By midnight, what you give I'll take and spend
        And name the salt wine sweet, and so have done.

*Spring 1939*

## Dawn Delayed

No more than leaves, as crisp as pages kept
    On shelves from papers out of date, once swirled
By wind, can sleep as earlier they slept
    Can I find rest, or harbour in the world.
No more than driven wind which drives them forth,
    From fruitless bough to bough, itself in quest,
Finds fair as camp one country south or north
    Can I lie in a sheltered place and rest.

Behind me lift the hills; across them blooms
   Distill their coloured breath, yet all the same
I go my heavy errand down these glooms
   Blind with eagerness to see some flame
Not foe to me, torn in midnight's cloak;
Enter some camp, breathe in some friendly smoke.

*Spring 1939*

## To a Wayfarer

Her track: beside the withered bloom. That way,
The one whose face you glimpsed and would obey.
Her tread is fierce—why thought you otherwise?
The watchers of the sun destroy their eyes,
Yet when their day, on shadowed path, departs,
The sun is stained forever in their hearts;
And if the tiger intricate of pace
Desires our blood, yet we behold his grace.
To follow beauty, peace you must forsake
To weld the heart with flame, the heart must break.

*Spring 1939*

## [Untitled]

To what avail were path and garden cleared,
Intrusive weeds forever being pulled,
The roses hid when hungry frost appeared,
The million-blossomed dandelion culled,
When all this soil enriched by weary hands
Falls prey to armies never underpaid,
Yet ever sacking randomly the land
Since in the wall the bloom of death's displayed?

I will forsake my garden, where no wall
Can seal the alien sprout beneath the ground,

To mice and mould by hyacinths resign,
And let the fruit upon the petals fall.
Decay and ripeness to the fly are keen
And similar: he chooses not between.

*Spring 1939*

## Fragments

Even as from the chaos of the wave
Purveying grasses grown beyond the eye,
In dismal gardens of dissolving pave,
Casts up a shell in shining colours dyed,
Then hurries it an instant hence

So were you pressed a moment and again
A flower upon the summer wind of me,
And like the summer breeze am I compelled
To bear your incense through the narrow halls
Where the massive shadow of the redwood falls,
Delighting nostrils that know not whence it came.

Wrists
Deflecting the sun.

The hated heel has trod our street
Heavily—nothing but wine of eyes
And tear of grape could rub it out. Perhaps not these.

The wood beneath your scarlet robe
Is bare, lips strong with lust
Have rubbed away the paint, Lord Christ.

*Summer 1939*

## To Alta, on Her Original American Sonnet

On instruments of wood and bone
On oboe, conch, bassoon and fife

The singer long has shaped the tone
That tells the joy and pain of life;
The savage in the night has blown
An eager summons to the strife,
And lonely queen made dulcet moan.
Immutable as marble rear the massive forms
The poet has constructed—no tide of time can break
The golden spar his hand from leaden life has made—
A color on a lip—the sudden spring which storms
Across the hills with flowery jetsam in its wake—
The regal court of night—yet in this day is laid
A deft and novel keel; a vessel unassayed!

*Summer 1939*

## Sonnet

The sunlit fields wherethrough I walked all day,
Finding the stone, finding the coloured flower
Are left behind me now; I cannot say
What was the hue of one forgotten hour—
The bird I killed because its wings were bright
In memory cries no more; I do not seek
Auspicious skies, but set my step oblique
And reach the cliffs of dream at edge of night.

And here I part the weeds whose guardian spears
Surrender to no path, though much by dark
Uncandelled by the moon, my swift steps claim
Admission past them through unchanging years,
And stare beyond the mist, and swiftly mark
A gleam, within me mirrored, of great flame.

*Summer 1939*

# [Untitled]

Curse you that are beautiful
Curse your flesh and mine;
Curse your lips no redder than
A flower upon a vine.

Name the secret heart you lock
Deep in a shadowed cell!
A heart of golden flame or ice,
But which, I cannot tell.

Callous child, who stares at blood
On the mangled beast of my heart,
Whose eyes are like a pine-filled vale
Where misty rivers start,

I could claw like any thing
Against a captor set;
And with a scarcely altered mood
I still could kiss your sweat,

Or bend a neck that's bent but once—
And that a memory
Which will not make my coffee sweet
Of morning till I die—

And set your foot with willing hand
Thereon, and think it well.
But who the prisoner in your wall,
That thing I could not tell.

*Summer 1939*

# [Untitled]

Oh golden beach and blue-enamelled sea
And guardian sky—not fearsome as by night

When toiling stars mill meteors to dust—
Rest of the heart, and of the heart's vain lust
Cease as the gull in his arrested flight;
Do not advance, loved day, but yield to me
Again and evermore the splendid kiss;
Abide, sweet hour, who bathes and binds the wound
Of being life and change were change is death
And almost seems to heal it. Lift no wreath
Of cloud to your calm brow, nor chilly stone
To shatter the tense and crystal pool of bliss.

*Summer 1939*

## Fragments

Through my leafed and branchey mind
A vine with pallid leaves in twined.
The butterfly will pass it by—
If only I might be so blind!

\*

Amid the vast complexity
Of cloud and hill and house and tree,
In coloured maze each way I see,
Why is my wound one hue in me?

\*

I stared into the well so far
That past the slime I saw the star.

\*

The lash the heart endures or dies
Incredible upon it lies:
And though the falling hand desists,
The brown and shameful scar exists,
Articulate from withered lip
Beyond the rustling of the whip.

\*

Drive not your chariot close, else all my earth
Blasted will be, and not of any worth
The seed thereon, which achingly I set
And shaded with my hand, and watered with my sweat.

*

And yet the tiger, intricate of pace
Desires our blood, as we desire his grace.

*

In this arena, scruffing arid sand
Striving with beasts,
I have observed high Caesar with soft hand
Lifting the wine to his unthirsty lips

sips

    feasts.

*Summer 1939*

## [Untitled]

Walkers in the meadow, walkers in the grass,
What know you of forests where no footsteps pass?
Settlements of Autumn, colonies of Night,
Holding under dark trees things best shut from sight,
Heavily above it wander in the blue
Clouds of every colour. It remains one hue.
Nothing breaks its surface—nothing flecks its field;
What it lacks within it ever stays concealed.

*Summer 1939*

## [Untitled]

Over me courses the mist, and the stars are obscured,
Under me tongues of the grass in succession repeat
Tales of a dynasty which to such days has endured
That defeat were the ultimate triumph, a perishing sweep.

Legends of African glades in the torment of spring—
Rumors of night in the fields past the great Chinese Wall—
Memories of man's predecessors, the slim leaves are whispering,
Imploring the wind for release as their arms rise and fall.

All is habitual, even the footsteps that fled
Hastily stairward might be but a shadow's light tread.
All is deluded and moonlit and ancient and fair:
Nothing suspects you are gone, or detects my despair.

*Summer 1939*

## [Untitled]

Mute though my mouth has been, yet have I heard
    The bugle's tone upraised in loud delight.
Dull though my eye has been it has not blurred
    The mountains spread like lions in my night.
More than the forest, worship I the wind
    Though it grow stagnant in the trees of me,
More than stars have I been stricken blind
    With the white moon who roves the winter sea,

Yet to the solid chest which is my thought—
    With symbols of strange lands carved all around,
Within whose pungent darknesses have slept
    Many a precious sight and precious sound—
More hours than one a nimble key have sought,
    More than a time have failed and cursed and wept.

*Summer 1939*

## Quetzalcoatl

I.

Like some still bird, between the mountain's hands
Great Tula—Citadel of Gods—lay caught,

No record telling when the Toltec lands
First knew the bearded lord whose words had taught
The race its craftsmanship. About her grew
As great in girth as men, sweet ears of corn,
And cotton-boles in coloured blossoms' hue;
Her pyramids were from the mountain torn.

Only the stars disputed her domain,
Earth otherwise was vacant. Eagle-high
The god called Tonitiuh from his fane
Stared out upon the sun with equal eye,
But though his breast a wheel of gold displayed,
From humble straw his servants' huts were made.

*Summer 1939*

IV. [*sic*]

The lord has left his throne these many days—
Though torn lips pray in rituals that fade
He shall no more regard with purple gaze
The eyes obsidian which unafraid
Beheld and worshipped him, The wind, dismayed,
About the courtyard fumbles, where the blaze
Of fire of sacrifice no longer plays.
In Tula's night no torches are displayed.

Yet all was done there, all desire unfurled
Through which the tortured flesh is deified;
All joys had being there—and scars:
The futile tears of that unwitnessed world
Which never heard of Caesar, though long dried,
Fell like our own; and to the selfsame stars.

*Summer 1939*

## Out of the Dark

Who that sees the waterfall
On the cliffside like a tall
Bowstring, knows the force behind,
Or the tension of the blind
Shackled tarn the boulders bind?

Who that sees a window flare
In the castle of the air,
By the lightning's torch made bright
Knows the floods of loosened light
That on barren pastures glare?

Who that hears the uttered word
From throat of man or bird
Knows that past the shore revealed
Tosses turbulence concealed—
Vaster anguishes unheard?

## Prophecy

You shall never be dismayed
By your secret blood displayed
On your finger poppy-red,
Without a sign of whence it bled.

Midnight's stain shall never steep
Brain and heart in place of sleep;
But neither shall it be effaced
And by the coloured dawn displaced.

You shall never seek a leaf
On a cliff, and see beneath
Incredible and bright, the land,
With cities smaller than your hand.

# A Gull from a Cliff

White bird, light condensed,
    Foam up-flung from a fountain,
What winged years and airy spheres
    Divide you from the mountain!

A ruined pyramid it lies,
    And seeks to ascertain
Above what treasure it was set
    As guardian tomb or fane;

What cities boasted to the sun
    In old triumphant years
From its tall top where only move
    Today the channelled tears.

The mountain bows with broken hope
    Toward the consoling sea,
And wears a threadbare purple cloak
    And yields to verdigris.

And I am made to sing his woe,
    Because I know his heart
When over him the crisp wings go
    To turquoise realms apart.

How soon a sorrow is ignored
    By creatures with a wing
Who tread the fields above the earth
    With little need to sing.

*Summer 1939*

## [Untitled]

Here sun and scarlet flower declare
A rivalry to win the eye;
Condensed from air, the butterfly
In aimless quest, has found them fair.
If to become a bloom of bee
Would mean to never have to choose
Between two things, to trick and loose
The persecuting Self, I see

The system's merit. Stalked by care
Or bayed by woe within the heart
The bird alone can wing, depart
From shadow into shining air.
Nothing murderous so besets it
But the fowl escaped forgets it.

*Summer 1939*

## [Untitled]

"We caught him prowling in the dark,"
  The man who wore the mask proclaimed,
"Disturbing our lady's sleep. Untamed
He said not why, but with a mark
Or two sketched here and there
Upon his flesh, I think we'll know."
The castle lord had turned to go
But saw the prisoner's mocking stare.

"What did you seek?" he asked him gazing
To where the agonizing tongs
Accomplice to the fire were blazing.
The bound man laughed. "I sang her songs

Of what had been and is. No pain
Of mine can burn them from her brain."

*Summer 1939*

## [Untitled]

Underneath this velvet floor
Descend the steps I know so well,
And stop against an iron door
Whose tongueless guardian cannot tell
What prisoner is there forsaken
Within a world the stain of night,
But not with any star as light;
Or in what battle he was taken.

And I, above, survey the fair
Long road where I went forth
In yesterdays to south and north,
And blind with sorrow, am aware
That till his end, I may not go.
I watch his eyes, but death dawns slow.

*Summer 1939*

## To Sleep

Sleep, alone no traitor in this camp,
Whose liberal wine if feverless and cool,
Why do we drink the bitter draught instead?

Why do we go to Life's dull teas so much?
Why do we smile and take the flowered cup
Sticky around the handle, where the poor
Kind blind but generous dear has failed
To wash it well? Why do we curl our mouths
At stories told us several times before,
And drink our tea with lavish cream infused

(Our hostess taking care to get it just
Precisely as we do not like it?) Of course
She's influential—she did a favour once
For Uncle John, but that was years ago.

Invest this town with unperturbed mist,
And still the arid street wherein were wrought
On a hundred anvils in the noisy noon
A hundred garish horns to foul the air.
Let us have an end of noise—of tears
An end forever—let mongers in the mart
Relax their cries, and edge in wonder up
To read your proclamation: *I annex
This land for ye unto the universe.*

It is not we who die, but pain and dread,
It is not we who lie completely wed
To grass and gravel, it is discontent.
And yet we heed the strident bugle call
Blown in a strife designed by other men,
And leap from rest to rummage for a spear
And yet we join in random projects to cast down
The unnamed fortress all the race has fought,
Armed foolishly with wooden swords and spoons.

Declare your regency, for fear this eye
Be spelled again by splendours of the flesh
(Which make men of the gods and gods of men),
By eyes a part of darkness and by lips
Which not for all my goods nor sorrowing
May I attempt an hour of all my years.

It is fretful midnight we sit up
Holding the hand of life, with inching stars
So slow to set—the window wide on naught—
The patient hungry for a hundred foods

He will not suffer after all consume—the white
Slow stars no farther, and all the town's eyes shut.

Make visible the fairest lights alone
Of all that town, like moons or fishes' eyes:
Only the fairest sounds give to the ear,
Slow and expanding in your rippled night. . . .
The speech of boats which bear the urban heart
As passenger, the outward-moving train.
Move with your wind, like dew upon the stem
The lights aflare in wards of mystery,
In suburbs of astonishment and dream—
Stars of a sky untroubled by the real.

But give no gate to dawn when he comes clad
In golden cloth: he is a spy
Hated by lovers all, but hated most
By me whose love unrivalled is yourself.

Waken us, Sleep, from all this dream of Man!
Have we no word to greet you for our tears?
We have too long lain prisoner—we fail
To spy the careless key upon the floor,
And overstay our terms by many a year.
But even torment whiles away the time:
Limbs turned askew are just as good as straight,
Or nearly so—and the prisoner of life
Accustomed to the rack, does not long much
To move from it, or if he longs, forgets.

*Fall 1939; last pre-Activist poem*

## [Untitled]

Yet ever my gaze returns
Upward, to the fallow fields
And the chill soil
Where is nourishment for no crop.
Like a bead of dew
Slid from the flower of a dancer thirsting for air,
That star reposes
On the balustrade.
On which star
Is your Throne?
How shall I search them all?

*Fall 1939; first Activist poem*

## Isolde

Springs uncoil wound tight in the throat,
Sear the hand with irons hued like sun on snow, like moon on
    cloud
Tear red from it with the curve of a serpent-tooth,
But first let it reach close.
The unanticipated hues
On the hinging wing
Intensify when the worm is broken.
And the undrained cup is more golden than Celtic hoards,
*And thou wert the goodliest knight that ever bare arms,*
*And thou wert—*

Where is a path from Death? Where shall I flee?
His sterile thigh
Rattles in the dusk
His frozen eye
Turns on our lust.

I who have lived among slow budding flowers, among indolent
    herons
Of the color-stricken marsh,
Have been snatched to the mountain,
Where black ice crawls beneath me to a gulf.
Who shall remember the corridors of your eye, the curves of your
    hand?

*Fall 1939; second Activist poem*

## Springtime

He breaks the woodland's morning hush
    With clear and silvery tones;
His ruddy breast and jet black cap
    Are in harmony with the cones.
He sings with all his might and main,
    And all songsters join in the chorus;
To start the morn with happiness,
    To gladden the day that's before us.

I wake, to hear the rollicking brook,
    Swelled by the melting snows,
Accompanying the music of the wind swung boughs,
    As on towards the river it flows.
The sun glints golden, as it tips the hill,
    And the glow seen from the vale below,
Bespeaks a glorious springlike day,
    And an end to winter's woe.

I rise, to see the earlier deer,
    As on green raspberry shoots they browse;
The chattering, saucy, lithesome squirrels
    Chase each other through the boughs.
The mink dive beneath shelving bank,
    Pursuing the muskrat about;

Reappear in the stream, close together they seem—
    Alas! The victor is but dragging him out.

I hear the foxhound's bay across the lake,
    After game they never capture;
With a swinging gate, wily Reynard roams
    Apparently at his leisure.
And cunningly wades across the bay,
    Or follows the flume to the shallows,
Whilst the hound are astray, baffled for the day,
    Hushing for awhile their halloas.

The sly, savage otter, with sliding dive,
    Speedily searches the pools of the river,
And slowly returns to the hollowed tree rout,
    With a fish in his mouth all aquiver.
The coiled black snake lives where frogs their home make,
    In shallows where lily pads grow rank;
With glittering, keen eye, long motionless will lie,
    Quickly seizing a victim he squirms to the bank.

The whippoorwill, with its weird night call,
    Starts as twilight shades are falling;
And the owl, skimming low, with big eyes aglow,
    Is seen for mice aprowling.
The bellowing bullfrog, on water-covered log,
    Receives response from miles away;
But the raccoon's call is more weird than all,
    Twixt sunset and dawn of day.

## *Poems for a Competition* (1942)

Prefatory Note

These poems received the award for 1942 of the Emily Chamberlain Cook Prize offered by Albert Stanborough Cook of Yale University to the University of California for the best unpublished verse submitted by an undergraduate.

The Committee of Award consisted of Dr. James Caldwell, Dr. Arnold Perstein, Dr. Howard M. Smyth.

The same poems also won the Ina Coolbrith Memorial Prize.

Dedicated to Lawrence Hart, *provocateur*

## Date Uncertain

The angular green
Of a mask used in Benin
While black warriors, banished from the compound, edge along a
   night-wide wall,
And comets eat the sky.

The black-breasted women
Herd about HIM.
He gestures,
They are trees;
He postures,
They are reeds
Spearing the sky of the river,
They are violent flowers on it,
Or teeth under the water.

The soft spider of his brain
Weaves rapid angles.
They are flies,

They are the elephant-tusked grove,
The elephant-trunked vine.

And he says, "Years,"
And Johannesburg is cracked;
And he says, "Old stones sacred in the valley by the boys' hut . . . .
Christ whipped away like a melon-thief, or a wife-thief,
With his blood drooled on the ground";
And he says, "Oh, their silly hats, glass,
Their women that never—"

The herd shrieks a laugh and
A tiger in the grove hesitates,
Losing a step of his intricate tread.

## Nostalgia

(*To be translated into Náhuatl*)

That white *tortilla* on the *metate* of the night
Patted and perfected by autumn clouds
Comes to my soul's nose with four hundred flowers
And I remember the soundness of corn.

## For D.

My thought and pillows are disarranged;
I seem to confuse your wrists with the line of a Kwan-Yin scroll,
Your mouth with a brown triangular butterfly,
Your belly with good linen
Spread on a hedge from dawn.

I will shut the window of my rained-on heart,
Since you occupy the bed which is almost legitimately yours.
I will not think of the sliding hands.
I will read a book
Or walk on Van Ness Avenue screaming.

## Lines to Diana

O break his porcelain magnet, the corrupt and spotted moon's,
The stars who guard his court are skulls on spears,
Driven into the rotting walls
Of balanced night beside the heart like a hinged crab,
On an ignored beach.

Burst his eyes with bullets,
That bubble of goldfish excrement,
Tear (like the tiger abused by Indo-Chinese monkeys)
Your vengeance on anything that can lament.

## The Gods in the Patio

(*Museo Nacional de Arqueología, Historia y Etnografía, México, D. F.*)

Fifty bones of a murdered world are on view today at eleven.
Guests will please smuggle cameras and check their tips.

Have the gods herded into some cave, their clumsy joints all
bent in the direction of flight? Is there a spider hanging its gourd
in the Jar of Tlaloc, where rain once shook golden rings? Are all
the Cholula plates broken?

O Tiger Knight, I saw your torso like a maize-ear, I saw the
rusty roses on your garment. I saw princes who would be beautiful if they were statues, who envied only the snake, the jaguar and
the ant. How long must they lie, the robbed and fragrant dead,
by the Snake Wall, the *Coatepantli*?

## The School Where Nobody Learns What

Oh, only be buried in Babylon,
And you'll see what I mean.

Seize a moment to lament,
There is scarcely time even for that.

Fill the little slate and call it done,

You needn't come back tomorrow.
The Janitor is anxious to shelve Johnny Ape's botany book
With Jennifer Pterodactyl's.

## For Leon Trotzky and Huitzilopochtli

Was death square then, or did it have blue fronds?
Were the preliminary feathers and flutes preferable to a hatchet?
Where the idol lies sealed in a pod of mud, where the delivery
    trucks go over it,
*Aquí, a las 17 horas se rindió homenaje póstumo a León Trotzky. El*
    *velorio en el mismo lugar esta noche.*

It is twenty-four years, O rabbits, it is twenty-four years
(Extricate your heads from the ribs and listen), since the October
    Revolution.
And men are twenty-four, but in Cracow, in Helsinki, who shall
    be twenty-five?
Do you in your imperative burrowing
Distinguish Pole from root and stone from Finn?
Are both but obstacles to nest-making?
Are even the dead attacked, who died in the gardens, in the pub-
    lishing houses,
Almost as if in twenty-four years
Death had learned nothing?
How do the flowers push through the blood-clots?
(Be careful! It is important that we live.)

## Sacre du Printemps

An insecure paving over the swamp,
Trees pewter and charcoal.
A frog adds a word to a dotard story
Whose beginning the moon has forgotten.
The watches of the stars mark only centuries.
Her lips expand a petal and search for the air's lips.

From an inch away he observes them
With the bright storm of his eyes.

## In Black and White

I.

I rose in darkness, blinded by my sweat
And left the bed where motionless there lay
The fate my eyes avoided through the day
And sought at midnight with hot palms beset
By nails; and gazed on San Francisco Bay.
The thought which crowded sleep from me was met
By panting engines and their metal neigh,
By diamond light on satin darkness set.

Their longer journey done, the jostling trains
Moved back and forth through labyrinths of track,
With dust upon their wheels from Kansas plains,
With laden cars from Utah at their back.
I stood and saw, with hands upon my sills,
A foam of lights subsiding in the hills.

II.

On Yerba Buena demon cauldrons glowed—
There was no land or water, only light
Embroidered thinly on the edge of night
To where new ships, put in unnoticed, rode.
Rivers of smoke above the freight yard flowed—
The sight was good. I bent and craned to see
What ship or train would take myself from me,
And leave upon some dock my unprized load.

I told the night, I do not love these sheep
That you have made me shepherd of: they mock
My toil. Then I, uneager for the leap
And saunter of my filthy-coated flock,

Went back to bed where lay all things but sleep;
Day being somewhat closer by the clock.

## Explanation to M.

Since I feared the flight or the fading
Of flowers wavering in your eye
Or the bees in your nostrils twitching their wings,
I circled through the wheat of your thighs,
Under that copper and suspicious crab, the sun,
Like one who fears shadow, like one
Who has lost his keys or a ring.

## *View from a Hill* (1947)

## I. For D.

### 1. From This Tree

From this tree
No further fruit.
Search the boughs, look where the ant looks;
Only as cold-veined snakes knotting on the mud,
Daggering their bird heads at a shadow,
Will they respond.
A fire has bounded past
And the bark is blistered.

### 2. Air for Variations

Well, and if every word I write I cancel out,
If I constellate every page with splotches,
There *were* hyacinths to give you
Before the drought.
I meant your hands should hold them.
I meant their purple tongues to talk to you drunkenly.

Even indiscreetly.
The ripping of earth should discover more than stones.
There must yet be some vine
Hid with its grapes while the noon's sword flashed,
Some skin tight as a pool surface
Over spiced flesh and three or four seeds.

### 3. New Directions

Today I went for a walk in Hell,
Explored the red precincts,
Because of the fine weather and your eyes.
There was an alley I had never seen,
With houses that must be old
Leaning their chins over the ember pavement,
Whispering aged lecheries together.
There were doors cluttered with ribs and cheek bones,
With the visible stench carding over them.
Because of your philosophical attitudes and your knees
I was admitted by all the servants.
I thought I knew every charred signpost, every monument of the
    place,
From the proper bonfires of the well-to-do
To the ragged flame of poets and social reformers,
Drawing a bitter persistent thread through the nostrils.
I did not know I could get lost like a stranger,
Ponder, wander mapless through Hell.

### 4. To a Friend on Sailing

Break with the alleys full of neon-lighted garbage,
With Nob Hill and the saloon where the drunkest bartender in
    town tells of his days as a chef.
Sail over Alleghenies,
Over fields and deltas flecked with rare rusted trash.
Like the child born, subsist alone

With the pavement of no city under you.

Measure stars leaded into the Gothic night,
Let red day, black darkness be the chessboard of your swift advance.

### 5. To One Rescued

Dropped by the tiger, you whose wounds brim red
In a lace of torment
Where the fang pushed in and felt your arm-bone's shape inside
    your arm,
Scattering the sinews, slackening the body's bow-cord:
Though the desert he dragged you through were fifty miles greater,
Though the day were fifty hours longer,
Would you call us with our antelope-hide shields,
Our clubs,
To break his low flower face
A second time?

## II. Fresco of Priests and Beans

### On a Feather Poncho

Birds with obsidian they did not swallow bursting them
A beak, a frog-jelly eye,
A claw delicately holding air—
Sag in the scale of a palm which evaluates death.

Lean feathers pulled, stared at, discarded on the planes of the wind.

The web in a hive of mummies
Swaddling oyster-shell bones,
And night furrowed a million times
And the sleet of stars in the hollowness
Drifted an inch.
Cataracts of years on Tiahuanáco,
Drowning her god's stone screams.
He too is nearly dead. The walls of his house

Are brown infrequent teeth of a skull;
Inside and outside are confused, the grass claims both.
Yet for a thousand blank years
He answered tear-clumsy lips
As a god answers.

## The Chichimecs

The Chichimecs live to the north of us
And do not sing.
They only catch rabbits, carry them in folded nets,
Eat prickly pears.
And when a man dies, they say
He had so-many rabbits, and
So-many wives.
Only the grass wrinkles our bellies,
By the rivers.
We scoop out fish with jade faces
Who walk under our hands,
And do not count our wives.

## Stela of a Mayan Penitent

While the Jaguar clambered down the night and the Turtle clam-
    bered up,
What silver honey did you browse on at the pace of trees budding
In your world that never heard of Caesar?
Bringing forth your senses like sacred palm-leaf books
Painted with bumblebee-gods,
Over and over in what seas did you turn tunawise
As the projects of the foam fell into ruin?
Did the flowers throw off their masks and augmented streams
    slake the night?
And now, with this cord of spines worked through your tongue,
    is it clear to you that one who walks out of the serpent-village of
    the jungle must stand as a shield against the fist of the moon?

## Tepuzteca, Tepehua

We do not even know when their
    eyeballs were eaten by time,
The Copper People, the Hill-Lords.
The roof of that century has fallen in,
    corn is dried on its floors.
They may have examined ginger-jars
    under resinous torches,
Before the end of that night they
    peopled like stars;
Their flute-accompanied corteges may
    have held up the muleteers
Ascending the Camino Real under the
    caves, with a bundle of Cantonese silk.
We do not find written anywhere
    when the last man or old
    woman complained last,
And was packed into the grotto of the
    dead with his bundle of food handy.
In 1580 Phillip II read the
    report which said, "this town
    is called Fallen Star,
"Because of a King they had, who
    was called Star-King. They
    speak Tepuzteco".
In 1750 the Viceroy of New Spain
    read the report which said,
"It is difficult to suppress
    the growing of contraband tobacco,
"For these hills are unoccupied".
We have a word of their
    language—it means "god"
    (or, possibly, "devil"),
And a paper bagful of

potsherds we think they made.
These pieces of dishes are petals
From one of the many flowers
    which here and there on the
    mountain of Time,
In summers of a different sun and
    winters of a different rain,
Have unfolded beyond the reach
    of our gathering.

## The Conquered

How he of the greenstone axeface now
Rearranged three hummingbird feathers
In his nose, and approved the accident of the solar yolk,
How Youngcorn's hair, and the shining waist of Heartflower
Seemed streets too well known.

How they stamped in on their hornless deer
From Snakehouseplain and Deadenemy Wood,
With the content faces of bats under mantles
Of kings coming apart in caves—
How a small piece fell out of his turquoise hat,

But how hefted the haft of dream-clubs,
Slicing his thumb on black glass incisors,
How he tightened his sphincters and hurled
Important hearts into marigold-carved stone tubs!

# III. For Rosalie

## blotted a beetle

field sprouted
with several kinds of flower
& a mushroom
N., N.E., E., S.E.;

spokes of grass
rimmed with a
(1.) red beetle sawing his tongue through trunks of violets
(2.) palaeontology of sparrow bones
   (a.) their hilts
   (b.) " shafts
(3.) arabic of a tunnel written underground. Feelers dodged into dark.

o her eyes were like
eyes with spiggots in them
peering through a melanesian gloom
on hybrid horses, and the nisaean plain
(receptacle of moonlight) blasting with plum-trees
where the $\left\{\dfrac{\text{minnesinger's}}{\text{messenger's}}\right\}$ aspect
blotted a beetle

**Table Set for Sea-Slime**

Clams claw their pots shut,
Sublimate their doors,
Slot their lophophores
On floors and floors
Of pearls and sycamores
At fours, and half past fours.

The small submergéd fowl,
The gill-hung owl,
The crawling towel,
Locks up its drawers;
Surprising as spoons pulled out on floors,
Clams slam their clocks shut, button up their wars
At fours, and half-past fours.

# IV. Five Years

### First Year: Sebastian

If only once
Arrows had strained between hemp and bark,
And blood gone salt behind sewn lips,
Fifty vertical granite spires on the Norman coast
Or five hundred domes in Cairo and Sophia overscrawled with
    gold writing,
Could not sanctify Earth.
Her seeds would be blackened.

If only once
Eyes had beheld the desperate rolling of eyes
—And not in a fever men cure; but in a fever where cure is for-
    bidden—
Had beheld the armored ants of pain exploring the marrow,
All the chrysanthemum-heavy mist,
Green-and-salmon,
Of the endless dynasty of Sung
Could not cover the spotted soil of the world.
Not the towers of New York with their knives of light upheld.
But this!
What fruit do you anticipate in the orchard of your arrows.
O likewise young soldiers?

### Second Year: Dream While Paris Was Threatened

Once there was a fiddler. By and by the fiddler came into the universe and looked at his watch and began to fiddle. And there was
Greece. He kept looking at his watch and walking in and out of the
universe and each time he fiddled there was a new culture. By and
by he came and sat and fiddled for four years and there was a great
battle, and then he looked at his watch which hadn't tarnished any
more than the stars had, and walked out of the universe for twenty years. Then he came back and fiddled energetically for a while.

And then he laid down his fiddle and laughed and walked out of
the universe, for there was no one left to fiddle to.

### Third Year: About a Mythical Factory-Area

Slow, like a glove off some Junker
To hand a hostage death
Beneath his own pear-tree.
The clear cannon-bells seeping
Along the sky
Tremble the scum of blood on cement.
Braided with tomcats exploding among the girders, the dark is so
     small there is no pocket for sleep.
Nor holes in heaven for God to weep through.

### Fourth Year: Letter to My Brother

In this sector of our years
Who sees but tangled bayonets, the treads
Of iron beetles kicking the sky?
From the Murmansk to the Black Sea of life,
We are woven in conflict,
Knowing not whether our movements are Advance
Or Retreat.
Guns sigh smoke all day,
But there is no battle until the battle is done.

### Fifth Year: Viktoria

But when our spears were cleansed and neatly stowed
And the needless guard had ceased to prowl the camp,
When the final tent put out its punctual lamp
And only we lay wakeful in our blood,
We heard a marshalling of bony mud,
A falling into files of rot, a tramp
Of feet out there unjointed by the damp;
A sprouting of the crop that we had sowed.

The plain our swords had smoothed was all awry,
All rooted up our neatly planted crop:
Star-numberless those troops that will not die,
But rise each night . . . What's to be done to stop
The dead that disinter themselves? to keep
By dark our daily gains—and still, to sleep?

## V. For E. and For W.

### "¿Que Quieres? ¿Mis Costillas?" (For E.)

More than the descent of star-dispersèd kings
Down walls of Babylonia between leaves
Of palms and feet of ocelots and sheaves
Of conquered wheat and wailing offerings
Do I esteem your ribs, that breathing box
Filled with the jewels of air which feed the flood
Of tumbling pearls and rubies of your blood
And bone—that gate my hand unlocks

With anxious thumbs, advancing to the soil
Of your sighing garden, filled with shadowy fruit
Among the spiny arbours and the flight
Of virgin bats, to sow in amorous toil;
Inquiring not what seeds will blaze in root,
Which fold in failure, stunted by the night.

### Chili Sin Carne (For W.)

Where Imhotep's words on plant nutrition
Bound up with Mrs. Hemans lie awake
On shelves in prim Platonic juxtaposition,
A figure from the brush of William Blake
Debates with me an indicated planet:
Is it the sun or moon which sank or rose?
And then ordains, as one who surely knows
"But can it be? It cannot be! But can it?"

Probing the nerves, the burrowed telephones,
I learn from them the answer they have learned,
"Only the trickster Greeks say Troy is burned,
Inter in verse these too-disturbing bones
With beetles of fayence and flavored tars,
Osiris-like in jackal-headed jars."

## VI. View from a Hill

### To the Builders of a Dam

Under the sky's plain, on earth's plain
You have fenced in the curved water's bloom.
A jaw-bone specked with rust roses is your unnatural concrete,
With the five petals extended over it where you permit.
But water knows many doors:
Where shadows are hammered in the turf
Are more trees than all your workmen.

### View from a Hill

Having done what was mine to do,
Like the snow falling,
Having fingered the earth, the fern, the soft skeleton of the twig
And having slid the latch of every wasp-visited gate,
I claim to know these fields.

There is no marred thing to hide
From my burning mirror.

If I trace out again any path,
My orbit will be not more unexpected than the sun's,
My curving trend than that of the long-named planets.

But Copernicus saw a star beyond,
And Galileo a star beyond that
Welled in shadow,
Like an orange gone soft and glinting.

## Recantation

I did not claim that besides this hilltop
With fog-twisted bushes a hundred years wet,
These snowflakes of light,
This water bearing the armada of darkness
Ever existed day . . .

A pool where a green body trails air in garlands,
A wine-warm hand next to mine on a table, lips knife-clean smiling
    at the evening,
A fist of music pounding the air . . .

But if I did, I lied; my tongue was drunk.
Some web of candlelight spun within my eye
Populated the thunder-hollow sky.

No *eppur si muove.*
There are only
Suspended at an angle above the luminous gore of neon
And the shops, the herding cars,
Wildernesses of night,
Tangles of black wind;
$L, = L\ 0\sqrt{}\ v/c\ -\ \tfrac{3}{4}\ +\ X.$
Describing an astronomy of skulls.

## On the Lights of San Francisco

Their hundreds marching on the hills
Burning the dark for eighty years
Move not in space.
They are an infantry sent against Time
By his worst-wounded enemy.

Scarce is the border overrun of his blue forest,
Scarce is the violent wing of the sabre loosened
Against guards jolted with waking,
When the trend of the wave is apparent.

And those who are not rent may yet find in a while, on the crumbled moon-regarded road, or in the peopled hedge along it,
  worse-poisoned arrows.

## A Escoger

Strophe:         Manifestly you cannot sit
                 Forever in this draughty antechamber
                 And your host off drunk in another universe,
                 But the question is, which door?
                 They are all so nicely hung
                 With the same everycoloured curtain
                 That the first or the third or the fourth
                 Seems adequate,
                 Save for a suggestion of mice
                 Or whispering, or bones not too well cured
                 Or other flowers behind them.

Antistrophe:     Whichever you choose will lead
                 To no amazing golden berries
                 Or rain of music, or flares
                 Of ports across the hills to the sea,
                 Whichever you choose, and you may not delay
                 forever,
                 Gives on a black garden where gargoyles have
                 gone mad
                 From the starlight:

Strophe:         Whichever you choose will be wrong.
                 But what else can you do with a life?

## In Order to Clarify

If my heart scowls now,
It is only because a certain epidermal contact with the enemy,
  areally limited, has been postponed.

Only because the enemy has successfully disengaged us, before we
    saw the whites of their thighs.
It is not because you are a possible gloss alongside etaoin–shrdlu
    reading it "night" or "day".
It is not, I insist, because you are the one beam to hold up the
    wall that leans over the prize begonias.

## We Kept on Reading "Tuesday"

The collapsing garden, the varnished bamboo green as a bug's
    underneath,
The chopped tassel of the banana,
Purple rotting to scarlet on one seceding leaf—
Ants like thoughts working within a wound,
Burying glass mummies in capsules,
All was suddenly shadowed from west.

Over so soon! There is no time
To write Harriet, or unclutter the calendar
Of days invalid, whose folly is no longer optional.
The sun, too long on the vine, drops down,
Column pines support (like Chichen's walls)
The parrot-colored lintel of the night.

Fish-eyes heaped up in a shell;
The skeleton-jointed stars hold the world.

# VII. For Barbara Mayer

## On Leaving Some Friends at an Early Hour

The brink is slid over,
The steep water abandons the cliff it tore,
And wanders into sleep.
The minutes resume their flow.
Circle of dark lake, dark scent in the air,
And possibly flowers.

That star hung from the eaves looks at me with animal eyes,
Puzzled.

## *A Stone for Sisiphus* (1949)

I and Percy B. Shelley
Both suffer the same belly
Ache; I and the Lake
Poets know it's fake.

## Sonnet to Siva

(*On accepting a temporary librarianship*)

And forth once more, splitting the Cambrian rock
The mouldy streams we all have tasted spew:
The soured wine is passed around anew,
We set our hearts to your long-accustomed clock,
We fit our faces to your gouging mask,
O Tragedy—we hasten to your knock,
For now we can resume our ancient task.

It is not bombs alone which break the heart:
Today we have a Poland in us all.
Tupper's a drunk; Don Pablo teaches classes;
Antonieta wants to study art—
And I shall sit at public beck and call
In the Benjamin Franklin, fiddling with my glasses.

*[1945]*

## Anniversary

I cannot sleep. The rising wind of years
    Through memory sifting, lifting the leaf's
    Brittle anatomy, blows together griefs
Of child and man, and wakened memory hears

Howard's voice above the desperate toss
    Of branch, and memory sees the god inlaid
    With brass bugs abandoned where we stayed
Some childhood year, leaving a sense of loss.

And thou, Vincente, legend-wealthy heir
    Of Teotihuacán mid shepherd folk,
Chilled with the stone mask the princes wear
    By the simple word a line of lightning spoke!
Nothing we love is given us to keep.
The wind of years is rising. I cannot sleep.

*[15 March 1947]*

## Invocation

Mother, Mother, Mother,
Pin a red rose on me,
That the flame may stay its leap,
My pale mind warm again with red,
My brush again attempt to draw
    a melon round enough,
A fern felt-out enough,
That my examining hand may somehow
    mold flesh into something to keep.

## Evening

The smear of stars, infertile eggs
Laid by an ant-queen kept under honey
In a padded throne-room.

The dream I had between sins, which fluttered like a tulip
Explored by a beetle;
Which was *all* my dreams
To the secure eye of sleep.

## The Coming Fructification by Night of Our Cyrus

Whose was the gloss of equating Hathor with the sky?
Only the confidences of borrowed birds
Locked in the mouldy granaries,
The ibis flattening its bill against day's edge,
Spilling the seconds like wheat between columned nights,
Only the dreams of frogs with sapphire feet
Could ever have swollen her nostrils with the sun,
Have burst her belly with pennants.
Only the beetle kneading the dung to spice,
Seething in sarcophagi could shift
And shape that Tree, could fold here in golden ferns,
Could stanch the weeping of the starry Calf.

## Of the Names of the Zapotec Kings

Of the names of the Zapotec kings
Not five have been preserved to us—
Yet their time was an island of gulls and crabs—
Property rights, courtship, and the problem
Of disposing of the dead.
It was the never-mistaking dance of flies
Before the eyed bushes of the jungle.

The Dominicans who came after the slaying had been cut down
To a reasonable pace,
To oppose the burning of incense
Before pagan figures
Also lived piously. One who did not
Quarrel with the abbot over the right spot to plant parsnips
Was certain to be transformed in Brother Paul's chronicle
Into an example of virtue.

Ah, Zapotecs and Dominicans, how could they have endured life
Before the Automat?

## Framed Portent

At that place,
Where night is wedged between tulips on a hill
Comets clang down the doors and corridors
And clamber their soggy fires down precipices,
Once at that place
The banana-colored valley and its oxen
And bronze-blooded men are a page turned over;
And the broom-flit shakes
Over the eyed lawn of your mind.

Conceal your lips:
The bat flings down in a web of needles
And the moon is gouged out of its colored peel.
Envelop your notebook in cheesecloth, I beseech you!
And see where among the columns uninvestigated
Two velvet lobsters confer on the spelling of Babylon.

## Orientation to the West

Trying to tread on blood the ant has cursed
Revolving his cratered eye to a round horizon of corpuscles,
We have seen the dark through copper tubes:
But twist the middle somewhat, joggle the end a little
And all this smeared vision will go straight.
We shall have a well up through the ravel-winged stars that have
    gathered above the Earth,
A stem through apartments of slime to a green blossom
Which need not split today.
And we shall see olives and fish with red edges, and strew black
    thorns on a wind, making the soul a bell with a stamen of stone.

*[1941]*

# Miscellaneous Poems

## Mourning Song

Grandma is dead, her bones dragged in his kennel
By the pious dog Death to prey upon.
Let us burn the wheatfield then, and burn the stars and birds
And avoid the Spring by going to San Francisco
And wind the clocks with ivy.
They have condemned her flesh for settlements of worms,
Who also have livers and lymph, and in a sense can be said to live,
As indeed, one could say of Grandma.

## Admittance

The arrow is no legend.
Like the hand of the sunlight laid on me
Is your name; your mirror face.
Even your name, o barkless white oak,
Your publicly-said name.

## The City

There are buildings with bronze rafters studding the grooves
    at the bottom of night:
Golden bladders of fish igniting shafts of the sea.
There are alleys flowing and flowering in serpents
Between the creviced brick brains.

The hundred insinuating words of the moon
Fall on indignant shutters. Behind them, hostages to the
    drawing-room,
Butterflies hook metal feet into vases,
Turn their wheels in the evening,
As on mountains encrusted with jade and aquamarine.

## A Tapestry

The peavine hair of horses curls
In the breeze four centuries old;
Chestnut eyes glance down across the rein.
A Greenland falcon teeters on the glove, his beak annoyed with
    velvet
And the scent of verdigris and veins muffled from him.
Bourbon lances, slippery for once with light,
Fisted by men whose duty it is to kill strangers
In strangers' lands,
Surround the banner of an abolished lord.
A dog dances past blue bushes of invented flowers
And lets down his tongue, finding the afternoon long.
This is no cloth for mouseteeth, though
We have learned too much to know it.

## Warning to Snake Killers

Queerly walking by a slow and pagan clock
Between the pyramid and church
The god was surprised and killed on the stair of his ruined shrine.
The Indian crushed the poison pod skull, he gathered the flowers
    of the movable skin with a ten-cent knife and threw away thir-
    ty tooth-colored bracelets,
But the stamen tongue wrote a symbol in red beads.

He dreamed that night that Tlaloc, in his heaven of the east
Peopled by those dead of dropsy, and all the colored shadows
    that have looked into rivers,
Turned an eye within his serpent mask
To the messenger of the fourth rain-jar
And ordered mildew spread on all the village corn.

## Respect Not the Leaf

Respect not the leaf nor the stone nor the day,
Reclassify the world according to pointed or blue or Mesopotamian,
Put a prism to stenches, reverence the wine-puddled ant-tunneled
    pear
And the combed edges of banana-leaves.
Day is black if you like; I am convinced
This bougainvillea
Weighs more than those iron-livered hills.

## Mythological Episode

O that frog or flower that stealthily
Snipped from the bone Black Tezcatlipoca's foot!

Trapped with his hands full of magic, what could he do
But wither a projected sun,
Drop two or three eternities into his purse unwrought,
And leave us to make sacrifices forever?

## Rainy-Day Pastime

Let us examine our bones, ours and our ancestors',
Haul them down from the attic.
Let us acknowledge we are tomcats mummified in alabaster vases
With powdered stuff, nutmeg and bay leaves, flavoring the sock-
    ets of our eyes—
The moon eclipsed that estimated the height of ivory-fetlocked
    chairs,
That watched rats fall down the slant of Chepren's tomb.
And bored ultimately with Cleopatra turned to despise the desert
    from a window.

The being at one with sunlight, munching blood and flowers in the
    priests' garden if we felt unwell (they watching for auguries) the
    explosion of spring and clawed love and snipe in the nasty-

footed rushes were sinews and sound and flesh. Today our white sticks are unencumbered.

The game is up, they have discovered us.
Here at the border station between cliff centuries we are caught smuggling . . . nothing, in innocent packages.
We have learned to hold teacups so artfully that no one detects the absence of tea.
A smith pounds rubies all day into the hilt of a sword cowardly with lead.
Bloodying the cold waters, abominating himself that he was not a mountain or a star,
Quetzalcoatl sat.
And said,
"The stars on the night are like insects beaten out of gold. We priests have hung our eyes amid them, and grope in the blind world blind."

## The Heart

There are sixteen spokes
Leopard-like with moss,
And one rim binds them,
    and they roll through many centuries
    on one hub.

And he was Niagara across the once confusing hills.
In the green night some twenty feet away a green star flew.

Then hold the four limbs apart on the stone and the knife without delicacy drives them down, and the tissue is rended and the flowers uprooted. Now the bones come into their viceroyship, and winds may carve at their leisure glyphs on the fleshless thighs, on the face, where they will.
It is worse than you thought.

The bones of the trees and their feathers

Chewing blueberry paws,
    a mouse
Leaves the hull of a corn-bread as hollow as an aborted chrysalis.

She works just like carrots in a rabbit-field.

## Mozart's G Minor

Sun green and grass gold a hundred birds flake down,
The eye cannot capture every beak, every wing,
The tongue cannot name them.

## [Miscellaneous Lines]

Seize the branch and knock its fruit off which never will get ripe.
An Inca garden where bronze flowers rust but never fade.

           *    *    *

A fungous appetite stole verticals from things and all sagged out to
The intelligence of beans.

           *    *    *

Let us lie low in the death where the locks of the flowers are by a
    jelly of black ants,
Where the patterns of the lighthouse walk out on the mist and
    walk back
And the drowned munch seaweed, the hands of the spiders reck-
    oning in the dust.
Do not leave your land.
The peasant who tilled for the sixtieth spring found pennies in a pot,
After the pig had been sold into Transylvania.
Go on picking up shells, so that you shall have all of them,
How should you guess that the one you sought was lost in Samoa
    before Duke William?

           *    *    *

## Letter for Last Christmas

We have stood several times
At the place where Penn Station goes underground,
And I have said, Belknap,
Howard is this or that.
But I never knew either of you.
You encompass your apartment-house with envelopes,
Exclaiming upon the wound-out words of Troy.
I buy my beer alone. Ah Belknap,
Is there no word from Howard since his death?

## [Untitled]

Of course it is abominable
That we should esteem chrysanthemums.
I said it first when it was only Spain.
Only Spain, where we hoped that Phillip had decayed at last,
So that the masses could stop.
But suppose one were not a partisan?
What term for the leaning boys intent upon the juke-box
To catch the song we all know?
What term for their hands
Shaping the statue,
What raveled words to wind them in?

## Colors

The color of plume with pollen smeared;
Swiss-chard color of Greek warriors lumped out of bronze in 600
     B.C.;
Where a car has leaked on a rainy street and driven off,
Or the painted faces and feathers of clouds
Shooting their arrows into the burning mummy of the sun.

## [Untitled]

Let us swell the peace with warmth,
Though not our heart,
Let us curl their green grain into pattern,
Nourish our knuckles with broccoli,
And forget that breath must be breathed in order to build houses,
    study stars.

## [Untitled]

These are the leaves
To bury you in the mind:
The new dog,
The hole he ate in the carpet,
The left-hand faucet
Instead of the right,
D—— calling at dusk
With the hint of something more at midnight.
Yet any wind lifts the small leaves.

## [Untitled]

The copper sherry, rippling flame
Like a shield turned all ways at noon—
The furious satin blade in the throat,
Splintering to light in the brain.

Cypress-stained water, unmoving, distilling
A mist as heavy as rain—
And voices across it; arrows; song
Bright with obsidian pain.

*[1942]*

# [Untitled]

Los años son un abismo de celaje
Oscurecido por la minúscula teleraña,
Un cielo de calavera blanca
Incrustada con mosaico de turquesa,
Tributo de la Tierra Caliente,
Y en el hueco de los ojos
Siempre el hilo cobrizo, teñido de uva;
Moviéndose; no olvidado.

## Poema de Salida

Mérida regada con el verde y morado interior de nácar;
La sombra minúscula de nuestra ala izquierda arando la tierra seca;
Arriba y más lejos que el neón, el brillo de la noche bruñida.
En abril los vientos de más allá de Campeche
Barren de la vista los nucleos de luz
Y confundo la catedral iluminada con el fogón de tres piedras en
    Chac Nicté,
Y tú San Hol, con tus ojos de animal que come frutas de noche.

## Intimations of Mortality

The millions of years ahead,
When we swing as dust between moon and sun,
As we soon must, will be less fun
(Being dead, I mean), less fun
Than setting thorn trees out in pots,
Than scratching cats' fleas, cats' ears,
Oh, lots less fun, I have no doubt,
Than ever going to church.

The millions of days ahead,
When we lurch about Mars
Like smoke fled!

(Visitors' old cigar-smoke
Ascending a cold parlour at night,
With the blaze of light ending,
The dog put out.)

*Fall 1947*

# NONFICTION

## Published Letters

*No Comment*

Dear Editor:

Astounding Stories is one of the least interesting and most "sensational" magazines I have ever read. The September, 1932, issue is a slight improvement, mainly because of Donald Wandrei. However, so infrequently do good authors write for you that I can frankly say you're terrible. Clifford Simak's story is about the most original story you have published. During your first six issues you would pass in the dark, but now you care nothing for quality, but desire quantity—of robots, rays, bewhiskered villains, heroes dragged through countless adventures, and the like. And for heaven's sake, drown Marchioni. Paul is the only artist of any merit. Wesso is good occasionally.[1]

Can't you dispose of the conventional ending:

". . . the ——— menace was gone forever. As they faced the sunset he put his arm around her, their eyes met. 'My hero!' she exclaimed. They clinched."

As you pay the highest rates among the fantastic magazines, you should have the best. But no, the drivel you publish is unspeakable. I speak mainly of the mercenary authors who use the same characters over and over and over. Raise the magazine from the cheap class in which it is. Stop publishing the same plots endless times.

---

1. RHB refers to Wandrei's "Raiders of the Universes" in the September 1932 issue. There was no story by Clifford D. Simak in that issue; RHB must be referring to "Hellhounds of the Cosmos" (June 1932). He also refers to the artists M. Marchioni, Frank R. Paul, and H. W. Wesso.

This will not be published, as you, contrary to your claims, print only complimentary letters. The few slams that get through are carefully censored with senile wit added by yourself. However, I at least express my opinion.—R. H. Barlow, Box 2382, Ft. Benning, Ga.

*Astounding Stories of Super-Science,* January 1933

To my mind you are deplorably lacking in imagination to so condemn some of the finest work of the greatest living fantasy writer. Must you be so literal, physical, in your interpretation of imaginative literature? Clark Ashton Smith, whom I have the honor of knowing, is primarily and foremost a poet, his work having received the highest commendation of such persons as Edwin Markham, George Sterling, etc. Truly, his colourfully nightmarish visions are far superior to the conventional type of—forgive me—trash—printed in the average mercenary scientifiction magazine. The mere fact that a few helpless ray-projectors, heroine consisting mainly of lipstick and legs, and a dastardly villain, are not dragged in by the nape of their respective necks certainly does nothing to impair the excellence of his dulcet prose, but rather is an agreeable relief.

*Fantasy Fan,* October 1933

I am highly pleased with your publication, and hope you can make a success of it. Glad to see you are printing Lovecraft's excellent article on "Supernatural Horror in Literature," and also his "Other Gods." Smith's tale was most entertaining.

*Fantasy Fan,* December 1933

The November TFF is decidedly improving and I look forward to future issues with much interest. I wonder how many collectors there are that can discriminate between the trash that seems popular and the best in Fantasy?

*Fantasy Fan,* January 1934

The March issue is very interesting. Howard's story is both unusual and well-written, and any poetry of Smith's is predestined to excellence.

I should venture that the fascination of the weird is through a vaguely masochistic pleasure that derives delight from frightening one's self! I believe the simile is ancient that our gaze will often return to the ugliest person in a room rather than the most handsome. Perhaps it is that constant saccharine palls. I claim it is untrue that "the beautiful, the good, is the aim of every true artist."

*Fantasy Fan,* April 1934

The July FANTASY FAN is one of the best, the Clark Ashton Smith tale being very good. My only objection is that you're wasting space on that ass Barlow in Baldwin's column!! But say, doesn't Mr. Pritchard have an eventful life?

*Fantasy Fan,* August 1934

Your August number is well up to average. The Morse story was well-written and interesting; and the two poems really quite good.

*Fantasy Fan,* October 1934

SaL gave me a few tips on how to insult the neighbors, who hitherto seemed impervious. Your rough and tumble policy is all to the good, so long as it doesn't become straight pyromania. I think that subtler phrasing of the blasts would occasionally deepen their effect; that the decorations are first-rate; that in over-reaction to the capons sex is treated like a novel discovery; that ROMANCE is the muddled offspring of mixed motives, being either a parody which half-wants to be serious (cf. And there the stars that quiver and start / Over the spires of her ruined land,) or incredibly poor poetry collapsing into satire—in either case ineffectual enough to be irritating; that olfactory adjectives are overused; and that savage satire of the sort you foster could be very useful. I think also you should keep it up.

*Sweetness and Light,* Fall 1939

Pedro! Pedro!

We do not have air raids, but during blackouts people shout "Pedro! Pedro!" or, as they would have it, "Peedro! Peedro!" Why is this? How long has it gone on? How general is the practice? Some say that it has to do with someone being locked out of the International House, others say it is the name of a dog lost a decade ago. Is the practice seasonal?

*Berkeley, California*

[EDITORIAL NOTE.—An article which has been promised for a forthcoming issue will deal with a related custom in college life. Information about places and seasons of this custom and any details about its age or supposed origin are greatly to be desired.]

## *The Time Machine*

(A Biographical Note)

The first publication of the tale that later became Wells' most famous short novel was in a paper issued at his school. The magazine, *The Science Schools Quarterly,* serialized a story of the same underlying plot, dealing with a Welsh professor. This was, broadly speaking, the debut of the story. It was later re-written, and some decade afterwards, after being published in both the *National Observer* and *The New Review,* appeared in a modest little volume published by Wm. Heinemann. Preceding it were two text-books and *Conversations with an Uncle* came out the day immediately before.

The book in its first English edition was a modest duodecimo volume measuring approximately $7 \times 5 \times 1$ ins. It was bound in a coarse linen-like grey cloth, and bore in purple lettering as well as the title a peculiar device of a rather emaciated sphinx. It contained pages 152 and XVI. The text, besides the title page, was virtually the same as that recently issued in *Short Stories of H. G. Wells,* but differed in several respects from that *Amazing Stories* used in their May, 1927 issue.

It appeared simultaneously both in the bound edition and wrappers, the former at the price of 3s, and the latter at 2s 6d.

## About H. G. Wells

A short while ago, H. G. Wells had a dream of the future which inspired the writing of his new semi-fantasy book, *The Shape of Things to Come*. It is an outline of the next century and a half, forecasting a World State eventually after destructive war. Published by Macmillan.

Wells writes in an almost invisible small hand.

A slightly demented person has been suing him for a decade, charging that he stole his *Outline of History* from an unpublished manuscript of his. Wells has had all the bills to pay, to say nothing of the annoyance.

Wells and Arthur Machen were both asked to contribute to an abortive magazine published in the '90s, and in one of the few issues appeared Wells' "The Cone"—Machen's didn't get in because the magazine expired. Wells' *The Time Machine* and Machen's effective horror story *The Three Impostors* were both quite in the limelight at the time. The short lived magazine was somewhat of a forerunner of the modern weird magazines. Machen was the subject of many amusing attacks, more fully reported in his autobiographical *Far Off Things* and *Things Near and Far,* even being accused of being deliberately unpleasant by some prudish ladies' magazine for his "Great God Pan."

The three H. G. Wells stories featured in *Weird Tales* during 1925 and 1926 were reprints,[1] though not mentioned as such when published. They were written about a quarter of a century before.

---

1. "The Stolen Body" (November 1925), "The Valley of Spiders" (December 1925), "A Dream of Armageddon" (March 1926).

# [Memories of Lovecraft]

From May 2nd to June 21st, 1934, I was visited by H. P. Lovecraft. I had long been an admirer of his work, and correspondent of his for three years. A day before his arrival we suddenly decided to add to the meagre furniture of his room with the purchase of a particularly repulsively-hued dresser, and so on the morning of May 2 we drove into town and brought the object back upon the front bumper of the automobile. Then I returned to meet my guest at the bus station. (He always travelled in this manner because of its cheapness.) He arrived at 12:15 noon, although the clerk at the station had told me that the bus would be late, and I had started to walk a few blocks in search of the current *Weird Tales*. I saw it coming, and hastily returned. He bounded out of the car and promptly greeted me. We made our way to a restaurant, and thence a short walk about town, discoursing various topics ranging from cheese to astrology. He spoke interminably in a pleasant but somewhat harsh voice, and proved to be a smooth-skinned man of face not unlike Dante. His hair was short and thinningly grey. We drove to the house and spent the afternoon in loud discussion.

Later that evening, after a row-boat trip upon the lake and a walk, he told me of a dream in which he was one of a band of mediaeval soldiers (altho' he says for him the Middle Ages are a perfect blank devoid of interest) crawling over house-tops in search of a monster-thing concealed somewhere, that was not only menacing the lives of the villagers, but their very souls as well. The searchers were led by a man upon a black horse who encouraged them actively and spurred them on. Finally locating the Thing where it was behind a chimney, the men advanced, obtaining foothold in broken tiles and thatched roofs. It looked at them with hate, for they bore Egyptian ankhs—it was afraid of their weapons, but not of the men. When it was cornered he saw for the first time it had wings like those of a flying-squirrel. It flew—or glided, and cast itself upon the man in the saddle upon the black horse, and looked up sardonically, for it had *merged* its identity and being with the man, and had the muzzle of the Thing in the armour of the knight. Then it laughed cacklingly and rode away.[1]

He told me of a plot-idea of his—based on disapprobation of the inconsistencies of time-travelling as usually written. This tale concerned a man who travelled to prehistoric times and found chiselled upon a rock words in English, *in his own hand.*[2]

Another dream of which he told me was that of being upon a high cliff by the ocean, where winds were blowing. A strange cloaked man was there with a number of large wooden balls; who claimed that he was a magician and could make the balls serve him. He was continually sending them off and once in a while they would return, rolling or flying through the air, and they would have encrustations of odd growths, or be slimy wet. There was no explanation to this dream, which terminated there.[3]

He compared age to a greased slide down which we went, unable to clutch for even a momentary hold or delay.

The whimsical appealed to him less than any other form of writing, and he possessed positively no sense of humor, looking on such as a childish pastime. The same applied to any type of game, for which he held active disliking.

He tells me he ghostwrote "The Curse of Yig,"[4] "The Last Test," "The Electric Executioner";[5] some Houdini stuff in W T[6]—

---

1. Cf. HPL to Robert Bloch, [c. August 1933] (*Letters to Robert Bloch and Others,* 66). The dream was incorporated into a story by J. Vernon Shea. "The Snouted Thing," in his *In Search of Lovecraft* (West Warwick, RI: Necronomicon Press, 1991), 25–28.

2. This is the plot-germ of "The Shadow out of Time" (November 1934–February 1935), although the writing is not chiseled on a rock but recorded in a book. The idea was conceived as early as mid-November 1930 (cf. *Dawnward Spire, Lonely Hill,* 268).

3. It does not appear that HPL ever incorporated this dream into a story.

4. As by Zealia Bishop.

5. Both as by Adolphe de Castro.

6. The only known tale ghostwritten by HPL for Houdini is "Under the Pyramids" (1924). HPL did do other revisory work for Houdini, but it chiefly concerned essays on spiritualism, witchcraft, and such matters, apparently unpublished and now nonextant.

"The Loved Dead";[7] that the latter was nearly suppressed in Milwaukee because of necrophilic theme.

He remarked also [that] Long is a Bolshevist, *poseur,* and has been even so mercenary as to sell letters of famous men to him; and his grandfather's cane.

When Howard Wandrei mentioned, in a letter, his forthcoming story "The Curse of the O'Mecca,"[8] Lovecraft observed, "O-Mecca? It sounds like an Irish Arab."

Concerning Derleth's affectations, posing, etc. he observed he would like to knock a little manliness into him, and he frequently expressed a desire to remove Long's abortive moustache.

"Francis Flagg"[9] is a Red of such virulence that deportation has been attempted, and if Walter J. Coates had not intervened, claiming that for t.b. it would be sure death, he would probably have been sent back to native Canada.

Long is self-consciously modern. For a while he was an aristocrat and claimed the writings of a patrician should be narrated definitely from that standpoint. Now he has swung to the opposite stand. To the former belong his best work—*Horror from the Hills* was of transition period. H. from H. embodies certain things *verbatim* from HPL's letters; notably the Roman dream.[10]

Long's sale of his rather miscellaneous library was caused by his radical activities—he was in need of money and his eye lit upon books as a saleable commodity—an attitude not accepted before.

Adolphe de Castro Danziger—the Bierce man[11]—he pronounced a charlatan, though clever. Bierce knew it himself; and

---

7. As by C. M. Eddy, Jr.

8. The tale is titled "The Hand of the O'Mecca" (*Weird Tales,* April 1935).

9. Pseudonym of Henry George Weiss.

10. Another account of the dream, as written in a letter to Bernard Austin Dwyer, can be found in HPL's *Letters to Maurice W. Moe and Others,* ed. David E. Schultz and S. T. Joshi (New York: Hippocampus Press, 2018), 357–64.

11. De Castro's was a friend of Ambrose Bierce. The two collaborated on a translation of Richard Voss's *Die Mönch des Berchtesgaden* (*The Monk and the Hangman's Daughter*). See de Castro's *Portrait of Ambrose Bierce* (1929), revised by Frank Belknap Long.

Sterling graphically portrayed the last meeting of De C and B; saying B. broke a cane over De C's head![12]

In the 1890's a book was issued (says L) with stories of now-famous writers—both good and poor. B. contributed; De C. had several tales. For some reason he is unable to tell me[,] all the extant copies were destroyed, or at any rate disappeared except for the two Congressional copies. So this same De Castro pulled a few political strings and had one copy returned! This, perishing of age, was used by HPL in preparing the stories for republication. De C. wanted them to survive in new life; but knew their inadequacy. L. was hired to rewrite them; and, taking the best one first ("The Last Test") "revised" it; then came "The Electric Executioner"—and afterwards de Castro couldn't pay him more so it stopped.[13]

He says he realizes his being a nonentity (!) but long ago gave up the idea of being noted.

He stayed up this past 3:00 writing!

"Whitehead wasn't afraid of the devil." He saw a snake crawling along the balustrade of his Dunedin house; and took a pair of gas-pliers, grabbing the thing about the head while it coiled helplessly about his arm, and plunged it into alcohol. This he presented to L. W. was a tin-god to his village, says L, and observed the word was ill-used; for he had reason to be entitled to be considered an oracle. He was also the most versatile man L. knew—played the piano well but didn't mention it.

"You would despise my library" he said—"it's just the kind you

---

12. Cf. HPL to Farnsworth Wright: "[de Castro], according to an anecdote recorded by George Sterling, parted from Bierce under the dramatic circumstance of having a cane broken over his head! When I saw his fiction I wondered why Ambrosius didn't use a crowbar." *Lovecraft Annual* No. 8 (2014): 13.

13. RHB may have misunderstood this matter slightly. A volume of de Castro's stories, *In the Confessional and the Following*, was published in 1893 under the imprint of the Western Authors Publishing Association (New York), an imprint organized by Bierce. It contained "A Sacrifice to Science" and "The Automatic Executioner," which HPL rewrote as "The Last Test" and "The Electric Executioner."

would."[14] He enumerated the contents in subjects; and said many of them were scientific or historical in nature. The one rare book he possessed was a first of Cotton Mather[15] for which $600.00 was rejected by his uncle.

His interest in 18th century was paralleled by Romanism.[16]

He possessed an autograph letter of Dunsany indirectly referring to a poem of HPL's.[17]

*Cthulhu* he pronounced Koot-u-lew—representing a sound never meant for human vocal organs in nearest form.

"Colour out of Space" was sent to Gernsback[18] because of Wright's rejections of other things which L. esteemed, and in anger at this! It brought only $25.00, and that after three dunning letters!

Gernsback never pays his bills, and owes Clark Ashton Smith $900.00 which a lawyer is trying to collect. So many are enraged in the industry [that] "to be a Gernsback lawyer has become as distinct an occupation as to be a corporation lawyer!"

Machen he pronounced Macken; R'lyeh with rising emphasis on latter letters; Azathoth—Nyarlathotep was based on a dream-name, as was also the first and others of the *Fungi from Yuggoth*.

We spoke a great deal—staying up till one o'clock, then my retiring while he wrote! In the afternoon we went to De Leon Springs and (after several amusing manifestations of our mutual absentmindedness) walked through the jungle-like growth which he admired very much; and I photographed him. Falling to canting on stealing, I jestingly reached for a flower on a blossoming tree be-

---

14. RHB was a collector of limited editions and rare books, things about which HPL cared little.

15. I.e., *Magnalia Christi Americana* (1702).

16. I.e., ancient Roman civilization, *not* the Roman Catholic church.

17. The letter was presumably written in connection with Dunsany's acting as Laureate Judge of Poetry for the UAPA in 1919–20. It may have been the one published in the *United Amateur* 20, No. 2 (November 1920): 22–23, although here there is no true allusion to any of HPL's poems.

18. I.e., Hugo Gernsback, editor of *Amazing Stories*. It appeared in the issue for September 1927.

yond my reach. Behold! He jumped up and picked it to present to me. "I'm simply ruthless," he said. "Ignorance of the law—I shall say I was told when everyone had left (the tourists usually depart March first and places are closed for the summer) I understood it was permitted to take whatever you wanted—in moderation of course."

An occasional defect in speech caused a "ch" sound to supplant "s".

His fondness for cats was everywhere manifest. "Bless Grandpa's old bones" he would say as an ejaculatory observation of affection.

"It must be terrible to worry about getting the money to have his suit pressed and get a new hat; and then also worrying about We Workers," he said of Long's sociological affectations. It appears whatever the phase—goldfish raising or socialism—Long is an extremist.

H. Warner Munn has such a belief in the supernatural as to have caused him to become Catholic after his marriage; and almost repudiate his earlier work as morbid and not nice. Recently he wrote a thing L. contemned ("The Wheel"[19] is an old thing) and said Munn was getting seedy.

Smith's exotic element results partly from Sterling and mainly from his father's early life in South America. The continual mention of the exotic flowers and creeping poisonous vines has resulted in S's style and mimicing. Says L: "He has not improved on nature—he has supplemented it." Smith never took a drawing lesson in his life.

He carried an astonishing number of articles in a tiny black bag.

Speaking of "The Picture in the House" he said (while of course there is an actual plate of the Anzique Cannibal Shop in such a book) rurals hold a horror to him. "They may speak servilely; but you *feel* they want to kill you." His loathing of gnarled, brutal rustics caused P. in H.

He wrote "Herbert West" as he went along.[20]

"The tragedy of the artist is that he cannot keep his own work.

---

19. *Weird Tales,* May 1933.

20. RHB means that HPL wrote the six-part serial in installments rather than as a piece.

An author can, through the printing-press; but an artist either has his work or someone else has it."

Wells' *War of the Worlds* he regards as the classic interplanetary story—none have been written—aside from "City of the Singing Flame"[21]—that deal with reverse procedure satisfactorily.

The *theme* of "In the Vault" was suggested by old C. W. Smith, Haverhill, Mass., the 82-year-old who issued such typographically ugly papers.[22]

"I'm afraid 'The Hound' is a dead dog."

"'The White Ship' is sunk."

We spent an afternoon on the other side of the lake in a small grove; and he offered assistance with certain of my literary efforts. He said in *speaking* he was not strict concerning pure English; but when he was on paper he took more pains.

"The Moon-Bog" was virtually written to order, through a meeting of amateur journalists on St. Patrick's day. The writing was specified to concern Ireland.

Frequently we would boat upon the smallish lake;[23] and usually be late for dinner. Thus one night he observed, "I'm rowing until someone reproves me!"

"The Outsider" was a series of climaxes—originally intended to cease with the graveyard episode; then he wondered what would happen if people would see the ghoul; and so included the second climax; finally he decided to have the Thing see itself!

A curious, half-jesting tone of melodrama entered his voice, as with dire meaning he would reach a climax in either the narration or reading aloud of a story.

An anecdote from Price,[24] repeated by HPL, was of Robt. S. Carr and Farnsworth Wright. C., it appeared, was financially embar-

---

21. By Clark Ashton Smith.

22. Smith was the editor of the amateur journal the *Tryout*, which was notorious for its numerous typographical errors and somewhat sloppy layouts

23. Which they called "the Moon Pool" after A. Merritt's story.

24. E. Hoffmann Price.

rassed at some hotel. To avoid paying his bill, Wright pretended to be a legal guardian over Carr; and intimated C. was irresponsible and dangerously mentally deficient. So they got out without paying!

He confesses to having cold-bloodedly invented Wilbur Whateley of Dunwich—but in many other tales—Cthulhu, for example—actual dreams are the bases.

"All American poets except Poe are minor ones."

"There was one of the worst instances of misdirected intellect," he said of Houdini. and deplored the fact [that] with all his accomplishments H. "chose to be merely a clever showman".

Politics have a drama in them—"That's why the Great Wall of China was built—that's why the barbarians came down from the North to sack southern cities."

His life, he claimed, was prosaic and dull—reading, writing and retiring.

Attempts to rhyme given words I selected:

> John and I were out fixing light wires near Schenectady
> I fixed up one and the other connected he.

> Attila the Hun is called by the Germans Etzel
> This comes from eating the pretzel.

> When we were out riding along the Star range
> I saw the moon rising up like a large orange.

My quest for something to kill time was a source of perplexity to him, for he claimed that he never had to do anything to kill time, but was always rushed to get what was necessary done!

He contended that he would not write, if he could find what he desired already written.

If he were to make any exception to "literature" in Sup. H. in Lit., it would be for "The Moon Pool".[25]

---

25. By A. Merritt. HPL alludes to the original novelette published in a pulp magazine, not the later expansion into a novel.

Of Wilbur Whateley in "Dunwich": "It was a Klarkashtonic monster"—he admitted.

Derleth's poetry he seemed to think fair enough, but he added: "Of course one can't tell the value of this loosely-constructed verse."

Representing evil entities as composite monsters he observed one day was a little childish; and yet owned that they must be more fully described than mere formless shadows. It must be handled very carefully, he said ruefully.

A plot in a weird story he called "excess baggage"—mood and atmosphere being all.

This highly ludicrous and rather pathetic incident I record for no useful purpose.

We had been in the habit of gathering blueberries beyond a shallow creek running between the swamp. Now HPL was no woodsman, as may be seen, and it was always perilous to trust his poor sight and lack of horse-sense. However, he often went along insistently against our polite discouragement. One such time—since he had nothing but his everyday suit, he arrayed himself in comical cast-off garments. Old mountaineer Mrs. Johnston loaned him her khaki trousers and with various other contributions, he set out with us. A series of recent rains had rendered the land very muddy, and the creek-channel had far overflowed, leaving a widespread thin puddle through which we had no choice but to wade. At the deeper creek had been placed a board to serve as bridge; and this was crossed without mishap. We spent some time gathering berries, but were through long before his dim eyes had attained even a half-basket. So we helped him fill it, and then all started home (Lovecraft, J.[26] and myself). He lingered for possible other berries, and fearing just such a mishap, I stood upon the makeshift bridge and called out its location to HPL. He replied that he saw it, and so we continued the quarter mile to the house—and deposited our berries in the common pie-fund, going then to change our splashed

---

26. Charles B. Johnston, the Barlows' hired hand.

clothes. We were quite tidied up, and still no HPL. Wondering at his delay, a series of confusions downstairs attracted me, and although I missed the scene myself (meeting him upstairs later) mother said he came in, soaking wet, and with most of his berries gone. In the God-awful rig he must have appeared very comical, though it had also a tragic air about it. Promptly he said to mother, "I really must apologize!" She, amazed by this vision of a thoroughly wet HPL, said in surprise, "What for?"

He then on to explain he had been homeward bound when he came to the creek. Not seeing the board, he was abruptly pitched up to his neck into cold water. The berries were flung up and upset, most of them going on the slight current. Quite unable to swim I think he must have expected promptly to drown—this, however, did not happen and he moistly and contritely returned. For the sake of decency I should omit this, but the tragicomedy of L. in that condition is amusing beyond conception. And to think he apologized for losing the berries!

• • • •

Mrs. Gamwell's stories of how HPL for a while insisted "I'm a little girl"—and of how he would be set on the table to spout Tennyson's "Come into the garden, Maud, for the black bat Night has flown."

O. W. Holmes saw HPL as baby, and I. Guiney[27] was friend of mother—often visited.[28]

---

27. I.e., Louise Imogen Guiney, a minor poet.

28. These last two entries were probably made during RHB's visit to Providence in September 1936.

## Obiter Dictum

I have just received what appears to be the October mailing.[1] To even the most tolerant eye it is not satisfactory. There are in it, perhaps, a half-dozen worthy papers; not all of these are regularly issued. The rest of the envelope is cluttered up with futilely small or juvenile leaflets. One is grateful for the effort of these lesser papers, but even with the handicap of size less superficial material might be employed.

In three of the larger papers, whose combined size would accommodate *Hyperion* or the *Ancient Mariner* twice over, space is employed variously for a tangled theological burbling; frivolities in no way concerned with the N.A.P.A.; and thrifty use of the mailing bureau as a means of vending objects that range from beauty preparations to books on parlor magic. Now this is really dismal! I am aware that good material is not readily had. But if amateurdom means to crawl out of its literary pigsty, external contributions must be sought until a clean-up is effected. Mr. Edkins has reviewed matters in the *Californian*—it remains to follow his suggestions. The level of the "little magazines", though not their freakishness, must be our goal. We must lay siege to them and ultimately embody them in the association. Theirs is properly our field, and it must be attained.

## Blake and "The Songs of Innocence"

> *They look upon his eyes,*
> *Fill'd with deep surprise;*
> *And wondering behold,*
> *A spirit arm'd in gold.*

The overwhelming genius of William Blake could not be confined to a single art. Its wild spontaneity took form both pictorially and poetically. Equally master in whichever field he chose, he thought

---

1. It appears that RHB contemplated sending *Leaves* through the National Amateur Press Association (NAPA), although there is no evidence that he actually did so.

of them in unity. Referring once to a creative work that he planned, Blake spoke of it as a "poem or a picture." Once his genius was free of the limitations of ordinary printing, he merged the arts more than anyone else had ever done.

As soon as Blake perfected his obscure process, wherein text and drawings were executed on a single plate and printed in rich colours, the stream of his genius gathered force, released by this new freedom of style. The *Songs of Innocence,* with its pastoral imagery, was the first of his colour-printed books, and after nearly a century and a half the fresh, joyous beauty enchants the beholder. The light happiness of the little book hides deep, penetrative thought, yet the music of the song is no less dulcet. "Piping down the valleys wild, Piping songs of pleasant glee," he gently leads us from the sweet beauty of *The Lamb* to the dark grandeur and deep symbolism of his famous *Tyger,* and yet the freshness remains. *The Lamb* is more than a happy lyric; it is a wondering heart confronting the starry universe, at the same time that it is a childlike song. "Little lamb who made thee Dost thou know who made thee Gave thee life and bid thee feed By the stream and o'er the mead; Gave thee clothing of delight, Softest clothing woolly bright . . ." But I must not quote, for if I might, I fear the whole book would be contained in this brief fumbling note. *The Lamb,* and its dark mate, *The Tyger,* are the outpourings of a great intellect in that simplicity which is more powerful than any gewgawed style. The few defects of meter and rhyme are spontaneous bursts of sincerity too great for any pedantry to bind.

Although this book was conceived and issued by him as a unit; the fragile loveliness of his decorations twining through the poems; it is not always possible for them to accompany one another. The severance is a mutilation, yet his greatness withstands even such unfavorable presentation. Let the lover of unaffected beauty take down this small book of joy and wonder, that his life be enriched and his perception of the universe made clear.

## A Seditious Book

John Strachey has recently written *The Theory and Practise of Socialism*. As the baffled Republican Party is beginning to realize, things are happening today; and one discussed-but-misunderstood trend is that towards Socialism in many countries of the world. Many people favor or oppose it without bothering to find out what it actually is, and how it works; and even if they are not of that benighted class which murkily conceives it is "taking all the money and dividing it up equally."

Those to dislike it shriek that it wouldn't work, and that, if it did, all the incentive to life would be destroyed. This incentive appears to be the slightly barbarous chances to get the best of one's neighbors (although capitalist economies put it more elegantly) and to steam under the Jolly Roger. Even if this were not a harmful attitude, it has little to do with the enormous classes of workers who do not live by profit, but through the sale of their labor. To many, it is a little incomprehensible that sometimes even miserably paid workers defend the system responsible for their misfortunes, but they have been told that it is unavoidable for some of us to starve and live in city slums while food is being wasted and destroyed, and materials and labor thrown about in an effort to patch the lopsided capitalist system. And they have not questioned it.

John Strachey has; and his book is a general outline of the kind of system under which we live, and where it breaks down, and what kind of workable substitute there is. Such books are not as easily read as *Tarzan of the Apes,* but they are more important because they affect us and our aspirations.

Things are happening today, and our lives are going to be a good deal better or a good deal worse. You must not get the idea that capitalism is eternal and unalterable. It isn't. Even if we paid no attention to it it would change, but machines that are not watched are likely to smash up very disastrously; and some things that have happened in Germany and are trying to happen in Spain would not be pleasant here.

# Obiter Scriptum

Or, Succotash without Seasoning

It has long been the custom for new papers to justify their existence and to outline their intended course. A good many periodicals which attain considerable circulation among the illiterate, would find themselves treed were they called before a literary St. Peter and asked for credentials. That no one may fail to comprehend the aim and scope of *Leaves,* this discursive network is inserted here, where it is not likely to be found.

*Leaves* is an uncommon botanical bit, modelled, I suppose, after Cook's *Recluse* of ten years past,[1] which (although it survived to no second number) collected a variety of material, chiefly fantastic, in complete indifference to popular taste. Such stories, together with discussions of the genre, and analyses of certain masters in it, will be the contents of *Leaves.* The reprinting of various Gothic performances, not now obtainable, is under vague consideration, and it will be noted that in the present issue all items are not new to print. For the few other pieces contained no excuse need be proffered: intrinsic merit and the element of variety both figuring in my choice.

There has long been needed a magazine able to present serious ventures into the field of the macabre and fantastic—a field which retains sizeable possibilities in spite of all the trash that has emanated from the newsstand. One cannot take into serious consideration the various cheap magazines which flourish on the corpse of literature . . . they are aimed at a definite commercial goal, and on this account, whatever the real taste and ability of their editors, cannot foster esoteric probings. Here might be recalled the lines of

---

1. When RHB learned that W. Paul Cook's second number of *The Recluse* was abandoned after being partially typeset, he sought to obtain the mss. of all the items authors had submitted for it. Some of those items appeared in *Leaves,* RHB's attempt to issue a magazine like Cook's, albeit mimeographed rather than typeset, from what he wanted to call the Southern Recluse Press. He published two issues and had planned content for two more.

Humphrey Littlewit, on the achievements of a popular writer:

> In former times our lettered brethren sought
> To starve their bodies while they fed their thought;
> Unawed by wealth, unbought by luxury,
> They own'd their brains, and scorn'd the slaver's fee.
> Poor, modest, proud, they held the princely pen,
> Masters and peers, and conscious gentlemen;
> And who, unbowed, would not their place prefer
> To the rich tradesman's fawning cur?
> But Time, the Goth, each harnessed virtue blights
> As his curst legions storm our guarded heights;
> Behold! Where bards free music once outpoured,
> A crowd of lackeys cringes round their lord;
> From gold-stained pockets beg their tawdry doles,
> And stuff their bellies as they sell their souls.
> What shall they write? 'Tis not for them to say—
> King Mob will give them orders for the day!
> Scrawling what's bid, they woo the unwashed throng
> In chap-book prose and loud illiterate song;
> Themselves in boasting, not in art, express,
> And reckon worth in terms of gainfulness.
> See! see! where once the honest dreamer tried
> To scale the slopes of loveliness and pride,
> To cast off earth, and reach th' ethereal mead
> High o'er the slopes where waddling porkers feed,
> Our newer band opposing objects find,
> And lose the freeman's in the miser's mind.
> 'Tis theirs to shine in tests of haggling skill,
> Their bulging purses, not their heads, to fill;
> To drown their yearnings and their freeman's bent
> In sticky swamps of servile excrement.
> Hail to the carcass, fed, though bound in chains;
> Pox on your dreamer's or your poet's pains!

We drink to flesh in one black Stygian gulp,
And sink our spirits in a grave of PULP![2]

-o-

That fantasy is a legitimate type of artistic expression has been amply demonstrated by the work of a hundred eminent writers; while its prodigious background of psychology and racial tradition is indicated in Lovecraft's masterful *Supernatural Horror in Literature*. Regarding dicta from certain quarters, Clark Ashton Smith has this to say:

> We have been told that literature dealing with the imaginative and fantastic is out of favour among the Intellectuals, whoever they are. Only the Real, whatever that is or may be, is admissible for treatment; and writers must confine themselves well within the range of statisticians, lightning calculators, Freud and Kraft-Ebbing, the Hearst and McFadden publications, WPA, and mail-order catalogues. Chimeras are no longer the mode, the infinite has been abolished; mystery is obsolete, and Sphinx and Medusa are toys for children. The weird and the unearthly are outlawed, and all mundane impossibilities (which, it may be, are the commonplaces of the Pleiads) have been banished to some limbo of literalistic derision. One may write of horses and hippopotami but not of hippogriffs; of biographers, but not of ghouls; of slum-harlots or the hetairae of Nob Hill but not of succubi. In short, all pipe-dreams, all fantasies not authorised by Freudianism, by sociology, and the five senses, are due for the critical horse-laugh, when, through ignorance, effrontery, or preference, they find a place in the subject-matter of some author unlucky enough to have been born into the age of Jeffers, Hemingway, and Joyce.
>
> Let us examine these amazing dicta, fathered, as they must be, by people whose literal-mindedness can be surpassed only by that of their "four-footed betters." Surely it is axiomatic that in thought or art we deal not with things themselves, but with concepts of things. One may write, like Villon, of Muckle Meg and the Fair Helm-Maker; or, like Sterling, evoke Lilith and the blue-eyed vampire: in either case, only figments of the poet's mind are presented. It is for

2. "Lines upon the Magnates of the Pulp" by HPL.

the creator, not the critic, to choose that image or symbol which suits him best. People who cannot endure anything with a tinge of trope or fantasy, should confine their reading to the census-returns. There, if anywhere, they will find themselves on safe ground.

To touch on other considerations: Why this thirst for literalism, for nothing but direct anthropological data, which would proscribe the infinitudes of imagination, would bar all that can lift us, even in thought, above the interests of the individual or the species? Does it not imply a cosmic provincialism, an overweening racial egomania?

Indeed, if all things fantastic or impossible are to be barred as literary subject-matter, where is one to draw the line? Many thinkers who lived before Freud, and some who live contemporaneously with him, have maintained that the world itself is a fantasy; or, in De Casseres' phrase, a "superstition of the senses." Gautier has pointed out that we live only by illusion, by a process of seeing ourselves and all things as they are not. The animals alone, being without imagination, have no escape from reality. From paretic to psychoanalyst, from poet to rag-picker, we are all in flight from the real. Truth is what we desire it to be, and the facts of life are a masquerade in which we imagine that we have identified the maskers. The highest intellects have always delighted in poetic fancy and philosophical paradox, knowing well that the universe itself is multiform fantasy and paradox, and that everything perceived or conceived as actuality is merely one phase of that which has or may have innumerable aspects. In this phantom whirl of the infinite, among these veils of Maya that are sevenfold behind sevenfold, nothing is too absurd, too lovely, or dreadful to be impossible.[3]

The game is eminently worth a whole candelabrum, but a certain knowledge of trumps is necessary to the skillful player. That something of maturity is absent from the common delineation of "the night side of nature"[4] needs little emphasis. Whether this fabulous territory is capable of further development remains something of a question. Such development, I think, must be in the direction

---

3. *Fantasy Fan* 2, No. 3 (November 1934): 37, 45.

4. The title of a book (1848) by Catherine Ann Crowe (1803–1876), an English novelist.

of subtlety; the barnacles must be pried off if the ship is to bear new cargoes. The late Robert E. Howard commented on this in a letter:

". . . the rustle of leaves when there is no wind, the sudden falling of a shadow across a door, the furtive trying of a window-catch, the sensation of unseen eyes upon one, these give rise to speculations more monstrous and terrors more cosmically icy, than any chain-clanking apparition, or convention . . . When a writer specifically describes the object of his horror, gives it worldly dimensions and solid shape, he robs it of half its terrors. Somewhere, somehow, there must lurk in the dim gulfs of our racial memories, titanic and abysmal horrors beyond the ken of the material mind. For how else are we able to half conceive and fear entities we are not able to describe? Seek to draw their images for the conscious mind and they fade away. . . . Humanity fears floods and starvation, foes and serpents and wild beasts, but there are fears outside these concrete things."[5]

Certainly, Lewis Carroll's parody verses,

"I dreamt I dwelt in marble halls,
And each damp thing that creeps and crawls
Went wobble-wobble on the walls . . ."[6]

effectively disposes of a certain school of horror-manufacturers. The monster that consumes people like some horrid kind of sandwich is a limited conception . . . although there is a pitfall of equal dimensions reaching out for the incautious foot—too hazily-defined material makes not for convincingness, and some ghosts must be of a different colour and substance than mist.—Here again I resort to the otiose practice of quotation; this time from Ernest A. Edkins:

5. Robert E. Howard to HPL, c. September 1930; *A Means to Freedom: The Letters of H. P. Lovecraft and Robert E. Howard,* ed. S. T. Joshi, David E. Schultz, and Rusty Burke (New York: Hippocampus Press, 2009), 50.

6. Carroll's parody of "I Dreamt I Dwelt in Marble Halls" or "The Gipsy Girl's Dream," a popular aria (Act 2, Scene 1) from *The Bohemian Girl* (1843), an opera by Michael William Balfe. Published in his *Lays of Mystery, Imagination and Humour* (1855). The text in the libretto reads: "I dreamt I dwelt in marble halls, / with vassals and serfs at my side / and of all who assembled within those walls . . ."

For some time I have been reading such contemporary stories of the weird persuasion as have come my way, and my impression is that they are mostly of inferior quality. Admitting that they are weird enough, in conception, I ask myself "what is it that they appear to lack?" Assuming that plausibility is not only possible but highly desirable even in the weirdest fiction, I think that many of them are deficient both in conviction and in that intangible something which, for want of a more definite term I must call "atmosphere." Perhaps the one quality is dependent upon the other. Gautier said that the inexpressible does not exist; it scarcely follows, however, that everything conceivable may be endowed with plausibility, nor can discriminating readers be expected to find any great relish in stories that are merely fantastic, without some saving grace of probability. In fairy tales for children this lack is a virtue rather than a defect, but weird fiction addresses itself to a less credulous audience. In fine, the reader says to himself, "this thing *might* happen," and is content to let it go at that; but if he says (however illogically) "this could *not* happen, and therefore the author is deliberately spoofing me," the story, I think, must fall short of its objective. The truth of the incidents need not be and in fact never is actually demonstrable, but it should not be implausible, *as the reader sees it*. This of course raises a tremendous moot point, and it may well be contended that since weird stories are generally a product of incredible phantasy, they only become credible to those who are willing to accept the paradoxical dictum, "credo quia impossible est." I shall not debate the point, but will merely record my own instinctive reaction: if the story seems to me to be wholly lacking in that daunting aura of dimly revealed but persuasive *actuality* whereby the stealthy horrors of Arthur Machen's creations, (for example) are enabled to creep into and for the time being dominate my customary skepticism, it fails to hold my interest. If this were only a gratuitous and obvious statement of the fact that Machen is supreme in his field, there would be little point in making it, but what I wish to underscore is the general failure of most writers of weird fiction to strive for some appearance, some effect of credibility; and my objection is to their bland assumption that phantasy in fiction requires no other support. It seems to me that stories of this type should always leave the author an exit; as when his quite incredible yarn purports to be transcribed from a manuscript found in a bottle, or to have been related to him by some mysterious traveller. Failing that somewhat shop-worn but still effective device, they must depend for plausibility on the evocative effects of sheer *atmosphere,* of nuances and implications, rather than of bald statement.

So many writers of weird fiction lean so heavily on grotesque nomenclature that I really think a study might be profitably made of the whole terminology, with a view to divesting it, as far as possible, from its grosser grotesqueries. Surely none but infantile minds are thrown into a state of receptive coma or condition of shivering ecstasy by such faintly comic vocables as Zuggoth, to mention the first one that comes to my mind. Nothing could be more fatal to the author's purpose then the employment of patently "shuddery" terms which, if they connote anything, are only apt to remind one of such absurdities as the "Wizard of Oz." It would therefore seem that weird names and titles should be chosen with the utmost artfulness and with a fine discrimination, different from known terms, but not *too* different. To repeat what I had occasion to say in a recent review, I much prefer that sort of darkly allusive prose wherein phantasy is enriched with a delicate imagination and shudders emerge from the incommunicable. For it is my opinion that fright evaporates as soon as it is catalogued, and that the hiding place of horror must be divined rather than revealed in the tenebrous caverns of the Unknown. Suggestion, adumbration, atmosphere, a certain *strangeness* that eludes analysis, these are the most potent ingredients of the *frisson;* Poe had the formula, also Arthur Machen and Lord Dunsany; but in reading the output of our current weird magazines, I get the impression that these qualities are no longer in favour. I suspect that I am behind the times in my tastes, and that such refinements of style may now be regarded as finical.

Another peculiarity of weird fiction appears to be its insistence on the quality of purposeful cruelty. In almost every super-physical bourne that is projected in contemporary tales of this character, the superior beings in their encounters with earthlings are seldom motivated by an intelligent curiosity, such as might be expected, and *never* by pity, sympathy, or kindliness. In the abstract, at least, it is incredible that vastly more advanced entities should malignantly *hate* us and take fiendish pleasure in destroying us, though conceivably they might be profoundly indifferent to us. True it is that in this un-regenerate world the strong oppress the weak, more often than not, but in most of us there exists an obscure hope, if not a belief, that in the long scale of progression, in worlds other and brighter than ours, if any, there must be creatures so infinitely further along in de-velopment that they would be more inclined to commiserate our unhappy lot, than to make it harder. The analogy is human and un-derstandable when we reflect that only brutal and insensitive people go out of their way to step on an inoffensive insect. Why, then, this almost universal representation of imagined spiritual entities as uni-formly cruel? Is it not, perhaps, the unconscious reflection of our own ruthlessness? Of course I quite see that there is more of an ata-vistic "punch" in the story of cruelty than in one of pleasant surprise, nor to I advocate the portraiture of angels of light instead of demons of the pit. But it occurs to me that a fine point of technique has been overlooked. We might assume that the Lords of the Unknown Spaces are so far removed from our tragic microcosm as to be sub-limely indifferent to our fate, as we are to the infusoria in a drop of water; but it is not also possible that these Lords of Space might be revealed to us as creatures of blinding beauty, rather than as crudely anthropomorphic monsters? Would not their intensely curious and quite *unconscious* cruelty be vastly more poignant, more artistic, more truly shocking, than tortures inflicted by sadistic super-beasts? Moreover, there is something slightly juvenile in our habit of por-traying these superior being as of Cyclopean proportions, and per-haps a more lancinating effect of bewildered horror could be attained if they were presented in the shapes of tiny and entrancing loveliness, working their terrible wills on us in a spirit of joyous ex-perimentation. The converse attitude of super-beings, monstrous in size and nature, pursuing their earthly victims with malignant ha-tred, seems to me to violate an unexpressed but implicit canon, since hatred generally involves *fear*—the whole concept being, in fact, as absurd as that of the Old Testament Jehovah. In weird fiction, I am inclined to think, the spiritual *chill* must be attained by other and subtler artifices. I am not at all sure that I have any definite idea of what form the new technique should take, but I believe that I can recognise some of its qualities when I rarely encounter them . . .[7]

Here is meat for disputatious anthropophagi; are there others to answer the dinner-bell?

## Note

Since 1921, the year of *Sails & Mirage,* there has been no new collection of George Sterling's mature poetry. Two volumes of fin de siècle amatory verse have indeed appeared, but these do not represent the final, most considered phases of his work. Except for a body of sonnets, the present collection embraces all that in the editor's judgment is worthwhile of the poems of Sterling's last decade, and collects for the first time such material as the author himself would have gathered into a final volume.

Thanks are due The American Mercury; Harper's; The Christian Science Monitor; Mr. Harry Robertson; The Nation; The New Republic; The Oxford University Press of New York; The Saturday Review of Literature; Scribner's; and The Virginia Quarterly Review for permission to include poems in this book. To any publisher who may have been overlooked, apologies are herewith made.

## The Children of Axayacatl

Dr. Bolton's Seminar
24 April, 1942

One must disregard most of the material written since 1600 concerning pre-Hispanic matters in Mexico, because it merely repeats old errors. This done, abundant Indian records exist, which are superficially chaotic, but which can be reduced to solid facts by sifting them and comparing a quantity of documents. Thus we learn many details about the family of the Emperor whom Cortes found ruling in 1519. Axayacatl (1469–1481) had many other children besides

---

7. An extract from "Observations on Weird Fiction," T.Ms., JHL.

the celebrated Moctezuma II and Cuitlahuac: at least a score of children by his five-odd wives.

Axayacatl's chief queen, heiress to the decayed grandeur of Tula in the modern State of Hidalgo, bore him two sons: Tlacahuepantzin and Ixtlilcuechahuac. These two are the subjects of much confusion since a god, a hero of the first half of the fifteen century, and a son of Moctezuma II bore the former name. Our subject certainly died in 1495, but details are strangely absent. Through an erroneous document which the chronicler Tezozomoc had at second hand and mangled further, his death is confused with that of his brother in 1507. The latter, Ixtlilcuechahuac, perished elaborately in battle to save the cornfields of the modern San Martin Huaquechula on the Mexican frontier in what is now the State of Puebla. Other notable sons of Axayacatl are Macuilmallinaltzin, whose story is obscure, though he seems to have been a candidate for the throne, and Tezozomoctizin Acolnahuacatl, who inherited a song.

Only one daughter can be checked on, and she *was* checked on, by her husband, and smitten down for her French Novel sins.

Any investigation of the richly-documented pre-Hispanic history shows the emphatic need for a key to all the jaw-breaking names of individuals in the Chronicles; such as the index of Caciques which Lie, Rafael Garcia Granados has valiantly begun in Mexico City.

## SELECTED BIBLIOGRAPHY

*INDIAN "ANNALS"*

*Los Anales de Cuauhtitlan* (Códice Chimalpopocatl). Published as DIE GESCHICHTE DER KONIGREICHE VON MEXICO UND COLHUACAN by Walter Lehmann, Stuttgart, 1936. The only reliable edition of this fundamental document, which covers a thousand-odd years of Mexican prehistory.

*Códice Aubin* (Codex of 1576). Pub. Paris, 1893 as "Histoire de la Nation Mexicaine". Also Mexico, 1902, in the Cuadernos of Penafiel.

*Códice Telleriano-Remensis*. Edition of the Duque de Loubat.

*PROSE HISTORIES BASED ON PRECEDING TYPE OF DOC-UMENT.*

Ixtlilxochitl, Fernando de Alva. *Obras.* Publisher by Chavero, 1892. A fertile but confused source which should not be relied on alone. Draws on Anales de Cuauhtitlan extensively.

Duran, Fray Diego de. *Historia de los Indios de Nueva Espana.* Mexico, 1867–1880.

Tezozomoc, Fernando Alvarado. *Cronica Mexicana.* Mexico, 1878.

*MODERN WORKS DEALING WITH BACKGROUND.*

Alcocer, Dr. Ignacio. *Apuntes sobre la antigua Mexico-Tenochtitlan,* Tacubaya, D.F., 1935.

Valliant, Dr. George. *The Aztecs.* New York, 1941. (Half technical, half Sunday-supplement, but the best work in English, and an excellent bibliography).

# Origin of "Guarache"

Origin of "Guarache" (2:7, 44, 58, 74).[1] Prior to the Conquest the Mexicoan Indian wore a sandal which may still be seen in sculpture and in codices. The *guarache* was introduced in the early seventeenth century when a Japanese embassy visited the country. The historical circumstances of this visit are given in Zelia Nuttall's *Earliest Historical Relations Between Mexico and Japan* (Berkeley, 1906). With the *guarache* came the grass raincoat, which is also found in the Philippines.

---

1. RHB's note relates to a query by Carleton Beals in *American Notes & Queries* 2, No. 1 (April 1942): 7, which reads in part: "The Mexican Indian uses a leather-thonged sandal, which he calls *guarache* (pronounced 'wä-rä′ che'). Without ever investigating, I supposed the word to be of Aztec origin. However, some years ago, on reading Lafcadio Hearn's two volumes of travels in Japan, I came across a sentence in which he spoke of the soft swish of the Japanese *waraji* on the stones."

James Cooper Clark touches upon the guarache in *Codex Mendoza* (London, 1938, v. 1, p. 57). He states:

> The word came into use in the first quarter of the seventeenth century when, in 1614, a Japanese Embassy arrived on the way to the courts of Phillip III at Madrid, and Pope Paul V (Borghese) at Rome. Quite a number of Japanese remained in Mexico until this Embassy returned from Europe, and during their lengthy stay taught the Mexicans how to plait sandals from straw, and rain-coats from palm leaves. Both these Japanese commodities have survived to this day amongst the Pacific Coast peoples.

I was told, moreover, some months ago by a Japanese that the word for sandal was the same in the Japanese language as in the Mexican.

## The Burro in America

The absence of a beast of burden, except for the unridable llama of Peru, was a principal retarding factor in the development of New World cultures. The Spanish burro has become so thoroughly a part of any Latino-American scene that it is easy to forget that it was an importation.

In a petition dated November 19th, 1594, found in one of the more than 30,000 volumes of MSS in the Archivo General of Mexico, Hernando Marin, an octogenarian, testified that sixty-three years before (1531) he had come to Mexico and *fue el primero que trajo plantas de España y burros para la cria de mulas.* On the basis of this earlier action he asked in the petition for the *corregimiento* of the pueblos of Mexicaltzinco or Atlitalaquian.

This note was drawn from a series of annotations on curious items made by the antiquarian Fernando Ramirez, in a manuscript volume "Monumentos de la Dominación Espanola," Mexican MS 159 of the Bancroft Library, Berkeley, California. The same volume contains many notes on the old streets, buildings, and districts of Mexico City, all taken from obscure manuscripts.

# Three Letters on H. P. Lovecraft

29 Oct. 1942
2521 Benvenue, Berkeley, Cal.

Dear Mr. Farsaci:

Your letter brings up many things of a former aspect of my existence; many painful things which I have begun to forget. I do not like much to go over them again, but your fair spirit of inquiry . . . makes it all most obligatory.

Howard Lovecraft was my greatest friend in my adolescence, and my guest in my home for weeks at a time . . . When he died he left a series of INSTRUCTIONS IN CASE OF DECEASE, of which the first item read "The first choice of my books and manuscripts is to go to R H Barlow, my literary executor," so you see neither Derleth nor Wandrei ever was considered, and that what they have done was due to my permission, since I knew they had contacts and abilities to bring out the volumes in an adequate way. It has occurred to me that you might publish the copy which Mrs. Gamwell, Mr. Lovecraft's aunt, wrote out for me in longhand, a few days after his burial. I am writing to get it from a law-firm in Kansas City . . . I may add of course I have the entire manuscript of UNKNOWN KADATH, and that I gave Derleth whatever text he has, as well as CHARLES DEXTER WARD. It is airy babble to speak (as I think the publisher did) of their "unearthing" it. All of Lovecraft's manuscripts in my possession (including those which he gave me during his lifetime . . .) are deposited in the John Hay Library.

Now you ask me what I have for your magazine. The answer is only those mss. which I copied on film, such as the enclosed specimen. The rest were too bulky and I was too often in Mexico, where all my interests lie these days; and I deposited them in the library mentioned. I have some fragments; some notes for INNSMOUTH, and maps and drawings; some prose (stories) from the Amateur Press of 1921, and his *juvenilia* on film. The INNSMOUTH notes, and the notes for his last story, never written, I might copy off on the typewriter for you, since I presume you have no microfilm reader. God knows where I'll get the time; I am a Teaching Assistant here and have 120 students to look after, and my own research . . . Meantime, you will pardon the brevity of this letter, and accept my real thanks for your sensible attitude.

Most sincerely yours,<br>R. H. Barlow

Lovecraft sent me the whole edition of the SHUNNED HOUSE about 1934 or 5; it had been lying in storage in Vermont, and the idea was to rescue and circulate it. A few were circulated; but the OUTSIDER volume made it no longer appropriate.

(Second letter—undated.<br>Ed.)

Dear Mr. Farsaci:

The DREAM-QUEST is the longest Lovecraft ever wrote: a wandering, dream-like thing itself, strongly influenced by Dunsany, and containing episodes and images which appear, some of them, in the FUNGI FROM YUGGOTH later on. (Such things as the shoggoths &c.) Kadath was a great mountain in a cold waste. It would be difficult to make a résumé of such a picturesque work even if I had the time to dedicate to it which I have not . . . I have some fifty or sixty pages of a typescript I began years ago; Derleth has a whole typescript for those problematical future volumes of HPL . . .

Lovecraft used many pseudonyms for his verse and letters, and a few times for prose sketches. Lewis Theobald, Jr. was one he used often; others used only a few times in some cases, were semi-comic and obviously fake names. I had a list of eight or ten of these, and have just searched for it to no avail . . . I have thousands of notes, mostly on Mexican archaeology and ethnography and history, and it is hopeless to look for a scrap of paper of seven or eight years back . . .

Loveman, by the way, has the longhand mss. of The SHUNNED HOUSE; the proof-sheets survived until about 1933 or 34 when they were lost en route to (I think) Rimel; and the printed edition, unbound except for a half-dozen copies which were distributed, is somewhere in storage among my things—in Florida or Kansas City I suppose. There is no point, other than a bibliographic quaintness, in circulating them now that the whole thing is available in THE OUTSIDER.

At the moment I have nothing further on the Gamwell testimony, and if I do not mail this at once it will get bogged down in the crushing amount of work I have lying around. I will write you as soon as I have something bearing on the matter . . .

Your *Cavalier* letters in the G. A. (for which thanks) incidentally, do look like HPL, though in an unusually high and moralistic and Puritan mood—which was not uncommon with him in his early days especially. I wonder if he might have partly revised the letter of some friend, instead of being the author alone?

Ever yours,

[R. H. Barlow]

2521 Benvenue

Berkeley Calif

24 Nov. 1942

Dear Mr. Farsaci:

I am up to my neck in proofs of a book, whose printer is being draughted, but am sending what I can. If you do not want the G. A. England Bibliography, please return it at once. I know it is rather long . . . You might use the M. G. Lewis list, too. It could be expanded.

Two films are enclosed, which you are to guard with your life! They are HPL's review of *Ebony and Crystal* and several pages of notes. These are photos of typescripts made by me five years ago. If you cannot find a reading machine (a RECORDAK is one of the trade-names which is prominent) in your central library, a photographer could make you prints large enough to read without making big expensive prints . . . There are two tight little wads of film of HPL material among my dozens of boxes of film, and I had to go all through them to get these items. What a mess! The review should be marked Reprint from *L'Alouette* No. . whatever it is. Any reprint should be cited as to the original appearance, of course, so as to make it clear to anyone who wants to dig up the original.

In return for these things, any of which you are free to use or not to use . . . I shall not "stipulate" that you print the enclosed letters from Mrs. Gamwell's lawyer. It is the quickest sort of evidence, in the absence of fac-simile possibilities . . .

I hope you can handle this stuff; you rather brought it on yourself! If you can diminish some of the slanders which have caused me a great deal of sorrow, more than I can say, I shall be in your debt.

If I have a chance I'll check on Max Brand's book (a book of poetry. Ed.). I won the two poetry prizes here myself, this year, with a "slender sheaf" called POEMS FOR A COMPETITION.

Sincerely yours,<br>[R. H. Barlow]

## Pseudonyms of Lovecraft

Lovecraft gave me this partial list of his pseudonyms about [May] 1934. Most of these were used exclusively in the amateur journals of the UAPA and NAPA, and many were used only once. This list may enable the industrious to track down items in the Fossil Library of Amateur Journalism, Benjamin Franklin Memorial, Philadelphia—where his own collection reposes. (I sent it there after his death, in fulfilment of his instructions.)[1]

H. Littlewit, Edward Softly, H. Paget-Lowe, Lawrence Appleton, John J. Jones, Archibald xxx (surname forgotten by HPL),[2] Lewis Theobald, Jr. Ward Phillips (from hoWARD PHILLIPS lovecraft).

---

1. Literally, per his "Instructions in Case of Decease," In *Collected Essays,* ed. S. T. Joshi (New York: Hippocampus Press, 2004–06), 5.237–40.
2. Maynwaring.

# A Hitherto Unknown Map
# of the Pensacola Coastal Region, 1762

In the *Sala de Cartografía* of the State Museum of Jalisco (Mexico) in Guadalajara, exists a vellum map bearing the number 25. It is the entire hide of a small animal, drawn on in red, green and black. At the bottom is written the following:

> "Carta reducida de la costa de Panzacola desde el cavo [sic] del norte, hasta el de S. Blas, corregida nuevamente, por D. Estevan de Ayarragaray, piloto de esta ensenada, y la dirige al exelmo Sor Marques de Cruíllas,***rrey de esta Nueva España, por orden del Sr. Diego Ortíz Parilla, governador del presidio de Panzacola. Veracruz, Marzo 9, 1762."[1]

This map precedes, then, by only a little the Spanish evacuation of Pensacola. It fell to this Colonel Ortíz Parilla to remove the inhabitants on the arrival of the British in July of the year following.[2] The Viceroy (Joaquin Monserrat) to whom the map is dedicated had equally tough luck, being removed in 1766 by means of José de Gálvez.

It is understandable how the map came to be made in Veracruz, the nearest big port, to which the whole Pensacola population was removed a few months later, but its presence in Guadalajara, where the writer encountered it, is less explicable. It is to be hoped, in any case, that some one may be led by the present note to investigate and publish the document.

*University of California,*
*Berkeley.*

---

1. Reduced map of the coast of Panzacola from North Cape to that of San Blas, newly corrected, by Don Estevan de Ayarragaray, pilot of this bay, who directs it to the most excellent lord the Marquis of Cruíllas, Viceroy of this New Spain, by order of Sr. Don Diego Ortiz Parilla, Governor of the Presidio of Panzacola. Veracruz, March 9, 1762. [RHB's note]
2. Described (on the basis of Parilla's correspondence in the Archivo General de Indias) by Wilbur H. Siebert, *Fla. Hist. Soc. Quarterly*, XI, 48–57 (Oct. 1932). [RHB's note]

# Autobiography

Introduction. The motives for writing an autobiography, unless one be famous and merely fulfilling a publisher's insistence, should be stated—especially when one chooses to engage in what seems an old man's pastime at the age of twenty-six.

I am beginning the present pages in Mexico City in 1944, because I have in my grasp for the nonce a good part of the material things I have desired—money, sex, a small reputation for ability, furniture, cat, servant, and the like—nevertheless, I have still many of the deep doubts and unhappinesses which have made my heart a Warsaw since earliest childhood. I wish to find out what I have done. I wish to remember and analyze the quite numerous phases of my life in order to learn their pattern—perhaps even to force them into a pattern—so that I may use that pattern in the choice of my future. This is my first reason for writing.

A second reason is that some of the things I have seen and experienced appear to have interest historico-literary and psychological in themselves, and I feel obliged (see below) to set them down. This work is a continuation of a psychoanalysis at the hands of Dr. Emanuel Windholz of San Francisco. I hope to be as exact and frank in this work as he tried to teach me to be in the analysis. I wish to write a document of some psychological accuracy in a competent literary style.

Other reasons: A feeling that at this time the fates decree that I write these pages, and a subtle feeling that my curious and uneasy life is not destined to prolong itself, accentuate my two main motives. This latter feeling contradicts the search for orientation feeling, but both imply that a climax has been reached.

One of my compulsions has been to know and see and do certain things; to have lived in certain places almost as if fulfilling a pattern imposed by the stars. I think I have done this in order to show myself a person of wide and sophisticated experience. I have lived, in a sense, consciously acquiring material for an autobiography. I must live in the Bohemian quarter of San Francisco; I must read An American Tragedy;[1] I must go on expeditions into the Mexican sierra—not because I enjoyed these things, but because it fitted the pattern.

A truth was formulated by a babe and fool, the gorgeous blond boy with whom I was infatuated at the age of eighteen. He, a jitterbugging, fornicating amateur athlete, commented, "I don't think you have an ounce of enjoyment in your whole body." And I don't, except in the smooth fulfillment of my varied compulsions. When I have a period of free time and the choice of activity, I am most discontent. At these times I am most prone to do something irrelevant which ought to be pleasurable—read anything lying at hand, or most often rush out of the house to consume the time in looking at new books in bookstores, or more rarely going to the legitimate theatre. At these times of "free choice" I am most wretched. Pleasure for me is a calm fulfilling the pattern of work, writing something or learning something, which I have convinced myself "must" be done. But fulfilling the work-pattern, since it is the most rewarding of my activities, is the most difficult. I invent a thousand sham-pleasures to keep me otherwise occupied, or I exhaust myself so that no activity can be thought of, but only blank sleep.

A mood which alternates with this urge to work like the literary blacksmith described in The Flowering of New England[2]—that individual who smithied 12 hours or 14, and pursued his literary life at dawn and midnight—is the mood of gregariousness. A chasm of loneliness opens alongside my paths of study, and a pebble is enough to betray my foot. I delight in the presence of many people; I can end a conversation only by effort, can never get rid of a visitor, and when I have seduced people by wining and dining them into cheering the house with their voices, I hope they will never leave.

---

1. The 1925 novel by Theodore Dreiser.

2. Van Wyck Brooks, *The Flowering of New England 1815–1865* (New York: E. P. Dutton, 1936).

Woodstock, California, Winter 1938–39. I went then to Lakeport, California, to visit the Beck brothers, Groo and Claire, who had published two or three small books, one of them the Commonplace Book of Lovecraft which I had prepared about a year earlier. My intention was to found a sort of Transcendentalist colony of Woodstock, centering around a printing press. Fine hand-made books of exotic content.

On the train I was in better spirits than usual, being somewhat purged by suffering, as one might say. Banks of wildflowers around Nayarit moved me to write portions of an essay about Mexico asking how one could be unhappy in such surroundings, and entitled "Snake, Eagle and Cactus," which I thought rather striking and recherché. On the train was a Canadian woman of rattlebrained aspect, and when we both reached Nogales on the slow (cow) train, and only the younger customs officials were there, they waved us through without opening our luggage. I sheltered myself under her scatterbrainedness. So Chicomecoatl passed the frontier. About fifty miles beyond I drank my first glass of unboiled water.

I bought another relay of my ticket in Los Angeles on the daylight train, and from there made a change to bus in San Francisco, of which I recall nothing. In Lakeport I was left sitting on my luggage on the sidewalk, because there was no bus stop. There a white-haired scrawny woman collected me, Mrs. Beck. Later in the library I heard criticism from the librarians: "Mrs. Beck's visitor was long enough coming!"

Lakeport was a small resort on a large blue lake surrounded by towns, and at one side rose a mountain called Konochti. There were willows along the shore. I sometimes sat on their roots and wrote unfinished scraps of poetry and prose-poetry designed to capture its beauty.

My mother had been in correspondence with Mrs. Beck and had arranged that I was to pay rent.

The Beck house was some way from town. It was to prove a curious parallel to Florida; a country house beyond the means of its buildings, with an ingrown family suffering from father trouble. In this case the trouble was that Mr. Beck had gone away years ago to Stockton, leaving four orange-headed sons, two of whom still lived in Lakeport and were big as oxen.

There were two or three dogs, very spoiled, a grand piano covered with junk so deep it couldn't be opened (no one played, anyhow), and a fireplace. Mrs. Beck, though she had raised four sons, hadn't any idea how to cook, and never ate herself, perhaps as a result. In the morning she drank coffee, because she was in a hurry to get down to the courthouse where she worked; at noon she preferred not to eat; at night she was tired, so she took only coffee. Since I had been ill and was more underweight than ever, I was to make myself eggnogs. This however led to conflict with Grandma Groo, who was antagonized at the start when I insisted on wiping the dishes for her, so she retaliated by counting the spoons of sugar I put on my oatmeal, and by hiding the eggs as fast as they were laid. Eventually I had a violent quarrel with the old people, whom I overheard say something very offensive about either Claire or myself, and I left the house intending not to come back. Mrs. Beck talked me into returning, however, and eventually the dreadful grandparents left.

I could not decide which of the Beck boys to fall in love with and vacillated continually. Claire had a mania for bathing, and I saw him once or twice quite naked. He had a nice prick, uncircumcised. At other times he found excuses to go downstairs from the bath to the living room, dressed only in skin-tight drawers, which also showed him off to advantage.

Things went badly from the start. Apart from the conflict over the eggs, I assumed that the boys were literary sophisticates like myself, and tried to read them poetry, as Lovecraft and I had freely done. They looked uneasy. Then Claire brought me a book which he wished to sell, and I meant to buy it. It had a paper inside, however, which I crumpled up and threw away after reading; then I realized that the book was not yet my property, and that the paper was something he prized. We were both dumbfounded by my highhandedness, and I retrieved the paper and smoothed it out, but it was an ill omen.

Correspondence with my mother had established the fact that dreamland was to be established at Lakeport; we were possibly going to buy a nearby house, and live there forever in the beautiful country. It was much later that I discovered I preferred cities. The quarrels and lack of productivity by the printing press in the Beck barn were of course a handicap, but still we were going through with it, maybe even buying the grandparents' old place. I visited it one very cold moonlit night with Claire.

I liked to go out at night but the boys did not care much to. Once or twice Claire and I stole quantities of walnuts, however, from a neighbor's place, in a gunnysack taken for the purpose.

Groo preferred to sit by the fire after doing physical work—this was late Depression, and no job was too menial. He tended to truck-driving and carpentering, anyhow. He would read his Amazing Stories, pet his dog, eat walnuts, and listen to the radio all in front of the fire at once.

The first break in this idyllic scene was a letter from Clark Ashton Smith. I had written him three times hoping to visit him at not-very-distant Auburn, and had lain out on the hillside memorizing Coleridge to recite to him. After my third letter he wrote two lines, saying that he had no wish to hear ever again from a person who had acted so dishonorably in the estate of his dear friend H. P. Lovecraft.[3] I gasped.

If I had not received this letter, and other blows of the same sort, originating with the half-informed and antagonistic Wandreis, and which continued for various years after, I should not have worked out new orientations. Its immediate effect was of cutting my entrails out with a meat cleaver, but its eventual effect was per-

---

3. The full text of the letter is as follows: "R. H. Barlow: Please do not write me or try to communicate with me in any way. I do not wish to see you or hear from you after your conduct in regard to the estate of a late beloved friend. Clark Ashton Smith."

haps salutary, though I am even today wounded.

Transition. Y.M.C.A. Hotel. San Francisco, Spring 1939. Once when I was in Lakeport I took a week or two off and visited San Francisco, living in the YMCA Hotel, on Turk Street. At that time I met Clyde Beck, the most cultivated of the brothers, though with a certain feebleness of physique compared to them and given to reading Celtic poetry and reflecting mournfully and smoking largish pipes and collecting knives. Eventually, after Christmas of 1938, I went to live in San Francisco at the same YMCA hotel, and saw a good deal of Clyde. He was just being divorced by his wife. We both drank a great deal on various all-night bouts, and dined together at foreign restaurants. In one of these—a "Mexican" place—I spoke to the waitress in Spanish, and it seemed she was Irish, to my embarrassment. Sometimes we had frightful hangovers. But it was Clyde's company, perhaps, that kept me from suicide. We were in a German restaurant the night of March 17, a year after the death of Lovecraft, I reminded us.

This was deep depression, as I have said, and there were WPA projects all over. I thought to learn a profession, the printing colony having wrecked on Mrs. Groo's eggs, and went to a drawing class or two. I was half reconciled to returning to the art world and doing commercial work. But the cheap superficial way of drawing which the instructor showed me as being necessary for making money disgusted me and I left off. Also, I wrote my mother to fish with my uncle and the Nelson Gallery in Kansas City, to see if I might work there. I got a favorable letter, was half decided to go to Kansas City, and even mailed a package of books back, but did not go for some reason or other.

Once I saw a man bring a sailor up to his room and thought of protesting to the management. A blond clerk and a Basque elevator boy—man, rather—caught my eye, and I took them out once or twice to drink at my expense.

While I was living at the YMCA hotel, the California World's Fair, run in competition with the Century of Progress (?) at New

York, opened. This was preceded by several weeks of advance publicity stressing the Old-West motif. Western dress and the wearing
of beards was encouraged; and there were even Kangaroo courts set
up in certain streets for the mock-jailing of the beardless. I obliged,
purchasing a bandana on Market Street which I wore about my neck,
used later to cover a small table, and gave some five years later to
Agustín Domínguez, a Huichol Indian in Mexico City. I also grew a
beard which made me resemble Trotsky in 1918, and which was my
second beard.

I insisted on these fancy dress attributes in places and at times
when they were not very appropriate, going so-clad to see a doctor
who had handled my father's case in Washington. He seemed annoyed at my garb, to which I alluded jokingly as a continuance of
the unbalanced condition in the family, and to my surprise, he recalled my parents only vaguely. "She's a little white-haired woman,
isn't she?" he groped. About my father he had nothing of consequence to say.

Nor did I part with my beard after the publicity campaign was
turned off. Groo Beck had grown a Christlike red beard, which excited me sexually, and when we went to live on Telegraph Hill with
Groo, the two of us kept our beards until pressure was put on him
by the Employment Agency to shave his off. I was then alone, and
the rest of the town back to cleanshavenness.

Groo suggested that I go to the Employment Bureau as he did,
and I went to the Women and Juniors' branch on 18th Street, and
was passed on to the dynamic Barbara Mayer, a psychologist. This
lost me my beard. She put me through a series of tests and inter-
views and won my confidence in a professional way. I asked her to
put me in touch with a psychoanalyst. She did so, at the Mt. Zion
clinic, and got me small amounts of pay from the NYA, one and
another job.

I had not been able to stand sleeping in the bed with Groo days
and weeks without making approaches, which he rejected. Miss
Mayer maneuvered to separate us. Groo was very attractive to me,

and I quarrelled with him a great deal. We often went to visit Clyde and his new wife, a flip blonde lassie named Joan. The first time I met them I brought champagne, which I could not afford. Groo knew nothing about liquor, and maintained he could never become intoxicated. Once he wore two hats and skipped down Montgomery Street, singing "Here we go gathering nuts in May," however.

Above us lived Doloret Roulé, a plump and unbalanced young woman who spent huge amounts of money and had a fat and lame lover, a Dr. Sharp. Other people on the hill were a lean young fairy named Leon, a woman who kept spaniels, and a pair of Irish sisters.

While Groo Beck and I had our apartment together on Telegraph Hill, he suggested we print a book. In the summer of 1939 we did produce a book, a collection of Sterling's poetry, from his manuscript which John Howell the bookseller had.[4] Groo did ninety percent of the work. Ultimately this book made expenses.

"What I'd like to do with you is stick you in college," said Miss Mayer, looking determined. I warmed to the idea. What was I to study?

The question of what I was to be turned into worried Miss Mayer, who was used to deciding people's lives and careers promptly and accurately. I said I thought I wanted to study anthropology, because "I wanted to know all about all the different people and languages in the world and I supposed that was anthropology." Finally she brought up my case at a luncheon with Dr. Grace Morley of the Museum of Art, which I often visited, and to whom I had made a nervous application for work after my retreat from Lakeport. Dr. Morley said there were openings for people specializing in a combination of anthropology and art—"and that," said Miss Mayer, "suits you to a T."

So anthropology was to be one of my subjects—but where?

---

4. George Sterling, *After Sunset* (San Francisco: John Howell, Publisher, 1939). 250 copies.

"Substandard Housing." Sept. 1939–May 1940. Eventually my mother came out and took possession of our small house, and Groo left, which was what Miss Mayer had been wanting, and I was talked into moving to a street in the west of San Francisco, near Japtown. This was a huge Victorian mansion, and I had a room and my mother another. And there was a crazy man who shouted about his diamond prick. I was stringing along with Kasanin, and taking classes—at first without notes, and walking out when I pleased, and losing my schoolbooks—in advanced Spanish and anthropology and European history in the Junior College. My first midterm in history was a C or C-, my second an A-, which dissatisfied me.

I was advised to eat sugar cubes by Kasanin.

For Christmas of 1939 I bought my mother a small radio, and left it with her as I rushed out to get drunk with Joan, Clyde being sick. She became sick also, and was unable to eat the turkey dinner prepared by her visiting mother next day. On this radio, which I borrowed, I listened to the Phoney War, and the invasion of Belgium.

At the Junior College I made friends with Gertrude Bolton, and with a young spiritual-looking singer, Raymond Keast. Gertrude was large and sturdy, and equally timorous. She wanted to have a football player in a sweat-soaked sweater as a lover; and to operate a salon, if someone else would invite the guests, which she would preside over in a red gown. She was very ashamed of not being able to keep her bank account straight, and was terrified before lecturing, though she gave no sign of it. She had many sisters, and her father was a boisterous and famous old man at the University in Berkeley. Raymond and I dined often with Gertrude and drank too much.

Miss Mayer, whom I saw continually, had got me on the NYA through a series of wirepullings and not very accurate testimonials. I received $18.00 a month, a standard pay for a variety of jobs I performed. First she had me work a short while in the Employment Office filing, which I did not like.

A "little theatre" building existed on ——— Street; this had been closed (by the depression. I presume), and was finally taken over as a youth center by the NYA. Various activities were carried on in the building: classes in dancing, puppet making. and the like; plays were rehearsed, though I think never put on. The director of this "Junior Theatre" was a professionally enthusiastic lady whose stage-name was Elizabeth Elson. Miss Mayer had me assigned to Miss Elson as a research assistant. A cornfed comedy was to be produced, and Miss Elson asked me to get material on Nebraska in 1900—a topic which I found dull and difficult. In time she said in perplexity that she didn't know what to do with me—I "didn't seem to want to do research." She complained to Miss Mayer that I didn't seem to want to talk about anything except sex. I asked her to lunch then and spoke of Picasso the whole time.

Eventually, Miss Mayer asked me to compile a guide book on free recreational activities in San Francisco, which I did and was doing in May of 1940 when Italy entered the war, because I remember leaving out some Garibaldi social evenings. This work led me to see much in San Francisco I had not known, such as natural history museums. and it amused me more than any other job I had had. The actual writing was difficult; as always psychological obstacles intervened. Miss Mayer went on handing me my checks for some time without insisting on any return. Finally I wrote out a draught while sick and actually mailed it to her to liquidate my obligations, as I left for Mexico the summer of 1940.

My dreams were still vivid and interesting to me, and a few days before France fell I dreamed this prose-poem:

## THE FIDDLER

Once there was a fiddler. By and by the fiddler came into the universe and looked at his watch and began to fiddle. And there was Greece. He kept looking at his watch and walking in and out of the universe and each time he fiddled there was a new culture. By and by he came and sat and fiddled for four years and there was a great battle, and then he looked at his watch which hadn't tarnished any more than the stars had, and walked out of the universe for twenty years. Then he came back and fiddled energetically for a while. And then he laid down his fiddle and laughed and walked out of the universe, for there was no one left to fiddle to.

I read of the armistice between France and Germany in Compiègne Wood in a little restaurant in Los Angeles as I passed through to Nogales and Mexico. I expected the capitulation of England within a few weeks.

## The Wind That Is in the Grass: A Memoir of H. P. Lovecraft in Florida

*The wind that is in the grass cannot be taken into the house.*

In March of 1937 I rode east from Kansas City in a bus and read and re-read those blurred lines in a small anthology of essays which held also the telegram telling me of H. P. Lovecraft's death. Now that Howard Phillips Lovecraft has been dead for seven years, and the flowers which wilted in the cold shadow of his monument are quite dispersed, even the one I kept, words should be written which would still see deep down in the whirlpool that comes to surround us all, words which would link memories of him and regret for him with the implacable later accretions. Old respect and affection, all apart from his calibre as a personality, demand a very careful evaluation of Lovecraft, but there is no time. The fact that there is no time, which is no one's fault, seems full of disrespectful meaning.

The publisher suggests I write "at least a little piece" for the volume, which must be printed at once, and though ten years have passed and Tlaltelolco Xalliiyacac in the rain of the cool summer night, with the *cargadores* asleep it the doors of saloons and La Virgen de la Macarena being played on someone's radio is in no way like the Florida countryside where Lovecraft visited me, I shall try to evoke that former landscape and the two vanished people who moved in it.

Early in the morning Lovecraft was to arrive, my mother decided we must buy more furniture for the large empty guest room, which with mine and the sleeping porch formed the upstairs of the house. I drove the old Ford eighteen miles into town and came back with a small pink bureau she had had her eye on for some little while. It just fitted the front fender. I then drove back again into town to wait for the Greyhound at the drugstore. We lived in central Florida, in a house covered with half-logs which Lovecraft later helped to creosote against termites, on a small unnamed lake of our property. The Eustis–De Land highway passed by our door, but we had no neighbors closer than three miles, and I had no friends nor studies except in a sphere bound together by the U.S. mails and the magazines of fantastic stories for which Lovecraft wrote.

Presently the bus swung in, and a tall, stooped figure with gray-brown hair and a protruding jaw emerged gauntly and hailed me. At another bus station I was to see Lovecraft for the last time, but this was the first time and there were hundreds of things to say, and opinions to ask as I drove homeward with my guest and his tiny valise.

Shortly after arrival and presentation to my parents and the pink bureau, he revealed to me that he had ghost-written an article for Houdini, the magician, an article built out of guide books and fancy which appears in the present volume,[1] and I in turn showed him my books and magazines, many piles of them treasured in a locked closet which I called Yoh-Vombis after a story by Clark Ashton Smith. Lovecraft said to me at a later time in a moment of annoyance that he loved literature, and that I loved books, in which here was some truth. The curator of Yoh-Vombis at that time considered bibliophily a serious occupation filing autographs of Wells and Verne with those of popular magazine writers, and searching for old *Weird Tales* along with out-of-print Cabell. It was indeed this bibliophily which had led me to write Lovecraft first, in 1931 when I was not quite thirteen.

---

1. The "article" is in fact the story "Under the Pyramids," published in *Weird Tales* (May–June–July 1924) as "Imprisoned with the Pharaohs" and first collected in HPL's *Marginalia* (1944).

That summer of 1934 I was seventeen,[2] and Lovecraft stayed well over a month at my delighted insistence. We rowed on the lake, and played with the cats, or walked on the highway with these cats as the unbelievable sun went down among pines and cypresses, or searched for obscure stories known to us both in the archives of Yoh-Vombis. Above all, we talked, chiefly of the fantastic tales which he wrote and which I was trying to write. At breakfast he told us his dreams; one of how he was a magician standing on a cliff over the ocean sending balls out into space and guiding them back, some of them returning with scars and mosses of seas and spaces unknown.

Life was all literary then; that is, all I cared to accept as life. We discussed the *Fantasy Fan* and Lord Dunsany, wrote letters and verses and stories, and did not go to bed until I was driven there by my parents. Although he did not care for games, once we wrote verses to fit previous rhyme-schemes; one of his called "The White Elephant" is in my stored papers still, for I saved even his note-pad jottings. Again, as we idled in the rowboat, he caught up my challenge to find rhymes for "pretzel" and "Schenectady," and found them in the German name of Attila and the ensuing doggerel: "John and I were out fixing light wires near Schenectady—I connected one and the other connected he." Our talk was full of offhand references to ghouls and vaults of terror on the surfaces of strange stars, and Lovecraft wove an atmosphere of ominous illusion about any chance sound by the roadside as we walked with my three cats, one of whom he had named Alfred A. Knopf. At other times he could be prevailed upon to read his own stories aloud, always with sinister tones and silences in the proper spots. Especially he liked to read with an eighteenth century pronunciation, *sarvant* for "servant" and *mi* for "my." My own absorption in dreams and dream-tales kept the conversation along those lines, though from time to time he spoke volubly and forcefully of history and chemistry, of the New Deal and Abyssinian War.

---

2. Actually, RHB had just turned 16 at the time of HPL's 1934 visit.

When he was not talking he was writing. Everywhere he carried a much-creased black bag which looked like oil-cloth and from this produced pads of letter paper, "Irish Linen" from Woolworth's, and letters to answer. His daily intake of mail was normally half a dozen longish letters. Beneath a pretended dismay at the size of his variegated correspondence, he delighted in it all, and answered all in detail. Sometimes they contained fifteen or twenty-page stories which he corrected painstakingly until there was no room left for interlineation. My own halting stories he corrected in the same way.

Lovecraft had been in Florida before. When I first came in touch with him he was visiting the Rev. Henry S. Whitehead, the polished writer of West Indian stories, at Dunedin on the Gulf Coast, and he reached the Keys on one occasion. He found an exciting contrast to his New England home in the soft pine and marsh landscape, with gray-green mosses choking the trees and hanging from their branches, and palmettoes crowding the sandy soil. The incidental killing of a snake was an incident to put in his letters, as was a blueberry-picking party during the course of which he fell into a stream and lost nearly all his berries—for which he damply *apologized!* His taste for antiquities was stimulated by the faintly fraudulent Hispanic character of Florida, and led us to take him to such places as De León Springs, where an 18th century Spanish windmill exists in an advanced stage of restoration, and New Smyrna, where portions of an unsuccessful mission stand. The pinkish walls of St. Augustine, a genuinely old and atmospheric town, held him entranced, and there on a more venturesome *ausflug* we visited the Chapel of Nuestra Señora de la Leche, and a mosquito-cursed graveyard full of the tombs of young people dead of a plague a hundred years before.

Lovecraft's *Letters* will contain, I suppose, numerous autobiographical passages, but as he himself recognized in commenting on Wells's *Autobiography,*[3] a man is not always the most objective re-

---

3. H. G. Wells, *An Experiment in Autobiography* (1934).

corder of his own life. A note concerning Lovecraft's customs may not come amiss.

He began his day by going to bed, since he worked at night by preference, long hours after our last argument was over. About his desk-lamp the moths of the Florida night bumbled and shredded themselves until near dawn, when he sealed the ultimate letter and refuted the last date of some pocket guide-book. Then he went downstairs to the bath to do a bit of frugal washing and wake up the household incidentally. He laundered his shirts thrice for every once he sent them to the laundry, and taught me the art of drying collars on a basin-edge to give the effect of ironing. (This I later put into practice as an art student.) He was always spotlessly clean, though most of his clothing had seen better days. He preferred whatever was unfashionable, separate collars and studs, high button-shoes, and the like, wearing a good deal of black. It was with inordinate glee that he discovered he could resuscitate a pair of trousers worn in bicycling in youth, a quarter-century before.

He arose about noon and breakfasted on vast amounts of coffee, thick with sugar. Sometimes he filled the hollow of a cantaloupe with sugar and thought it passably sweet. Other eating preferences are mentioned in letters and stories—his absorption of ice-cream and his detestation of fish. Once Frank Belknap Long smuggled scraps of fish into a salad to test this eccentricity and Lovecraft left it uneaten, thinking it spoiled. He had a rather delicate stomach so far as unsavory and unsightly things were concerned; I twitted him once on the marked distaste he showed (strange for the author of "The Hound" and "In the Vault") when he helped me remove a decaying heron which floated in the lake.

Claiming that really considered prose could not be written on the typewriter, he composed in longhand, generally with a fountain pen, in a minute script with many interlineations. For paper he used the backs of old letters, family ledgers, or new-bought schoolboy pads. A fair number of these manuscripts exist, since I began to ask him for them as early as 1931, and he passed them on to me as soon as they were published, instead of destroying them as he formerly had done. He gave me one of several longhand copies of "The Doom That Came to Sarnath" (1919), which he had made in preference to typing it out. "Juan Romero," "Iranon," and the "Other Gods" also exist from this period, since they did not see publication at the time. Of "The Strange High House in the Mist" (1926) I have a much-interlined and revised typescript; the rhythms (he said) became too obvious in the story and had to be toned down. The two long novelettes, *The Case of Charles Dexter Ward* and *The Dream-Quest of Unknown Kadath,* he sent me in 1934, I having requested him to let me type them bit by bit in exchange for the originals. Some of the resultant typescript he proof-read with me, remarking that it was not every author who had the privilege of supervising his posthumous works. Most of the other manuscripts written before 1931 were destroyed, "The Colour out of Space" and his other great stories, as soon as they were published. He told me of two exceptions, which were given to Samuel Loveman, "The Shunned House" (1924) and another—perhaps "The Rats in the Walls."[4] After 1932, as I say, he gave me all of his manuscripts, at the same time protesting against what he called my misguided activity in collecting rubbish. The *Fungi from Yuggoth* came into my hands along with the prose, and consists of an interesting set of draughts which would lend themselves well to facsimile reproduction some day.[5] Two manuscripts only of this latter period went to other people, since with a typical desire for temperance he explained that *should* by any chance this old rubbish have any value, he would not approve of a monopoly. Consequently he gave two manuscripts, whose titles I forget, to Baldwin and/or Rimel.[6] One of

---

4. HPL gave the manuscripts of "The Shunned House" and "Under the Pyramids" to Samuel Loveman. He probably destroyed the manuscript of "The Rats in the Walls" after its publication in *Weird Tales* (March 1924).

5. Now published in *Fungi from Yuggoth: An Annotated Edition* (Hippocampus Press, 2017).

6. HPL gave the manuscript of "The Thing on the Doorstep" to Duane W. Rimel (who lived in Asotin, WA) and that of "The Haunter of the Dark" to Donald A. Wollheim (who lived in the New York City area). The former is now in the

them kindly loaned me one manuscript after Lovecraft's death, and I had a microfilm made. The other manuscript I have never seen.

When I arrived in Providence in March of 1937, shortly after Lovecraft had been laid in the family plot in Swan Point Cemetery, his aunt, Mrs. Gamwell showed me a group of personal papers kept in a cabinet in his room, and took out one which she had been horrified to see him write by chance a few months before. This was a used envelope marked in pencil "Instructions in Case of Decease." Inside were two leaves of notes, beginning abruptly "First choice of all my books and manuscripts is to go to R. H. Barlow, my literary executor." Other instructions concerned books to be returned or bequeathed—a Mather *Magnalia* to the late J. F. Morton, a collection of amateur papers to the Fossil Library in Philadelphia, and so on. Mrs. Gamwell copied out this list in longhand for me, since she wished the original as a sad memento, and her copy I still have.[7] Had I published it then, some misunderstandings and ill-feeling which caused her and me distress, might have been avoided. I fulfilled the instructions, sending one book as far as Polynesia, and, taking two or three cardboard cartons of books, as well as the unpublished manuscripts (mostly notes and juvenilia) from a metal box under an armchair, returned to Kansas City where I was studying.

A year or two later I decided that my many removals were endangering the papers, and deposited them, together with the microfilm materials and his file of *Weird Tales* 1923–1937 in the John Hay Library in Providence, next door to his last home. They may be consulted there today by properly qualified students. Only one manuscript remains in my possession, after making various deposits—the notebook in which he pencilled "The Shadow Out of Time." He had destroyed one draught of this story and threatened

---

John Hay Library; the whereabouts of the latter are unknown. He also gave a copy of "Dagon" to Emil Petaja and "The Shunned House" and "Hypnos" to Samuel Loveman.

7. This copy of "Instructions in Case of Decease" is now in the John Hay Library. HPL's original is apparently destroyed.

to destroy the second, so when he showed it to me in the summer of 1935, I had it typed and returned him the typescript. At that time he was making his second visit to me in Florida, and I sounded him out by drawing parallels with T. E. Lawrence. He agreed that under certain circumstances manuscripts could justifiably be taken away from their authors, and this was certainly the case with the "Shadow," for I had it copied, and later on Donald Wandrei submitted it for publication, both without consulting Lovecraft.[8]

It is not possible, in the couple of days allotted me by the exigencies of the press, to write a real memoir of the man who virtually moulded my intellectual life and many of my tastes and habits. An evaluation of that striking personality, which is only partly shown in his stories, would be difficult in any case because of the handicap of close perspective. The fantasies he wrote have become models. As an unobtrusive guide treads knowingly the stair to an Etruscan tomb or a Zapotec chamber, Lovecraft conducts us by means of his dexterous prose to doorways of awe and wonder and flings them suddenly wide to us. But he was much more than a story writer— barring certain accidents, such as his connection with the amateur press, he might never have gone back to writing stories at all after his adolescence. He is more important as a man who had the integrity to ignore the Machine Age and its frenzied leveling-out-to-rubble of life's rich irregularities, who had the courage to study and think and converse and write, and to stimulate others to study and think and converse and write, in accordance with the deeper traditions of a more orderly age. He was the twin of the "Last Puritan," except that he knew what he wanted, and frankly admired that character.[9] His intimate acquaintance with astronomy, history and literature, as well as a host of other interests, made him a civilizer

---

8. RHB later gave the manuscript of "The Shadow out of Time" to an anthropology student of his in Mexico; upon her death, the woman's sister donated the manuscript to the John Hay Library. It served as the basis of a corrected edition of the story, *The Shadow out of Time* (Hippocampus Press, 2001).

9. A reference to the novel by George Santayana.

among barbarians, a closet Quetzalcoatl, a cloistered Akhnaton, whose impact may be felt now only in the volume of *Letters,* since, alas, the wind that is in the grass cannot be taken into the house.

# Henry S. Whitehead

In 1647 the first Whitehead came to Virginia, not long after the Anglicizing of the original name, Caer-n'-Avon. From Virginia the family spread to New Jersey, and in Elizabeth, a "Whitehead-settled town" which still has its Whitehead Street, the Rev. Henry S. Whitehead was born, March 5, 1882.

All but the last of his five decades were spent in New England or nearby. He was educated in Connecticut, and at the Berkeley School in New York. He attended Harvard and Columbia, graduating from Harvard in 1904 in the class with President Franklin Roosevelt. At college he received football injuries which were to trouble his last years. In 1905 he wrote his first short story, and sold it within three days to the first magazine he sent it to—though he never was able to collect payment. He began to work, about this time, on a reform newspaper (Democratic) in Port Chester, New York, beginning as a reporter, and rising to the editorship by 1909. He held various political offices also, and was Commissioner of Athletics of the A. A. U. 1905–1909. In the latter year, however, he resigned from fourteen different organizations and entered his second professional career.

In the autumn of 1909 he matriculated at the Berkeley Divinity School, Middletown, Connecticut, and three years later was ordained deacon of the Episcopal Church. His "deacon's year" was served as curate of Trinity Church, in the mill-town of Torrington in the same state, and he returned to Middletown as rector of Christ Church from 1913 to 1917. At the same time, he was Chaplain and assistant psychiatrist of the State Insane Hospital. In 1917, he went New York City and for two years was Pastor of the Children and Evening Preacher at the Church of St. Mary the Virgin on West 46th Street. He had continued writing—chiefly for Episcopal journals—throughout the decade since abandoning newspaper work, and in 1919 published a collaboration entitled *The Invitations of Our Lord.* A second book, *Neighbors of the Early Church,* was published in 1921, while he was in Boston as Senior Assistant of the Church of the Advent.

He left Boston in 1921 to serve as Acting Archdeacon in the Virgin Islands, to which he returned every winter, until his health broke down at the end of the decade. In 1921 he also began his serious short-story writing. His *Good Manners in Church* was published in 1922, and the winter of 1922–23 he spent substituting for a friend in Chattanooga, Tennessee. He was back in Connecticut soon, however, with an appointment as rector of the leading Anglo-Catholic parish of New England—Trinity Church at Bridgeport, Connecticut . . . a position he held from 1923 to 1925. In 1923 appeared the first of his *Weird Tales* stories, of which this book is largely formed. These were based on his West Indian experiences and in time completely displaced his other fiction (of the *Outdoors* and *Adventure* type). He became a popular figure in the mystery-filled pages of that journal during the decade that was left to him.

From 1930 till his death in 1932 he lived in the small town of Dunedin, on the Gulf Coast of Florida, where he gathered and arranged the possessions acquired during his busy life. His Dunedin home was a perfect thing in its appointments, with furniture built to his own design. At the same time (1930) he came into correspondence with H. P. Lovecraft, with whom he developed a rapid friendship. In the summer of 1931, Lovecraft visited him in Dunedin, and the two spent many delightful hours in discussion and debate, especially under the stark moon of the Gulf.

These last three years, however, were years of wearing and Protean illness. "Life with me at 48," he wrote, "seems somehow too short." Old football injuries "in the midriff" harassed him; an operation for stomach ulcers was performed; for a while cancer was suspected. In addition to this, he underwent twenty-eight blood-injections to rid him of a tropical disease. A deceptive improvement followed for a few months, in the summer of 1932. At the end of November, however, he complained of an indefinite "malaise," and on the twenty-third of that month died; the immediate cause being a fall which produced concussion of the brain.

All his papers were found in perfect order, but this was soon disturbed by hands which destroyed his files of correspondence with Lovecraft and others. The fate of a number of unpublished stories (including an incomplete novel, *The Good Wine*) is not clear, though five years later some of these still existed.

Whitehead's was "a finished life, rounded, closed, artistically complete." Shortly before his death he told a friend that he had always wanted to build three things—that he had built them all—and that he could never stay to enjoy the fruits of his labor. Among these things was a church. The death of Dr. Whitehead was the first death among the serious *Weird Tales* group. A young poet wrote these words to Lovecraft on learning of the event: ". . . a noble and generous spirit gone forever—completely wiped out, as I shall be in a few years. Farewell to both the dreamer and the dream—no more star-flecked West Indian skies for him now, no more music and wonder and the passing of gods. Gone, wiped out. And forever."

Dr. Whitehead—he held the Ph.D. degree—was notably virile, both physically and mentally. He weighed one-hundred and fifty pounds, when in poor health. Mountain-climbing and small-game hunting delighted him. At eighteen he could "lick my weight in polar bears." He was on the football team at College, and in the half-decade before entering the ministry, was Commissioner of Athletics of the A. A. U. In later life he could be prevailed upon at times to startle social gatherings by tearing a deck of cards in two and then quartering them. Once he did it with a deck of linen cards.

This same masculinity was notable in his attitudes. The continuity between his two careers of journalist and priest is to be sought perhaps in his warm gregariousness. I never trained with the longhairs or the near-pious gang," he wrote to a friend, "and what are known as church people, to the majority of the public give me severe shooting pains all over." His friends ranged from ships' surgeons to safecrackers—"all kinds of people—I love 'em all and delight in their society."

In the Virgin Islands he was a sensation. Making his parish visits with a chauffeur in livery imported from New York, he ". . . put old St. Paul's back the way it was in its palmy days, when Alexander Hamilton and the great gentry of the Islands drove to service in their coaches." Everybody came to hear him preach.

His mature years in the Antilles gave him the material for his stories. He had family connections with the Virgin Islands: a great-uncle had administered Great Fountain Estate on St. Croix under the Danes. Not long after the Islands were bought by the United States, Dr. Whitehead went there, and was there each winter for nine years as acting archdeacon. There he moved among hybrid races and tongues and traditions of Africa and Europe, in the ancient portals of the New World. He explored equally the Danish manor-houses with their balls and receptions, and the negro huts with their dark lore of Obeah and Voodoo, a world described by Seabrook in *The Magic Island*—which Whitehead called ". . . straight and true as a die. . . ."

Though his best tales treat of the supernatural, Whitehead wrote as a realist; a reporter. He loathed "armchair exoticists," and wrote with ire of the popular stories of one *Weird Tales* contemporary concerning ". . . China, a land of Mr. ——'s sentimental imagination." His own stories are almost ethnographic. Some, indeed, set down verbatim what old residents of the Indies told him.

The character "Gerald Canevin" is Whitehead himself, a harking back to the ancestral Caer-n'-Avon. "I use the form 'Canevin' because it is easily pronounced and is made up of 'cane' and 'vin,' that is, cane-wine—RUM, the typical product of the West Indies. O, there was a Methodist in my Madhouse that time. . . ."

Whitehead was a craftsman in his life and in his writings. "He likes form, like all High Churchmen," said one observer. In counselling a young author he cited Leonard Cline's words about ". . .

the beauty of order and direction and movement, the boundlessness of fulfilment possible only within the marble limitations of form." Much of his work was in the essay pattern. His goal in writing was "to turn out stuff that is not hackneyed, and that is worked out in good form." He considered himself a professional writer. His literary ideals seem to have been shaped by his early work us a journalist, rather than by any excessive bookishness. His private library was a rather casual assemblage. The style of his private letters is almost Rabelaisian—in the true sense of that suffering adjective.

If the material of the stories in this book is a reflection of his experiences in the West Indies, their formulation is due to the existence of the magazine *Weird Tales* and its imitators from 1923 on. His supernatural stories were largely written with that outlet in mind. Before *Weird Tales* was founded, he had read a scattering of writers in the genre—Stoker, Hodgson, Jacobs—but the stimulus of that journal, and his correspondence with such contributors as Price and Lovecraft, was decisive.

His position in the literature of the supernatural will be established by the present book. That his stories are the product of a cultivated and reflective mind and of an organized and dexterous pen is evident. "God hath created all things, visible and invisible," he wrote in a story, and in a letter added ". . . and the idea . . . that such 'creation' of the Invisible is limited to 'Angels' is—merely Fundamentalist." As a priest, his ear was highly trained to catch the whisperings of strangeness and unworldliness implicit in the ancient and febrile Indies; as a journalist, his hand was highly skilled to set those whisperings down for the enchantment of kindred souls.

*City of Mexico, 27 September 1943*

## Restoration of Santiago de Tlaltelolco

The ancient church of Santiago de Tlaltelolco has been opened for public worship after nearly a century of use as a government warehouse for *pulque*. The great significance of this

monument to Mexican history may be realized from the fact
that it was built in 1600 by the noted Franciscan historian,
Fray Juan de Torquemada, on the site of the smaller, primitive
chapel of the original Franciscan College of Santa Cruz de
Tlaltelolco, established shortly after the conquest of Mexico.
Professor Barlow, of the University of California, now doing
research in Mexico, describes the inaugural Mass as follows:

The benches, which were not more than twenty, were filled when
we arrived. At the north door one of those printed signs, so common throughout Mexico, implored aid for the restoration of the
desolated church: here in Santiago Tlaltelolco it seemed especially
real. We had seen the temple when only a sea of broken chairs and
lame desks, the flotsam of a hundred government-office cleanings,
swirled in grime beneath the mouldy frescos. This was when we
had begun our excavations to the west of the church, in quest of the
pre-Hispanic pyramid. Of late we had learned that the temple was
again in Franciscan hands, and that the wilderness of rubbish was
being cleared away, to be piled compactly under the north vaults, and
eventually removed. Then one morning an army of women with rags
and brooms and pails were at work on the filthy floor; an altar was
improvised and a small chalk sign appeared in the unaccustomed
open door: Mass would be said Sunday, November 19, 1944.

As we squeezed into a row of women with scarves over their
heads, at the back of the last row of benches, we felt the cold despite
the ten o'clock sun in the doorway. Mass had been said at six and
eight the same morning, by the priest in charge, Father Jácome Mon-
tiel, but this ten o'clock Mass was to be said by Father Wheeler,
O.F.M., an enthusiastic guest. Since there was no sacristy, Father
Wheeler struggled into a grass-green chasuble to the left of the little
altar, which had been set up against a blocked-up doorway leading to
the former convent. Over the plain wooden altar a white cloth was
spread, on which stood half a dozen gilded wooden candlesticks, one
of which did not match the others very well. A few glazed vases, ap-

parently new, and painted with photographically exact roses, held pink paper flowers shaped like lollipops. Under a small velvet canopy reposed the universal image of Our Lady of Guadalupe.

But this was a camp in a desert: there was undeniably very much more wall than altar, and this wall, which stretched to all sides and above and behind us, was decorated in some places with ruins of old frescos, but chiefly with cracks like veins of anthracite, with mildew, with scaled octagonal windows, and with the sockets of blind niches where once the saints looked out. At the east end of the church, where formerly a many-tiered retablo spread golden wings, rags of paintings two hundred years old were tacked crookedly—figleaves on the nakedness of the wall. Here Torquemada had officiated, and here two turkey eggs under an inverted bowl had been found by treasure seekers who tore up the floor a few years back.

Though a small Indian boy clutched a stalk of white flowers and stared at the altar, and another less Indian boy skirted the small flock collecting coins, there was no altar-boy. Vestments and other needful articles were handed to Father Wheeler by a university professor and lover of Mexico's ravaged antiquities: Sr. Pablo Martínez del Rio. In the audience were his confreres in the investigation of Tlaltelolco, and a nobleman and a Cora Indian lad. A representative of the last Indian state to be conquered—the Cora were subjugated only in 1722—joined a representative of the conquerors, the Marqués de San Francisco, in worship at Santiago. The rest of the small group were men and women from the *barrio,* a flock which had sprung up like flowers after a desert rain.

At the right of the altar a tall wooden cross, like those placed in poorer Mexican graveyards, rested against the wall. The number "6" was scrawled on the plaster a little above it. Between this cross and a fantastically tall and rickety ladder left by a workman, Father Wheeler began the ten o'clock Mass in Santiago Tlaltelolco, whose doors had been padlocked violently when Maximilian was still an Austrian prince at Miramar, eighty-five years before.

*University of California, Berkeley.*

# Fragment of a Letter to a Young Poet

. . . Your letter convinces me that you are in danger of going completely sane. By levelling the mountains you have filled in the abysses, but it means living with the wheat and bermuda-grass. What are your ends, beyond avoiding *arroz a la Mexicana* at meals? By scrabbling through documents for the answer to When was Ixtlilcuechahuac born, or What does the date Seven Monkey mean, you are classifying what ought to be myths, and therefore solid, by the ephemeral realities of the Bertillion System. There are hundreds of pebbles to pick up, but when are you going to get around to building your wall? You can never explain anything by learning. Better to discard tape measures altogether and contemplate over the horizon of your navel beetles rolling dung-balls. True, there are a few reasonable pastimes for the scholar—learning Chinese genealogies, especially if they be fictitious, or inventories of temples destroyed by the Goths, but as soon as he comes upon a vice-president or an economic motive he should leave off. Wheat is valuable only as a poetic image: as a foodstuff it was classified best by the ultimate lady of Versailles. Do not share in the impracticality of the ant. Learn the names of all the Mesopotamian cities and see how many mounds once had mayors and political parties and see if the desert has not reckoned them up in her Annual Reports.

Anything which on the other hand may be misinterpreted is worth while. Only things which mean themselves are quite infertile. Try never to understand what people think they mean; read pages of the telephone book backward and say they are new king-lists, punctured illegibly on clay, from Chaldean towns. If you choose to have bones in your house instead of flower vases, it would be well to paint them various colours. Never believe anything which is true and never allude to what you are talking about. Know the Common Divisor of pincushions and comets, and that the Real and Significant is whatever amuses you two seconds. Join as a professional turncoat in the defense and the sack of the same castle—what matters is the smoke. Be quite hardheaded and you may weep at anything; if you are very discriminating you may even praise the fashionable. . . .

# [Statement about Poetry]

Some while ago I was asked for a declaration of how I make verse, or what we shall call poetry. Apart from the fact that my product is hardly of the calibre which would make explaining it of interest, I doubt if it is possible, and I am sure it would not be discreet, to explain the poetry-writing process accurately. But I'll take a stab at it, and in the plainest of prose. Though the use of poetic devices in the writing about poetry is almost unconscious, it "explains" poetry only to those who already understand it, so tuck yourself in for a nice nap; I mean, prepare for flat and nasal Calvin Coolidge prose.

When I have an indication to write a poem, it springs from something visual or auditory, usually: with something I see (perhaps only in a dream or imagining), or with some pleasing clang of words. If it is visual—some striking combination of colors or textures—I feel an urge to paint it in words, for I have a painter's eye. But since I feel that even a good color photograph of jam on a bearskin is inadequate, some little meaning, some little allegory regarding the thing seen occurs to me, and I make some evaluation, accidental or deliberate. With me sensory stimuli are first and foremost visual and I rarely use a taste or touch stimulus as departure point for a poem.

As I said, less frequently a poem may be touched off by a trick phrase which occurs to me, perhaps in a half-dreaming state. This leads rather to horse-play, as in the following quite unusable gibberish which I jotted down half-asleep, "The read-letter day Saint, Nathaniel Froghorn, base and viol." In reality, the ability to put words to working by themselves without any task-master, so well exemplified in leaders spiritual (e.g. Father Divine or Mary Baker Eddy), economic or political, I lack. This ability is present in many children, I think, and some adults.

So much for the principal ways in which a poem gets touched off. Now for the plot and the way of telling it. I do insist on a plot. If the bark of the tree has caught my eye, my first thought will be what color and pattern it has, but the next one will be perhaps "it has been there a hundred years," and possibly, "the man who always meant to cut it down died last summer." Said Wells, "By taking any object and letting my thoughts play with it I can make a story." By doing the same thing one can make poetry. It is rarely necessary to invent a meaning for a sight or experience which has excited me sufficiently to cause me to want to write a poem. If in poetry we talk about two things at once—eating cherries and kissing—we may be talking about three or four things also. I am conscious of ritual and symbolic meanings, not all of them clearly sexual, in most sights and activities.

When I come to the actual writing of a poem, though I have a rough lay-out in mind, I may rewrite this lay-out and suppress and add to it as felicitous concepts or phrases appear, until I have something not consciously premeditated. This may be an advantage: it is what is known as "spontaneity." In reaching for cream of wheat on the shelf, blackberry brandy and tabasco sauce may tumble down to brighten up the meal.

The phrase which I have just written, which is a conscious departure from plain prose, may introduce a final word on how I express whatever I try to express. I prefer to make little allegories and I have never been able to buy candles successfully, or tinned fish from salespeople. But surely one of the main features of poetry is saying things by talking about other things. Lovecraft taught me to say exactly what I had in mind; Hart underlined that expression was strongest when put in retina and esophagus-twitching words. Thus I would not say "we remember the food," but "we remember devils' food cake and oysters," or even better, "our brains are clogged (or burrowed, or studded) with oysters and cream pie." At this stage of a poem, the poetry begins to appear. All sorts of little devilishnesses and indirect ways of saying things occur to one. A word takes an unexpected turn, and another plot is included—perhaps the plot I shall keep. And then this new plot requires different words. However, though I may transmute the subject matter of a poem as I build it up, the mood or flavor of the various strata is probably more or less constant. The writer of the Song of Songs begins to describe a lady's neck, and gets himself delightfully off the track, so that we no longer give a hoot about the lady at the end of the second line. "Thy neck is like the tower of David . . ." he begins, and then he leaves the neck and goes on to the tower ". . . builded for an armory." This in turn suggests ". . . whereon there hang a thousand bucklers, all the shields of the mighty men." This is authentic tabasco sauce— genuine pre–Pearl harbor blackberry cordial.

Well, that's why darkies were born. I hope you are sorry you asked me. Fortunately, it cannot go on forever, since it is eleven thirty and there is a map to work on for the new *Tlalocan*.

[from a letter to Rosalie Moore, 15 May 1944]

## Angel Hernandez, Artist

Angel Hernandez was eight years old when his mother came to cook for me. He was born in Otlatla, in the State of Puebla (Mexico), where people speak nàuatl ("Aztec") and he learned that language first.

Angel had never drawn any pictures, so that he was very pleased when one day I gave him crayons, pencils, and paper. He became so prolific that in a few days I had to put him on rations, and give him old proof-sheets and other emergency supplies.

Angel's drawings drew only suspicious censure from his mother, and after a few months when he began to go to school, teacher kindly showed him how to trace from books and how a tree perforce must be drawn, and his drawings ceased to be of any interest, and he gradually gave them up, which pleased his mother. Then his mother brought three more children out of hiding to live with us, and it ended by her going back to Otlatla. So Angel will grow up to be a shrewd peasant, and not a thief in the labyrinth of Mexico City slums. But he will not draw any more.

Angel made about fifty good drawings and almost no bad ones until he was taught how. I have all of them except three which I gave to a professor from Cambridge University. The present drawing bears my pencil notes which contain Angel's own explanation, in not very choice, and sometimes invented, Spanish. It can hardly be translated, though an English version might go like this:

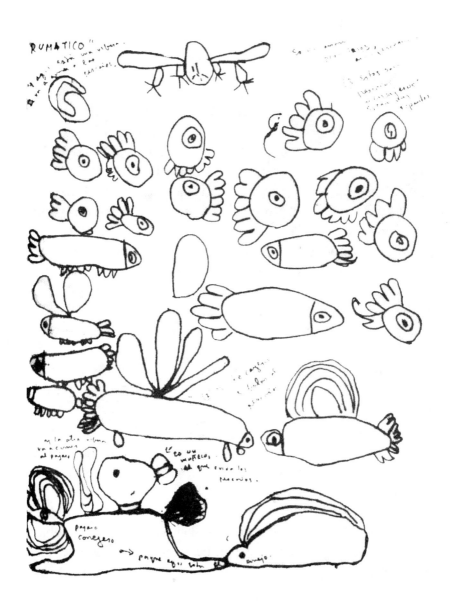

"RHEUMATIC"
1.  (upper right)  It is a fishing airplane, a damage-doing (?) airplane.
2.  (center)  And three bullets fell into the fish.
3.  (upper right)  These are messenger fish. They are very frightened.
4.  (upper left )  And here is a viper. It is going to eat the fish.
5.  (lower center)  This is a man-doll; he who takes care of the fish.
6.  (bottom)  Rabbity bird, because here is the rabbit.


# The Malinche of Acacingo

Below Tenancingo (Estado de Mexico) lie the small settlement of
Acacingo and, to the west of this, the Cerro de la Malinche. On the
latter exist various carvings, or remains of carvings, for in one place
an outcropping of petroglyphs has recently been blasted with dy-
namite by someone eager to detach salable portions. Elsewhere appear fortifications, sentry posts (reminiscent of Nezahualocoyotl's
Bath), and a shrine. These are on the west side of the hill, commanding an ample view of Tecualoyan, Zumpahuacan, Iztapan de
la Sal, and other towns in the southern part of the state.

During a brief visit to the Cerro I was able to make a drawing
of the shrine, which somehow missed the vigilance of the early
church and has not yet been mutilated by the traffickers in antiquities. The simplicity of the monument—a single stone, perhaps 1.5
m. tall and 1.9 wide—is balanced by the magnificence of the setting, a cliff-wall facing towns and rivers and cloud-filled space to the
west and south.

This carving, "la Malinche," guards a trickle of water, and from
her two bunches of plumes one recognizes Xochiquetzal, the first
woman to bear twins and a popular goddess in nearby Morelos. At
the nape she wears the water-goddess fans, *tlaquechpanyotl*; her face
is framed in a serpent helmet with stylized eyes. Whether the object
in her clasped hands be the pendant of her necklace, another object
appropriate to fertility goddesses, a heart, or something else, I do
not know, but I guarantee the accuracy of my drawing. At the

meeting point of her index fingers appears a shallow hole where some precious stone perhaps was embedded.

The date, 2 Acatl 1 Tochtli, I relinquish to the reader of these notes. The year 2 Acatl is, of course, that of the New Fire ceremony, and the whole style of the monument looks to me immediately pre-Hispanic.

*Escuela Nacional de Antropologia*
*Mexico, D. F.*

## Journey to the Place of the Fish-Masters

Since everyone said that Vera Cruz was a lair of luggage-snatching extortionists and mosquitoes, since Yucatan was too far from the capital, the North too sterile, and Guerrero and Oaxaca States fresh in my mind, I had been toying with the idea of seeing Michoacan— the Place of the Fish-Masters. I somehow expected this realm of the Tarascan Indians to retain its early uniqueness. Historians of Mexico dwell either on modern revolutions or pre-Conquest pastorals— and no wonder; the colonial period withers century after century, gauged only by the fungoid spread of churches—so they give the impression that the Spaniards have never come to most of the land. One must go and see the church built on Cholula's pyramid and find the finest pottery of North America in pigsties and adobe walls; one must go to Tlaxcala and see that it hangs about soda-pop stands and not on the decision of the quarrelling Senate about the pathetic "alliance" proposed by Cortes in order to realize that the old Indian cultures are destroyed. Hence, I conceived Michoacan, which I had never seen, as a fertile parkland where the cruellest of the Conquerors would one day ravage and slay until his brain had turned to gold, but not as a place where this had happened five hundred years before.

Spring vacations at my college forced the issue. I was free for ten days, and I had an accomplice. My friend George had come to Mexico City to rest up from his rural abode in Taxco, whose puttering streets, Chinese-landscape mountains and star-oppressive nights retain their charm despite the garish Neo-Babylonian colony infecting it from the U.S. He had come also to pawn a camera, but like most government services, the National Pawnshop was closed for the holidays, so he joined me in my planless permeation of the provinces. He even added a fictitious goal—the city of Guadalajara, in which he had a trunk containing he didn't know what. Our route would lie mostly through Michoacan, with a little of the State of Mexico at the beginning and a little of Jalisco at the end.

George is a dissipated antiquary, who if caught off his guard knows the genealogy of every Balkan prince, a collector of tequila bottles and curious personalities. He, if anyone, knows the details of Queen Victoria's underwear, and knows who else knew and how. His household is an ameboid organism always assimilating or discarding an Armenian Methodist barber, a cook suspected of poisoning people out of temper, or a chicken born without feathers. His heart is big enough for all. Someday his friends are going to buy him a sideshow to keep his back yard if they can ever be sure which is his back yard, since he migrates as often as the early Celts. His interest in the background and local minutiae of every place he sees, his infinite ability to improvise bawdy anecdotes, his amused contempt for the traveller who goes through his pockets for microbes every twenty minutes by a stop watch ("My friends are going to be delighted when I catch elephantiasis some day, I suppose," he muses); his acceptance of collapsing beds and kangarooish buses as part of an adventure—all of these talents, tested on our trip, make him an ideal travelling companion.

At first we were not going to take any baggage except a red and green striped fibre bag such as our cooks carried to market, but after stowing enough of our trifles to fill a bin with friends and ex-landladies we still had enough for a suitcase which we would carry by turns. I regretted this burden, and knowing that the barnacles picked up in voyaging always double one's baggage, took only such essentials as a shoe-horn, a telescope, a German grammar, a copy of Shelley in the Tauchnitz edition, and a shirt. George had to lend me an English school-tie on the first occasion for cleaning-up. I feared all during the trip that in some lost *cantina* I'd be approached by some reminiscent "classmate" dying of a pestilence contracted in the *chalchihuite* mines who would ask me if the Botany Prof. still wore tennis shoes to formal dances.

On Saturday, May 24, 1941, we peered back from the bus window, as well as those dwarfed apertures permit, at the Valley of Mexico, its fields flecked with the clusters of little houses which have been sacked and rebuilt and burned so many times, forming pueblos each of which had its local dynasty as the Aztec tribute-lists tell. I thought, as one always must on entering or leaving Mexico City, of Cortés and that first unimaginable sight of those vanished lakes and forests bearing the sullen Aztec capital with its hundred malformed gods. Then we swung away to the South, and the hills piled up about the Valley and our journey began in a rain. It grew cold in the hills near Toluca, one of which is a white-gleaming crater holding an icy lake where the gems of Barcelona are reputed to have been hidden by Republican refugees. I have heard from a man how he found empty cardboard boxes there bearing the names of Catalan jewellery stores.

We got to Toluca around three and hungry, and went to a cheap restaurant as one had always better do in Mexico unless he goes to a very good one—the middle class ones are unwarrantably expensive and have musicians. At once dogs and beggars swung satellitically about us, begging and snatching all the odd buns and scraps of tough meat we were not actually chewing. The waitress picked her way among them. They were no more the management's problem than, say, the flies. An old woman who had brought a bag asked for my salad, which I surrendered, and did it up in a *tortilla* brought for the purpose. Then she pushed her campaign to the over-fiery *mole* sauce from which I had extracted the islands of meat. As she disappeared floorwards beyond the edge of the table I wondered how she could put the messy brown liquid in her bag. After a while I leaned over and discovered her wiping it up on more of her edible wrapping material, which she disposed of by eating. She was undoubtedly very poor, and too old to be ashamed of bothering gentlefolk when they were eating and she was hungry. Not one of the crew of the café paid her the slightest heed, and she and five dogs and George and I shared two 85 centavo (17¢ American) meals in great coziness.

Once the December before while I waited in front of this restaurant for a bus a large Indian swayed up to me. I glanced at the *cantina* and stepped back, but he lurched toward me again. He made a rough sound and thrust his hands out, not for alms or to show me anything as far as I could see. On his left cheek grinned a deep scar, as he made the sound again and again thrust out his hands, trying to grapple with me. They were large and strong and colored like gilt wood that has tarnished in a church. They were all I remembered from the trip, those hands, splendid and useless, and the scrawny boy who threw a rock at the idiot who showed them as he stood there making rough noises.

Afterward George and I walked through the market, one of the largest in the country. A fairly new cement building overflowed into hundreds of little shacks and tables and awnings where people sat on their haunches all day to sell rope or the omnipresent worn-out chickens, which, one thinks, surely can't survive more than a couple of trips to market, since they are trailed about head-down and swooning. I might have bought a *sarape,* but all I found were commonplace, and piled up in a grandiose post. Moreover, the woman who sold them squawked at us in English, so of course I didn't look at them. When five or ten sarapes are piled up before one man who has made them, one may settle down to haggling in a respectable way, but larger establishments are harpies swollen on the blood of brainless tourists. Moreover, the larger and more worldly the dealer, the more ugly and decadent his wares, screeching with harlot colors and mildewed motifs. We noticed a woman talking an Indian language, who stopped when we passed her, and many people with hare-lips. George showed me that women wore men's straw hats over their headscarves, and when a woman scooted by on feet that seemed to be self-governing, said that was the "Toluca Walk." He had named it. There was much mud and the rain chilled down at intervals.

We also visited the local museum, which was a mixture of zoological, botanical, geological, archaeological and historical exhibits, many of them worth stealing. Curiously, no one had. In the patio among cacti, where an unsociable eagle roves, are several cages of animals on the raccoon order—*cacomixtlis.* I had one once, which, bought to celebrate the departure of a room-mate, proved to be as much a problem as the room-mate had been. They are cowards in the day, but great hilarity descends upon them at nightfall, and they break flowerpots, swing on curtains, and sound generally like drunken burglars. Besides these was a penfull of dishonest-looking snakes and a dreamy alligator, whose peaked look may have been due to the chill climate or to his diet, for when we asked the boy in charge what it ate, be said "We don't know."

There were many pieces inside the museum dug up at Coixtlahuaca nearby, "the place of houses on the plain" where a round temple of the wind-god exists. They were dominated by a lifesize figure of the wind-god, of subtly rounded black stone, wearing the melon-shaped mask of his blowing lips. I do not remember any Spanish sculpture so fine. Coixtlahuaca must have been deserted before the Spaniards came, because these statues are not broken. The museum also displays a feather textile which professes, not very convincingly, to be pre-Conquest. In the historical wing is a random collection of paintings—saints with their insides being pulled out on hooks, their eyes being pried out and other routine pieces painted with a good deal or red paint and abandon—relieved by a few rhythmical "primitives" of the last century, especially the departure of the French marshal at the end of the Intervention, and several curious stirrups shaped like brutal doll's faces.

We supped in a Chinese restaurant full of British war posters: pictures of oversize tanks and battleships blowing up, all of which said exactly the same thing, that Britain would win the war. She would not win it with those posters, we thought. Then we went to a movie called "The Insurgent" where people wore costumes and read proclamations of Ferdinand VII and yet it came out all right. It was richly photographed, though the *taros* of beer with which we topped it off and a long fervent conversation about New Orleans and Florida and the Seven Years' War blurred my memory.

Toluca is the capital of the State of Mexico and has a cathedral, only the cathedral is full of pigs. Its grey stone walls lack continuity, like a building in a dream. The front is all right, though one wonders when they are going to get a roof on it. Inside it is not all right: it is garden patches and shanties, with chickens and cotton drawers hung out to dry. Perhaps one third of the walls are done: one of them timidly mentions the date 1867. The workmen have not come back. One who threads his way back to the right of where the altar would be finds a doorway carved with lush saints in false beards and stone panties. Another deception, he exclaims, having caught you, and pushes in looking for the bottle factory, but this time it is a real church. It looks as if they had been going to make it into an annex; in any case it is a good thing if you hold with church-going that they did not tear it down.

Before Cortés, the Toluca Valley was peopled by the Matlatzincas, who sacrificed people by squeezing them in nets until they came through or a part of them came through. They were a later stand of the Toltecs of Tula after the eleventh century, and lent such ample military aid to the neighbouring Tarascans when the latter were in a tight spot that colony of men was asked to settle down near the present city of Morelia. In the 1470's the father of Moctezuma conquered the Matlatzincas a couple of times.

Saturday the train for Morelia, capital of Michocacan, edged warily into town and people jumped off to buy bananas. George and I had awaited this instant in ambush on opposite sides of the track. Now we clutched and heaved our way in, hoping that one of us might get us seats, which are not entailed in tickets in rural Mexico. We sat down victoriously and soon savored the sliding landscape, a good deal of which sifted through the windows as the day progressed. At stops, being frightened into hunger like all the travellers, we bought oranges and bananas and buns, which must have been found in an attic, baked eggs and roast corn through these windows, from the women who besiege all trains and buses. George dawdled with that most typical bloom of the seedy century's end which produced *The Hill of Dreams, Dorian Gray,* and *A Rebours:* Moore's *Confessions of a Young Man.* I studied the German subjunctive, Ersten and Zweiten Forme. We drifted on through dry country. I was practising giving orders to an imaginary dog when the train balked suddenly. Bundles with people among them scrambled off and rushed to another train. "How nice to have so much room," we thought, and then seeing that absolutely no one else had stayed, we thought perhaps the engine was going to explode. So we got off also. It was a transfer point which no one had bothered to announce, and the other people got the good seats that time. At evening, entering Michoacan, we passed an ominous region—a brown desert sprawling clear out of sight, void of even a weed. It proved from the map to be the ex-lake of Cuitzeo—why gone dry, we did not know.

We found Morelia crowded, as expected, because of the celebration of its 400th anniversary. The previous year its citizens had done very well celebrating the 400th anniversary of the College of St. Nicolas Hidalgo, and if historical items do not run out the tradition seems established. We went to a place George had once lived in, where, he promised me, a stuffed nigger boy served as hall-tree, the bathroom was full of pigeons which roosted on the door so it couldn't be shut, and a derby hat with the date 1871 inside lay on the hall table. However, we learned that this hostelry had been weeded out, probably by the Sanitary Commission. We went thence to the *Central,* built around a patio where one might hold the Olympic Games. Its corridors were obstructed by low-hanging cages of bad-tempered mocking-birds.

The walls of Morelia were spotted with pink and green posters announcing events of the cuatrocentennial. Among them was a performance of the new left-wing theatre and ballet group being nurtured in Mexico City by the Electrician's Union. We decided to attend this. At first we were treated to an empty stage and a series of screams and groans which curled our nerves like hairpins. These continued for some little while, then the female producing them was lugged on by a bent little peasant in the conical hat and cotton pajamas of the Chiapas region. She died after a while. It appeared that we were being oppressed by a league of drunken doctors who jokingly caused abortions and mine owners being mined in turn by yellow-haired "floosies." These applicants of Caucasian social injustice were finally wiped out by us aborigines in some uncomfortable detail. Carried away by the blinding of the mine-owner by the bent little peasant and the rush of rebellious is crowds by torchlight into the strongholds of their oppressors, we were ready in a trice to demolish the next aristocrat we should see. We subsided, however, during a very long ballet—obscure posturing to Bach (which might have been seen in any city in the path of the Ballet Russe's annual change of feeding grounds) followed by a costume piece. In this latter, skull-visaged ladies hiding behind sweetly-composed falsefaces borne on something like lorgnettes—faces like those of girls who have just learned the runs in *Amaryllis,* devils and lovemaking peasants and pieces of a giant which walked about quite unassembled, were all vanquished by an exuberant young wench Revolution who had the prerogative of stuffing the rest of the cast into the mouth of Hell because she had mastered the obscurer pamphlets of Lenin and had a rifle besides.

A simple kind of black and scarlet blanket had taken my eye as we teetered into Michoacan—it was of a chastity which the products of looms near the capital have lost. Along the arcades of Quiroga, where I saw them afterwards, they hung the colour of the startling underwings of moths whose backs are brown as old grass, or the colour of a fire department's washline. On Sunday the 25th, we went to the market hoping to find one of these blankets, but found mostly a dreadful stench, possibly rising from a row of leather-dealers' booths. It rained: we fled back to the hotel. There the clerk called on me triumphantly with a man he had found selling the usual garish junk admired by proprietresses of boarding houses for American tourists. Impervious to the charms of green and yaller and purple all beautifully mixed up, I followed the man back through the rain to the central arcade where he was established with some cronies. At length he sold me a pure black and white blanket, not what I wanted, but with merit of its own—thereby doubling our luggage.

Rain had George and me in and out of the *Central* a dozen times after that. The whole swollen population of Morelia watched the sky anxiously, because of a special event slated for the afternoon. A token of this event wavered past us on one of our sallies downtown—a truck stuffed with brass-players who brandished a sort of wheel covered with pink and yellow and lavender streamers of crepe paper. It was, George explained, made of the little spears or *bandarillas* to be stuck in the bulls that afternoon at the ring. Special fighters had been brought from Mexico City to divert all the Mexico City folk who had come to Morelia. The fight did not seem likely to come off—in a little saloon where we took refuge and beer during a shower a man looked out at the sky and said "goodbye, bulls!" and back at the *Central* they said it had been abandoned. We were about to give up when I saw two picadors—the mounted "fighters" leaving our hotel in their fortified costumes topped by round helmets or hats with shaving-brushes stuck in them. We took a chance and went out to the ring on the edge of the city. There a discontented crowd was pushing around and eating fried pork-fat called *chicheron* or a kind of *ersatz-chicheron* made of wheat, which has the same merits of the original except the possibility of giving one trichinosis. The crowd scowled at a chalked-up notice that the fight was off. Skies were clearing, and some official who rashly came by in his car was surrounded and bullied until the sign was removed, whereupon we all fought our way in. Tickets for Sun and for Shade are offered, the latter costing more. We bought Sun tickets, not counting on the sun's coming out, as it rather perversely did.

Morelia has a small bull ring. The effect of the pillars sheltering and encircling tiers of seats was distinctly Roman, as was the beast-fight itself, though 1500 years before the Romans wore underwear the Cretans were very fond of some kind of dance or fight with bulls and painted them in their frescoes. The arena had to be mended, and smoothed like a tennis-court. This was done sketchily, because more showers wavered down, and a few moments later a man walked below us with a thing like a coarse fish-hook trailing green crepe-paper, made to stick in the bull as he came into the ring, in order to anger him. The wheel of colored spears we had seen in the morning was now propped against a pillar. Only the musicians were lacking. Apparently these had gone home, because without any formal beginning a horseman dashed violently across the ring to "ask permission" of the "authority" to hold he fight, and without the Carmen music, the little train of fighters wandered in. The leaders were one Silverio Pérez and someone else—popular young fighters who alone had permission to kill the bull. There followed some underlings to distract the animal strategically, and the picadors from our hotel on shaky and blindfolded nags. All were clad in eighteenth century style, gold brocades on green and pink and brown, knee-breeches, shoes with pompoms, false pigtails which had atrophied to another pompom on the hat-brim, and two-color satin cloaks, red inside for the bull. These figures trekked over to the wooden barricades spotted at intervals close to the ring-walls, established themselves cautiously behind them, and the first bull trotted in.

He was a hefty, sleek thing, annoyed but not Apocalyptic. With the hook in his shoulder trailing green paper strips he was like a be-frilled chop in a restaurant. After considering the fighters, he responded to a waved cloak with a couple of swipes which the waver dodged, and the fight was on. The bulls merit no sentimentality— they are so unintelligent that only persistent provocation gets them going, and the moment it ceases they stop and stare like villagers at a train. After plunging furiously at a cloak and its wielder, they will let him furl it and turn his back to walk away without any memory that he was the tormentor. The momentary stimulus stopped, they stop.

The routine is this: first everyone shows off by waving cloaks, and the bull is induced if possible to smack into the wall of the ring, while the audience on one side hopes he will jump into the audience on the other side. Then the picadores enter, rather foolish-looking big men on nightmarish blindfolded old hags stumbling around in padded overcoats which (one hopes) will keep them from visibly disagreeable mishap. These picadores prod the bull with spears, so that he will tire himself lunging at the horse. Their legs are protected by a kind of stovepipe, and the chief danger is when the bull lunges into the horse's belly, because sometimes the latter is overthrown. This afternoon one of the picadores who kept goading the bull after the audience had yelled at him not to tire it too much, was nearly settled for by a terrific charge which bowled the horse over, the rider falling over the bull's back and sprawling stiff on the ground. The bull was lured away by other fighters and no damage done to the fallen man, nor was the equine Father Time as much hurt as I had anticipated, only getting a leg crippled. Blood was much in evidence but one could never tell whose: the bulls bled some from the shoulder, some from noses bashed against walls. This tiring-out accomplished, the third phase of each fight was an elaborate ceremonial, the really dangerous and skillful part, in which the fighters walked out to the baffled and glowering bull with one of the *banderillas* or paper-frilled spears the length of a cane. They postured mockingly with these in front of them, very audience-conscious, raising and twitching them at arm's length. Then they run straight into the malignant horns, and out again, and if the play is well done, the spikes project one from each shoulder, and the people shout, and if it is badly done, they are on the same side, or it is the fighter who gets stuck. A pink pair, a yellow pair and a lavender were thrust in this manner into each successive bull, and each jerked and wheeled about to rid himself of the festive-looking torment. By and by he began to tire, and the man who had the right to kill him with a special little sword, took this sword and proffered his cloak upon it to the bull a few times, avoiding the violent and immediate head-sweeps, and then sought to kill him by one blow behind the skull. This was not too well done with most of those we saw: as the sixth and last bull was being dispatched, people piled over the benches and into the ring like monkeys loping through a jungle toward a banana grove. Presumably they jumped in to offer advice. I followed and saw the bull go down only a couple of yards away, spewing blood hopelessly. Then his executioner was carried off by the crowd.

All afternoon an increasingly saturated (with pulque) bun-peddler had been making up for the absent orchestra, until it finally came back, with whoops and yowls. Ultimately as some bit of nice horn-dodging resulted in hats being thrown in the ring, he gave a screech of ecstasy, dumped his bread-basket in, and jumped in after it to clutch and hoist the fighter up by the knees. Then everyone cheered him instead of the fighter; his bread was collected by volunteers and chucked back into the basket, because he couldn't afford to waste it, and the show went on and he went on hawking the buns. George told me that other objects are thrown in, as well as the jewellery which rich and excited ladies are supposed to fling to the fighters. A countrywoman of ours, for example, once hurled her panties into the Mexico City ring, and was defended victoriously by the crowd when the police came after her. Sometimes also, the bull-fighter throws his hat to an onlooker before the fight, an honor signifying that the next bull will be dedicated to the hat-catcher. Once it landed in George's lap, and he asked his neighbors what to do. "Put five or ten in it and throw it back," they advised enviously. "Five or ten centavos?" he asked. "Gracious, no! Five or ten pesoes." So etiquette did him for all he had.

When we got back to the *Central* we saw the star of the day, Silverio Pérez, again. At close range he proved to have gold teeth and a kind of horsy look which I fear endangers him with nearsighted bulls. He, like the picadores, was stopping at our hotel. An hour after the fight we watched him confer impressively with them, climb into his roadster, and drive furiously out of the Olympic Game patio into the street. "He'll be in Mexico City in three hours," we thought, but late that night found the car parked on the other side of the street.

A poetry recital seemed to offer variety, and I wanted to investigate local literary schools without having to work very hard at it, so I said I was going to the same Teatro Ocampo where we had seen the ballet, and listen to a literary programme. George, however, had to see a firework "castle" on a frame as high as a telephone post, which was to be set off in front of the pink seventeenth century cathedral. "Go on to your intellectual nonsense," he said. His satire was justified: the stage produced only a series of scared young men in borrowed evening clothes who forgot their most impassioned lines, and one massive youngish lady who chanted with cornfed supplications about how butterflies ravished her—a quite impossible feat. At midnight I struggled out in the midst of the third narrative poem detailing Morelia's history, and bought two pancakes and a bottle of green fizzwater on the empty plaza from one of those nocturnal woman vendors who huddle about with flickering lamps and small tables of beans and tortillas.

Monday, the 26th, followed, though the British were losing Crete. Since a series of little Chinese restaurants had served us mostly flies and waitresses who lingered at other tables to have their bottoms pinched, we breakfasted in a booth at the market. These usually contain a couple of tables and a charcoal fire smothered under enormous earthenware pots, one of tripe, one of pork, one of indestructible beef, and some kind of vegetable stew. Aside from sauces, a few drops of which are enough to season a roast ox, one can eat most market dishes, or make something himself out of eggs. Eating in a market, one may imperiously direct the cooking without any objection from the cook; running out if he fancies to another booth for a little grated cheese, or to a fruit-stand for a melon. She will provide the knife and spoon and never hears of corkage fees. Tortillas, indeed, are always a separate negotiation, being bought from perambulating basket-bearers at around a centavo each.

After breakfast we went to the local museum, which had some fine clay figure and animal pieces, the latter being bulgy dogs, a prehispanic foodstuff no longer on the market, so far as I know. The ceramics are the high-spot of the artistic remains of this region, though who made them is uncertain. They are an evolved form of the most ancient pottery forms of the western hemisphere, the Archaic culture which differs unrecognizably in other parts. A sort of stirrup-shaped jug handle here is oddly similar to Peruvian forms— indeed, the solution to the whole question of North and South American relationships in pre-Conquest times is suspected to lie in Michoacan. The linguistic isolation of the Tarascans, the decoration on the only two vessels found at the old capital of Tzintzuntzan, the lack of any really primitive remains underlying Peru's high culture are obscure background shapes which same future investigator's torch, kindled in Michoacan, may light up. Other things in this museum are a scary two-story fresco on the Dali order, having as always with Mexican frescoes no divinable connection with the building housing it; a flock of pious paintings, some of it good Baroque stuff; many relics of the priest Morelos, and a guide whose witless gabble and aggressive label-reading nearly provoked me into pushing him through a showcase. To be treated as if I were the National Illiteracy Problem set me foaming. Of all the ineradicable pests I have met I wish him quickest in the hands of the Gestapo. Nothing could insult him enough to silence him. "That's an idol," he said, pointing at an idol, or of a case marked "Morelos' Boots," "Those are Morelos' boots," he would say. He seemed surprised that we didn't tip him. Dodging his clamorous pursuit around showcases, George and I agreed to upset him by going in different directions, so that one at least would get peace. I saw a copy of the Nelson's Looseleaf Encyclopedia of the 1590's, the *Nuremberg Chronicle,* which had hundreds of illustrations, each appearing four or five times with different captions; a few drawings of petroglyphs, and a couple of the insipid Tarascan pictorial manuscripts, late sixteenth century.

In the local library, which took us hours to find because it had no sign, the personnel was equally ignorant but exceedingly courteous, even hauling out the contents of their display case when I showed interest. One tome contained engravings of mermaids, tritons, and less routine inhabitants of the sea. The library is rather large with shelves of stuff from disbanded convents which remains to be catalogued. I read something more of the history of Morelia, which was founded as Valladolid, on May 18, 1541. The first viceroy of New Spain, Don Antonio de Mendoza, had gone there a year previously to meet Pedro de Alvarado (whose massacres had brought on the expulsion of the Sad Night and the whole siege of Mexico City) to discuss expansion north and west, and fancied the place as a town site. There was already a mission on this site of Valladolid with a little religious school. Years later when the provincial capital (a few years at Tzintzuntzan, and then a long while at Pátzcuaro) was finally brought to the present city another school merged with this first one; the result was the College of San Nicolas Hidalgo, the oldest college on the Continent, which claims 1540 as its foundation year. We looked into this celebrated institution, which was crowded with the students of a special spring session, and saw a number of rather Frenchified paintings by local artists. Picasso and Matisse are quite popular in the hinterland.

Since my vacation days were limited, we asked about buses to Pátzcuaro, the next major stage in our journey. These were parked about a square. One driver said with a vague gesture "The Pátzcuaro bus is in front." "In front" being found a block away, we bought tickets. I was thereupon bamboozled into tipping one of those diabolical young extorters, who hang officiously around buses and must be slapped off like horse-flies, to hold a seat. He did—for someone else. After the bus pulled out, with me scolding impotently out the window, I found myself entitled to sit with some potatoes in the back of the aisle, while a little boy dangled his feet down my collar. I crouched over and read Shelley—which peeved me all the more as we sped toward Tzintzuntzan, where we had asked to be let out until the next bus. The driver observed in an off-handed way, about five miles beyond it, "You wanted to get off at Tzintzuntzan, didn't you? That's it back there." We went on to Pátzcuaro.

In Pátzcuaro, which is on a large lake, there was a choice of hotels: rickety or expensive. We chose the *Concordia,* one of the former, and were assigned a room that looked like a hastily thrown up stage set of a mountaineer's cabin, with one bed and one series of boards with a blanket spread over them. I callously assigned this to George, who is the more three-dimensional of us. "This looks sort of like the Tyrol," he said, indicating the timbers. "But I sound like Queen Victoria. Wherever she was, it reminded her of someplace else. When she was in Scotland, it reminded her of the Rhine, and when she was on the Rhine it reminded her of Scotland."

Dumping the suitcase which we lugged in unhappy turn, we set out on a side-trip, another bus trip to the lakeside. There we came on a party of young gentlemen bathing, all of whom modestly scuttled into their clothes and went home. This occurred in the back yard of a Southern-California-trying-to-look-like-Mexico-house, and we went in at the same spot. The wind blew and the sun went under, and George did too, and I, half-immersed like a skittish seal in some unnamed little American bay, dared move neither way until I could decide which half of me was colder. After a little ginger soaping, I got dry on old newspapers and wind. George marooned himself on a stone to do the same, and then tried to put one sock on, standing like a stork. All of this turned out badly, and he stalked ashore through the mud with no visible gain in cleanliness.

Pátzcuaro is Japonesque, with white wooden eaves shadowing cobbled streets. Situated in timber country, there is little of the mud and wattles architecture so common north and south of it. A great industry in this region is scraping and whittling out useless wooden objects polished to look like real mahogany—mostly boxes decorated with incised lines.

That night we went to the Plaza, a sort of Campus Martius lighted only along one edge and corner by the candles or little oil lamps of fruit vendors, like campfires in the desert. I was enchanted into buying a green melon, which I then had to eat in order to prove to its former proprietors that I wasn't fool enough to buy unripe fruit. George succumbed to peanuts, for sale in great heaps, though there couldn't have been more than half a dozen customers afloat. He offered them to me, and I took some innocently enough, just as if they had been something inconsequential. He scowled, and after a few minutes said, "I always rather resent it when people accept them. I am generous with other things but not with peanuts. I go around corners when I have them. How I hate those women in Taxco who see me and scream 'Oh, give me some peanuts and take half the sack.'" I understood. We were peaceful there in the big dark square with those laudably inadequate lights. In our cities we never let the darkness in. George said that he had gained his peace of mind again, which he had lost during Holy Week. I remembered something of that myself, having got drunk especially for a party and then having found the party called off when I burst merrily in with five additional guests. At that reminiscence we both went and had a glass of beer, and another walk around the square, and then I couldn't find the hotel and he wouldn't tell me, so we walked around twice more before I spotted it.

We subsided into bed, though George couldn't subside very far on account of having the board element of our bed-and-board combination. Quiet and darkness ensued, and images of the lake and hills drifted past me . . . broken by a thump in the corner. "What's that?" I asked. "A rat," George suggested. "Sounds like a whole colony of them," I said, remembering once when I had popped out of bed and put my socks on only to find that my feet came out the other end. I told him of this. He put on the light and hung the more edible-looking clothing out of their way. Not a whisker was visible. Out went the light and back they came. I thought of the Pit and the Pendulum, and put on the light and shoved my bed into a defensive position. Then I put the light out again. Back trampled the rats. In retrospect we decided that they must have yearned for the soap, which we would gladly have given them. All night they sprang furiously at the wash-bowl, falling short each time, abandoning this pursuit only to make horrid scratching sounds on the ledges formed by the two-by-fours parallel to our prostrate forms. Would they leap over upon us? It was too much: we put the lights on and left them on as long at the Light Company was willing, or perhaps able, which proved to be four o'clock. Then the *Valse Macabre* set in till it began to get light. They never did get the soap nor us, but at dawn they seizcd my toothbrush and fled. I cannot otherwise account for its disappearance, which upset me greatly. I had had it only a year.

Tuesday, the twenty-seventh of May, yawning into the market at eleven, we found a little booth where a breakfast of cream and rice with crude sugar cost ten centavos a cup, to which I added a communal melon at thirty centavos from a fruit-stand. Then we sought out the local museum, which is situated in the original building of the College of San Nicolas Hidalgo, before the removal of everything important to what is now Morelia. One cannot easily tell the age of such buildings, whose yard-thick walls are duplicated to this day. The Cathedral, abandoned in Queen Elizabeth's day, likewise failed to show its age. Having been finished up as an ordinary church, we took it for something recent.

The museum was dedicated to regional arts. Regional arts, of course, means lacquer here—a process known to the lake-dwellers before Cortés, and though much adulterated by mere painted stuff, charming and restrained in its better days. New designs have got large, over-pictorial, and sprawly, so that Olinala ware takes precedence. We saw hundreds of pieces, and I was abashed to discover that a kind of pea-green ware which I had fancied was placed among the decedent products. A regional kitchen flaunted festoons of clay pots on the walls, and a chapel with sky-blue-pink walls held a Christ dressed in a kind of butterfly-shaped loincloth with spangles. Doves and scrolls bedizened the walls. There was a great deal of pottery from a place called Capulá, which I determined to visit, though I had so much pottery already George said I'd have to start a tea-shop. There was also a Moorish-looking geometrically pierced screen, made of wood. Wood also served for the little house constructed in the patio (again very Japonesque) which had beds inside, something more remarkable than the building material, for if most Mexican peasants live in mud houses, even more sleep on straw *petates*. That is why, I think, that servants never know how to make a bed. They think they are making *petates*, and just lay the covers on, so that one's feet grow cold and one's temper hot at three a.m. A show-case of silver fish necklaces set me on the smith's trail. When we left the museum we sought him out and bought a couple of pieces, both variations on the shield of Ihuatzio, a village across the lake where a ruined temple has been uncovered. The ornaments consist of canoes with two dumpy, determined paddling figures in derbies, and three fat fish dangling beneath. Then we went to have a glass of beer and were given little withered minnows as appetisers, followed by lunch again in the market. Our neighboring diners looked at us, and concluding that English was another Indian language, felt no self-consciousness in dropping their Spanish also and talking Tarascan.

Then it was time to leave Pátzcuaro. We sat on a concrete bench and awaited the bus to the lake and the train station. A horse with sides of meat impaled on two spikes jutting from its saddle ambled past us several times. I wished we had him to carry our suitcase; which I soon turned over to George, because I wanted to get out and see a monument on the way to the lake. It commemorated the last Tarascan ruler, Tangaxoan II, and has besides the heroic figure of the chief (who for a wonder doesn't look like a Crow or a Dakota) plaques at the base showing the division of the kingdom by his ancestor Tariacuri, Tangaxoan's genealogy, his meeting with Cristobal de Olíd and peaceable surrender to this first Spanish emissary in 1523, and his death at the hands of the twisted Naziesque Nuno de Guzman in 1550. It was made by one Ruiz, and was one of the ablest monuments I had seen in the country.

I met George at the station, and we decided to try to crowd another expedition in before the train came. I wanted to see Janitzio, one of the half-dozen fisher-peopled islands, so we decided to make a flying trip and chance missing the train. Renting a motor-boat for the half-hour trip, we set out westward from the dock. The lake was choppy, with a west wind. Encased in the rubber sheets with which we were provided, we caught an occasional wave in our laps and squinted at the metallically bright water. On our left as we headed for Janitzio, a tree-covered mound rose not far from shore—an ideal site for Bacchanalian revels, I thought. After a long time we caught up with a dugout holding nine men and a couple of women, all rowing with the most ineffectual little paddles ever devised, mere discs of wood the size of tortillas, and not much more durable, fastened to slender poles. Teaspoons would have been better. The rudder descended from the elevated bow through about a yard of air before entering the water, yet despite these handicaps, such boats have been navigated for centuries on the lake. When the Chichimec (barbarian) conquerors descended on this region about the time the Aztecs came to Mexico—say the fourteenth century—and founded Pátzcuaro as the result of a dream, they took over the use of such boats from still earlier people. We left the stubborn rowers behind and pulled into the shadow of the island, where all wind ceased. Janitzio proved to have about fifty houses, with tiled roofs, cobbled streets and fishermen mending nets along the shore talking animated Tarascan. It looked like pictures of Italian Mediterranean towns. The island was parched and dust-laden from the shore to the squat cement tower in human shape, like a Statue of Liberty *enceinte,* commemorating the patriot Morelos. Little boys here are supposed by some excitable souls to shoot arrows at palefaces who fail to give them pennies, so we watched for ambuscades, and concluded with some disappointment that it was as much a myth as that of Mexican women wearing mantillas or the Typical China Poblana costumes.

We scrambled into the island church on the ascent to the statue, which is a kind of observatory, and saw a tiny figure of St. James dressed as a *charro* or Mexican cowboy, with the tight striped pants and embroidered jacket and umbrella-wide sombrero tradition demands. He looked like the moderately prosperous and conservative old gents in rural parts, or the elegant show-offs on Sundays who ride along the chief boulevard in the capital on Sundays at eleven. Instead of the usual little silver arms and legs and sacred hearts, livers and vermiform appendices, St. James had offerings of dolls' clothes. In front of the church, three unoriented gravestones were built flat into the cobbles, bearing dates in the 1830's.

From there the climb led past a soft-drink stand under construction and two little girls who chimed in Spanish "We'll sing to you in Tarascan for ten centavos." George's wind gave out a little after leaving the church, and he told me to climb alone, but when I got to the top he was already there. Inside the cement figure of Morelos was a winding stair bordered by frescoes of events in his life, somewhat poster-like affairs with a text it would have taken half a day to read. I bounded past the history, still hoping we could get back to the mainland for the Uruapan train, and surveyed the lake and the surrounding islands from a vantage-point near Morelos' ears. Still further to the west lay Xaracuaro, the seat of the pre-Chichimec inhabitants, and two or three lesser islands and promontories. Due east was Tzintzuntzan, the old capital of the natives, hidden behind a hill.

On the return flight we stumbled past some grass mats with minnows such as we had eaten in the Pátzcuaro beer-parlour, drying on them; past the two little girls who began to sing uncertainly at us, past two little boys with the same idea, and arrived at the dock only to find the boatman, instead of leaning nervously forward with oar in hand, quite absent. In a little while he idled up with the local school-teacher. Would we be so good as to take the young man to shore? He had an important errand. Yes, we cried, if he'd hurry. He loaded nine cartons of Coca-Cola bottles in the boat leisurely. This seemed to be his errand. We set out into the spray again at a much faster rate than before because the wind was with us. The school-teacher talked to us as if he had been reading an interview with himself in the *New Masses*. The Indians were very backward—we are a very backward people, aren't we?—the boys were encouraged to play in the streets instead of to come to school. Their parents mistrusted the school and made lots of trouble. All the islands were served by this one school and three teachers. . . . We left him unloading Coca-Cola bottles and scuttled to the station, where the train was nowhere in sight.

After a while, it bore us dustily to Uruapan, whose streets were crowded as if in carnival. An animated business in bananas was going on after nine at night, a curious thing with these chicken-houred tradesmen. The town stayed this way all during our brief sojourn. Some of the people may have been waiting for their turn at a bed, for we encountered a hotel crisis. One had recently burned and another been shaken to pieces in the earthquake which had just destroyed Colima. The rest had been wickedly occupied at once by our train companions, who reached them by taxi instead of waiting for the bus from the station as we did. After casting about awhile, we followed one of the know-it-all little boys despite my longing to scourge them out of the way like orientals at a coronation, and found lodging at Corregidora 9, the two of us for three pesoes, with no rats.

Idols infested my dreams—I disputed the right to buy them with an American who manufactures much of Mexico's popular art, and awoke at four a.m. on Wednesday, with the issue unsettled. This day, the 29th, we pushed down the street of the fruit vendors, who didn't seem to have gone to bed at all, to the Cooperative. The Cooperative is a place where they make lacquer, the town's most noted product. Besides the doorway between banana-stands, it hid another around the corner, which I took from its carving to be a church entrance. These two display-rooms were connected through a patio. The patio was large and contained one chicken and three or four girls who sat on some steps and rubbed dreamily at wooden dishes with oily rags to make the colors stick. These lacquer-makers had obtained the proletarian freedom which the play in Morelia appeared to favor. While George looked for something to replace his coronation plate which he had broken one morning with the alarm clock when it went off ("The thing frightened me," he complained), I tried out this route through the courtyard a couple of times, making up my own mind what to buy, and nearly having to buy the chicken which I stepped on. The lacquers were mostly platters— black with red artichokes on them. One flaunted a Plains Indian head. Somehow Mexican craftsmen of the humbler sort feel their ancestors lived in tepees. We bought some pieces singly and jointly, obscuring finances a little more. One did not bargain much here.

Then we went to another place, on straight capitalist lines, and regret to say found better pieces of lacquer. They cost more, however. They held more and smaller areas of color, and some designs were copied from the eighteenth century heyday; crawly little black patterns on a green background, like a jungle seen through ferns. I insisted on seeing still others, and the owner finally brought out two sedate white bowls with brown and white leaf-patterns inside a restraining circle which left the centre bare, and a great bird, like a doubled-up ostrich, on a cobalt background. The latter was very Indian, a copy of a sixteenth century piece, and all being irresistible, had him send them to me at Mexico City, C.O.D.

There is a curious oriental effect in Michoacan. The lacquer is part of it. But lacquer here is no novelty of the Spaniards. It was made long before them. Some of the other elements, the long-eaved houses of Pátzcuaro, the gates like *torii* before wooden houses, may have been introduced to the early seventeenth century when Nipponese ambassadors, en route to Madrid, were caught between boats for a year or so in New Spain. At this time the grass raincoat and the *huarache* shoe, often assumed to be native, were introduced.

At noon the little boy who had led us to Corregidora 9 was led by us to the bus, where we piled him on some luggage to hold down a seat while we ate. How useful these small and intelligent youngsters can be!

It rained on the way to Zamora: there we found an express bus for Guadalajara—a spacious and underpeopled affair, though none of these plush and mirror bordels on wheels in which the hardy Pittsburger roughs it. Had we the cash to transfer to this marvel? For suddenly we had spent all our money, each counting on the other to keep enough for prosaic ends. We didn't have enough, really, but we took it and left the hotel that night as a distant and academic problem. The place at which we had to stay, as a result of this extravagance, was an insect-ridden madhouse full of screeching housemaids and indefatigable bed-bugs, which George escaped by drinking half a bottle of a liquor he had bought to take back to Taxco. He lay back and laughed at me as I fought them sleeplessly. Knowing nothing of this nearing doom, we rolled through Jiquilpan, a priggishly beerless town due to its ungrateful son, the recent President Cárdenas, and a while later saw the lake of Chapala. This sixty mile long body is the haunt of fishermen who use certain celebrated butterfly shaped nets. Nearby is a valley of Henri Rousseau lushness, George says, which scarcely anyone can find.

The speed of the bus rose with the driver's spirits as we neared Guadalajara. I took to reading Shelley in order to avoid gaping in terror at the accelerated landscape. The *Ode to the West Wind,* which I had begun sulkily to memorize out of Morelia when I had no seat, kept me busy until evening. When next I looked up we had completed the week-long descent from the mountain-top which is Mexico City, and were in low, park-filled Guadalajara, at a bus stop clamorous with infant bandits. Somewhat west rose the towers of the Cathedral, which is so ugly it is worth going miles out of one's way to avoid it. Any medical museum would be overjoyed to have it in a jar of alcohol.

## Parícutin

Austere Parícutin holds his court amid dust. Long before one comes upon the year-old volcano or his outposts of lava, one enters the evil snows which deepen until there is no plant or animal track left. Once entered upon, this dust is in his nostrils and in his lungs and in his eyes and in his shoes until he turns his back upon the golden volcano, hours later, and goes back to Uruapan. Our bus was climbing out of a dry stream bed when I first noticed the dust. It lay in a film on a broken tree, and blew in the windows, which the passengers began to close. The road was bordered with pines hacked away when the new road was built, and the dust lay softly on them. We came out, after a little, on a valley of ashes where the dust lay thick, and moved far off in a shadowy pavane. Pines stood in the coiled snowscape at the feet of the hills hopelessly. Reflecting on their fate, my attention was shifted to my own: out came the handkerchiefs of the bus passengers—two red and yellow bandannas (the middle-aged American couple), a blue one (the *militar*), and a soiled one which had perhaps been white (the Mexican in a pith helmet—presumably an engineer). Driving now along an ample highway of grey powder—all the bushes were dead—we passed eight or ten poor little houses, like cracker-crates made of the thinnest wood. These were dead also, their shingles heaped with grey powder. Looking at them through the choking air, I wondered if this were the town of San Juan Parangarícutiro.

Visibility was low like that of a Turkish bath as the valley widened. The soft Dali landscape showed a few tracks where a starving coyote had limped by. Someone's land, needlessly fenced in, bordered the road on the left, a *milpa* where no maize would ever sprout again. Beyond it more woods which didn't know they were dead yet, and beyond this dust over flat land. Then we saw the lava.

As if from cities bombed by planes which had only just fled, smoke rose from the dung of the volcano. On the slopes of the hills which led up to him, deep drifts of ashes lay furrowed like a brain. And above them rose Parícutin. All the passengers shouted.

The grey dromedary hump of the first crater, now dormant, wheeled out of sight again, but the bus began to overtake some of the denizens of the place—denizens of the dying town ahead. Three Tarascan peasant women walked on the roadless desert in a garment of dust; we waddled past a man on a burro laden with dried stalks of fodder from some far-off town which had no volcano. And so, crossing over a withered creek, we came to San Juan Parangaricutiro. The first thing we saw was the graveyard, a wall with an arching gate and a few old wooden crosses. The people of the graveyard were being buried again, along with their descendants. Next we passed wooden houses of the Tarascan country: Abraham Lincoln's birthplace built by brown people with purple bangs and eyes humble with oppression. The walls were squared logs and the steep roofs shingled. There were many of these houses—San Juan had been a big town. A blue skirt on a wash line and a banana plant were the only things not grey. One doorway showed shelves of canned goods—more than a San Francisco grocery in war-time—and another held a group of women and little pantless children who had arranged themselves there to see the bus come in. The tiniest boy jumped and shrieked in ecstasy at the sight of us. In the plaza beyond, as we came to halt, we saw all the men of the town congregated with horses. Perhaps there were fifty horses scuffing the ashes before the church.

A stone cross rose in the plaza. Upon it were carved two bleeding hands and a jawless skull. It may have been carved hundreds of years ago. The church, one tower of which will never be finished now, loomed on the east. In the doorway women were selling charms as if the town were any town. I pushed past their commercialized piety and stepped inside. Among the artificial green marble pillars sounded, surprisingly, quiet organ music, and candles burned on the high altar, as if the town were any town. Two men in cotton pajamas came in after me, and falling to their knees abjectly, began crawling toward the lights and the music, their sandals scuffing loudly on the boards. But louder than the litany, louder than the dragging sandals, was the panting of the volcano among the hills.

San Juan had not been abandoned, though all the papers said so, but was trying to live on the very thing that had destroyed it, Parícutin and the money of people who come to see it. To this remote Tarascan-speaking town, Hungarians and Canadians and other people were flocking. Only the wars in the world kept San Juan, which was out of the world, from a boom.

Parícutin gasped and rumbled insistently, hidden beyond the dead hills, as I stood in the plaza. Horses were renting very dear, and when I had secured mine, most of our caravan of uncertain horsemen had gone ahead. I attempted to overtake them, and only lost my hat. My guide scrambled after it, and we fell to talking of horses and hats and volcanos, and I was glad to discover he coveted my hat—purchased that morning in Uruapan as a precaution against falling ashes. We made an exchange, and I kept his, which fitted me.

The road was short, up a series of sterile hills, under a fallen tree resembling a triumphal arch, and across a bridge or two—all the path over ashes of unknown depth. The clanging of the volcano grew louder, and suddenly I saw its smoke climb into the afternoon sunlight of the last day of the year.

Atop an ultimate hill I overtook two other riders who had stopped to stare at the red wound from which no one henceforth quitted his eyes, so long as it was to be seen anywhere. The pilgrimage of the moth to the candle became suddenly understandable. A little farther on, as we renewed our pace, a blasted promontory jutted out into a sea of ashes. It was a place where the Tarascans would have been building a shrine, if their fire-god had not been killed by the Spaniards four hundred years before. As it was, the promontory bore a quick-lunch stand. This was a long new shed, dismally roofed with grime already, thrown up to dodge into when ashes happened to move over that section, far up in the wind. Inside, at three or four competitive counters, one might buy buns lugged out from Uruapan, beer, or (at one place of especial elegance!) a drink from a diluted bottle of the evil beverage called *charanda*. At the quick-lunch stand before the volcano I had arranged to meet my friend the photographer.

He was there, his nose smudged with ashes, eating a large bun sprinkled also with ashes. We promptly wiped out the *charanda* business by buying the whole bottle, a tactic which so astonished the woman selling it that she forgot to overcharge us. We drank a little: the air was very cold and the sun was sinking rapidly now, but the light of Parícutin grew. His noise was like that of an uneasy freight-train—he gasped out poisonous gases and gulped in fresh air and coughed rhythmically. Two months before, the dromedary-shaped crater had gone dead—an unfinished Fujiyama—and a new crater clawed its way out of its parent's side. It was this new crater which cast up a foam of liquid rock momently, having already reached a quarter of the old cone's height.

It was possible and necessary to go down the hill past the geologist's shack and wade toward Parícutin on foot. My photographer friend had done this in the morning; now he wished to go again. The five candles of the quick-lunch stand would guide us back. So we left his sleeping bag in the charge of the woman who dealt in buns, the bottle of *charanda* tucked well inside it, and sliding down a hill which had lost its shape, began at nightfall to trek among dunes. The gasping of the volcano was louder now, and with each gasp it heaved lava into the sky, a changing filigree of gold against the hollow heavens. In a shaft of red light this fountain of rocks played incessantly. As our feet scuffed and our throats choked on ashes, down there in the colorless netherland, the red light of Parícutin and the white light of the stars lighted up the sky. Orion slid up over a precipice of lava, where something was smouldering like a campfire, and Rigel mingled his weak but eternal rays with those of the transitory giant. There was also a little moonlight. It was like a dream of walking across the bottom of the sea.

We climbed and descended a series of sterile mounds which felt like mattresses. No footfall echoed, nor did any sound come from the hail of newly smelted rocks which bounded first golden and then red and then invisible down Parícutin's sides. I could not tell how far we stood from the volcano when my friend halted to set up his camera. After a period of fumbling and lighting of matches, which the cold wind put out at once, the volcano was perpetuated on the little patch of celluloid, and we pushed on. These halts came some dozen times: once in a gully from which we could see only rocks flung upward like pancakes by a dextrous darkey in a restaurant window in Memphis. But even when one could not see it, his eyes kept searching for the volcano, and when he saw it again, he stared at the monotonous dancing rocks as if he had never seen them before. He came to watch for little variants in the changing mosaic of golden fragments inlaid in the night—as they rose, large masses stretched out, doubled upon themselves and broke, to rattle silently over the crater's lip, or fall back formless into the crucible. Now and again, like fireworks gone wrong in a festival, sparks which were in reality tons of rock shot out beyond the ordinary range of fire, and skipped off alone down slopes which they momentarily bejeweled.

Stopping and pushing on, little by little, we began to walk on warm ashes. The need of getting the volcano with his hat in his hand, or reading a novel, or addressing the multitude from a balcony led us closer. Behind us the five stars of the quick-lunch stand began to merge with other constellations, but the next shot, or the next would be the culminating one. So we ventured closer to that uneasy Mecca, whose crowds jostled in the sky and perished unceasingly, and the ashes grew quite warm. Then a stone fell from the sky *behind* us. It looked like a golden brick, and it was at last clear what sort of noise the stones made when they hit, for it was only a dozen meters from us; and as I say, it fell behind us. We decided upon a flexible line of defense.

Before, any point had seemed safe, now no point did. We ran back to some previous hills, and then to some others, and there my friend began to set up his tripod, while I watched to see if any unusually high stones lifted out of the volcano. Having been blooded by the whistling brick, we could hear other stones falling at intervals, where before we had seemed to hear silence. Little scraps of what seemed to be stiff sponge fell down on us whenever the wind blew the volcano's smoke over, in the pale sky. From time to time a hillock loomed in our way, as we returned across that dirty desert, eclipsing the quick-lunch stand. It began to grow dark with smoke. The only appropriate thing to do was to get lost, and this we did. One descent led us only to a queer soft precipice, and no quick-lunch stand shimmered grail-like beyond. Back of us the volcano continued to juggle its fantastic oranges, a safe distance away, and we should have been close to the promontory we had first descended, but only a pool of red shone off in the rocks to the right, with the sullen look of a cat's eyes when it is eating. There were no other live things in that world of ashes, so when we noticed that we had been making footprints, we followed them backwards and found ourselves.

At the quick-lunch stand there was a bench made of a split tree, not very wide, and on it one might rest and look at the volcano more, which had now begun to pall somewhat. There was, however, nothing else in sight except in the sky. My companion asked the woman who sold sooty buns for his sleeping bag, and began to dig in it for the bottle of *charanda*. He found it, and we drank a little. Though it is not very refreshing, *charanda* is useful for killing bedbugs in cheap hotels in Jalisco, I had once discovered. (The next day, in Uruapan, he examined the bottle and found that the woman had rummaged in his bag and changed the bottle for an inferior one, worth some three *centavos* less.) After the *charanda,* my friend began to nod, sitting on the narrow bench. I saw an attractive plank propped up in the end of the shed, and laid hold of it delightedly, whereupon a large growl, of an unencouraging cast, leapt out at me and caused me to desist. I could not explain why I had bargained to stay all night before that now frankly monotonous crater. When, a little later, two boys speaking Tarascan hauled a horse out of the darkness past the shed, their chins snuggled down into their blankets, I saw my opportunity to escape.

# Appendix

## Fragments

that mighty one above the _____ powers of men

_____

Groonta

_____

The Summons
A Memory
Till a the Seas
The Fugitives
Marionette
#13 Garoth

_____

The Traveller

_____

The Dreamer
The Watcher
(tail-piece)

etc

perhaps
The Prophet?
The Minotaur?
25 copies

## A Memory & a Dream

A Memory
A Dream
Pursuit of the Moth
*The Bright Valley

*The Root-Gatherers
A Dim-Remembered Story
*The Night Ocean

(No Right to Pity[)]
FRAIL TRIBUTE: Sonnets

*unfinished

# National Defense

*H. P. Lovecraft and R. H. Barlow*

[HPL:]

so that you might not forget, but take it home with you.

Omit reference to figures or statistics of any kind

Make comparison at outset

Fire department—best insurance against disaster of any kind. Maintenance effects a saving—expense much less than that of damage without it would be. Same with warfare. National defence is insurance against the disaster of an unsuccessful war. Have been lucky in past—successful termination of war. No military policy, but good fortune caused success. In world war unprepared, but allies held front so that preparation could be effected. Took year to put troops into field, & even so some arrived untrained. If military policy had existed, taxpayers would have been saved millions—expense of training camps, munitions factories, & machinery of draft. War ended, need of natl. defence manifest. Natl. defence act law 1920. Provided force large enough to defend country in case of emergency—not large enough for aggression. Young men often say will not fight unless in case of attack. No one has ever proposed any other kind of military policy. Those in charge of country would never stand for war of aggression—future same as past.

Natl. Defence act         (3)    Reg. Army
Component parts—         Natl Guard
                  Organised Reserves

comprise several field armies depending on type of emergency aris-
ing. Key commissions held by civilians preparing selves for possible
service. Extension courses _____ by reservists offer promotion.

Reserves made possible by patriotism of civilians who pursue studies in addition to business

Case of War
    Reg. arm. and Nat Guard would serve first—hold line until re-
serves ready. Details of reserve training in file with W. D. 9 areas
have plans prepared & consolidated under Natl. Defence scheme.
All prepared even blank telegrams for mobilisation. By this plan expensive training camps needless—training already effected by reserve officers & enlisted men. Mobilisations

brigades
divisions        sent to threatened areas.
camps
armies

    Great saving easily visible. No training camps—no exp. of
transportation. Indust. mobilisation in time of peace—methods of
procuring equipment—supplies—munitions— Preparation to expe-
dite the supply troops when mobilised. Much in papers about excessive profits in wartime revealed by sen. investigating
committee[.] Plan for prep. in peace take profit out of war. Also
movement take profits out of all prep. Profitless—war less liable
than in past. No doubt of laws against banking loans to belligerents
abroad, less warfare—assurance of peace[.] Fire dept. comparison—
None unless necessary. Suppose something better for fire protection. Then adopt—but nothing better came. If improvement
though[t] of—still use old till perfected.

Pacifists decry war, & rightly. If war eliminated, econ. progress hastened to genl. advantage. But until war can be abolished & broth. love & golden rule prevail—nations not fear—jealousy—envy—greed—inord ambition— Until millennium—no fear outside aggressions—only common sense perfect & perpetuate nat. defence best means protect citizens & country.

Therefore forces as prescribed should be kept up to prescribed level.

Though reg. army incr. 65,000 men, level of all nat. def. not maintained. Reg. only 42%[.] Nat Guard 40%—_____
69%[.] Cong. should be urged to insist forces kept up to min. level. What use enhance bus. if nat def. neglected?

In closing wish to say—hope we & children & descendants down path time sing. grand anthem "America["] (text given)

[RHB:]
In speaking to you on Nat. Def. I would like to bring the subject to you in a way that you would not forget, but take home with you and sit down and think of the ideas that I have tried to present to you.

I purposely will omit references to figures and statistics of any kind. Let us take, for example, your local fire department—best insurance against disaster of any kind. The expense or maintenance is much less thru prevention of fire than that of damage without it would be. If you did not know that this department was paying for itself, you probably would not retain it. The same is the case with warfare—best defense against war that our country has. Nat. def. is insurance against the disaster of an unsuccessful war. Have been lucky in past—successful termination of war. But that does not mean that in the future every war in which we are engaged

The country has entered in haphazard fashion in every war that has been waged—world war and if we had not had allies to hold the front until we went into it we would have been in a very precarious position. Took year to get troops into field, and even so, some arrived untrained. Now, if we had had a military policy before the

w. w. started, tax-payers would have been saved the expense of many training camps—munitions factories, machinery of draft and terrific cost of military training camps.

When the w w ended it became evident that a Nat. Def. policy was much needed. Best minds prepared the N. D. Act, which became a law in 1920. This act provided forces large enough to defend country in case of emergency, but in no case was it large enough to wage wars of aggression. N.D.A. is purely an act for defense, not offense. Young men often say will not fight unless in case of attack. No one has ever proposed any other kind of military policy. Public opposition in this country would never stand a war of aggression any more than it has in the past. You are all well acquainted with what the regular army is National Reserve, which in time of war would be the greatest army in the United States . . . number depending on type of emergency which arises. Civilians, through prior training . . . in case reserves are called into XXXX Service through taking advantage of full pay . . .

These reserves are only made possible by patriotism of civilians who are interested in their daily bread.

If war declared, reg. army and Nat. Guard would be called into immediate action—hold line until reserves ready—given extra training to form brigades, corps, and armies as prescribed by the NDA. Details in regard to mobilizations, concentrations and training of National Reserves are on file in the War Dept. Nine areas have plans prepared and consolidated under Nat'l Def. scheme. All details have been arranged even to blank telegrams for mobilization. By this plan, expensive training camps are needless—training already effected by reserve officers and enlisted men commanded by officers in these (?) reserves and . . . enlisted men who also hold positions in those reserve

brigades
divisions        sent to threatened areas
camps
armies

I believe in these few remarks you will be able to see the great saving in dollars and cents due to an industrial mobilization in time of peace that all methods of procuring equipment—supplies, munitions. Preparation is being made to effectively, economically, and in all details supply troops when mobilized. You of course have seen a great deal in the papers about great profits in wartime revealed by sen. investigating committee. Plan for prep. in peace to take profit out of war—move on foot to take profit out of prep. in time of peace, for war. War will be made so that profits become less likely to . . . War less liable than in past.

Prevention of loans—bankers, US, to belligerents—making impossible for firms in US to deliver munitions . . . elim. of war and assurance of peace. Fire dept. comparison.

Suppose you had in view something to prevent the ravages of fire. Would adopt system—but present nothing better than Fire Dept. affords. If improvement thought of, still use old till perfected.

People called pacifists decrying war, and rightly so, because if war can be eliminated, econ. progress hastened to everybody's profit. But until the time comes when wars have been abolished, golden rule practised as well as preached—jealousy, envy, greed . . . ambition[—]nations not fear one another—until the Millennium—no fear of outside aggression—

(Until this) only common sense for our country to preserve and perpetuate NAT DF as the best means of protecting our country. Therefore forces should be kept up to the level prescribed in 1920. Though regular army has been increased (65 000 men) that level is not held at present. Reg. army is only 42% of that strength. Nat. G. is 40% [. . . 69% (?)]* I believe that every patriotic citizen should urge his congressman to insist forces kept up to min. level. What use enhance business—beautify and protect cities—if N D neglected?

---

*[Under the bracketed words, RHB has written: "see note HPL"]

In closing I wish to say that I hope we and our children and their children down the paths of Time as long as time shall last will sing grand anthem

AMERICA

# National Defense

*E. D. Barlow*

In giving a few remarks on National Defense I hope to present the subject in such a way that it will be remembered and reflected upon after these paragraphs are laid aside. I will purposely omit all reference to figures, statistics, and technical matters as far as possible, and try to show in a very general and concrete fashion just how the actual problem bears on the average citizen.

The best common comparison I can think of is with a city and its fire protection. An effective fire department is the best possible insurance against costly and prostrating disaster. Its maintenance requires money, but costs much less than the damage which would occur if it were not maintained. Prevention is cheaper than a conflagration. If a city did not know that the fire department paid for itself, it would probably not maintain it.

So with a nation and its military forces of defense. These forces form the best possible insurance against the disaster of an unsuccessful war, and ought, aside from all sentiment, to be maintained as a matter of ordinary business judgment. We have been lucky with our wars in the past—each having been successful despite the almost total lack of a real military policy on our· part. But only through some system of co-ordinated preparation can such successes be made sure. We cannot always rely on the sheer good fortune which has happened to help us before.

The World War amply proved what kind of a disaster might some time befall us. It caught us unprepared, and would have formed a paralyzing blow had no allies been present to hold the front till our own preparation could be effected. A year was required to place our troops in the field, and even so a substantial number reached the front without adequate training. If a proper military policy had existed, the country's taxpayers would have been saved millions—the expense of special training camps, and of all the haste, waste, and in some instances inferior materials resulting when private companies are suddenly called upon for supplies and munitions which they are not prepared to furnish.

When the war was over the need of a real policy of national defense became plainly manifest. The best minds drew up a carefully considered plan, which in 1920 was officially adopted as the National Defense Act. This act authorizes forces large enough to defend the country in any emergency, but not large enough to wage a war of aggression. The purely defensive nature of this plan has perhaps been insufficiently emphasized. Today we often hear high-school and college students, vowing never to bear arms except in case of an attack upon this country—as if any other sort of military policy had ever been proposed! The fact is that those in charge or likely to be in charge of the nation would never sanction a war of aggression. In the future, as in the past, public opinion will always limit our military enterprises to a defense of the territory and the civilization we have.

The forces which the United States would, according to the National Defense Act, put into the field in case of war, consist of three distinct parts—the Regular Army and the National Guard, with whose nature the general public is well acquainted, and the less known but crucially important corps called the Organized Reserves. It is the latter which would, in time of war, form the country's greatest military strength; being a flexible organization capable of adjustment to emergencies of every type and degree of seriousness. This reserve ensures the formation of field armies in any needed quantity and suited to any sort of operation, yet calls for no expensive special staff or feverish eleventh-hour training when the emergency actually comes. Key commissioned and enlisted men's positions are held by civilians trained in peace time and in addition to their regular occupations—largely through extension courses offered by the Regular Army and affording increased opportunities for promotion. This is made possible by the patriotism of citizens who are willing to divert enough time from their business and personal interests to master the exacting studies involved, and to hold the assignments without pay except during an active training period of two weeks—sometimes annual and sometimes biennial according to the funds provided by Congress.

On the coming of a war the Regular Army, National Guard, and Organized Reserves would join to form one vast force—the Armies of the United States—with all three components acting in predetermined harmony through organization into the brigades, divisions, and army corps which constitute the tactical units of that force. The Regular Army, and the National Guard, already organized and intensively trained, would be called into immediate action to hold the line until the Organized Reserves are ready for field duly. Details of this process—concentration, mobilization and training—are on file in the archives or the War Department. The country had previously been divided into nine geographical Corps Areas, each of whose commanders has complete charge in peace time of activities within his area—the training of the Regular Army, the supervision of the training or the National Guard, and the organization and training of the Organized Reserves. The War Department has co-ordinated the plan submitted by the nine Corps Area Commanders into one large mobilization plan for the entire country. So thorough is this plan that it includes even the filing in the War Department of prepared telegrams ready to use in initiating the war-time mobilization of troops according to its provisions. By this plan of the National Defense Act expensive training camps are rendered needless, the training having already been partly affected by Reserve officers and enlisted men under the supervision or Regular Army officers in time of peace, and being completed by the gradual special training of the various units from the smallest to the largest—company, battalion, regiment, brigade, division—as they are formed during the process of concentration and mobilization. As soon as a company is assembled it will receive its training in the tactics of that unit. When that company is grouped into a battalion this new unit will master battalion tactics, and go on upward—the men absorbing without confusion each larger phase of training as they come to it. In effect, this is a progressive system of concurrent concentration, mobilization and training. Finally, brigades, divisions, corps, and armies are mobilized with the least possible delay and sent to the threatened areas.

The great saving in dollars and cents inherent in such a plan ought to be obvious to every reader. There will be no costly training camps, no vast expenses for the transportation of trainees and supplies to those camps, and none of the other sudden and excessive financial drains common in past wars. Instead, there will have been a quiet industrial survey in time of peace—a survey including methods of procuring equipment, supplies, munitions, and everything else necessary. Everything will be ready and co-ordinated when the troops themselves are mobilized.

At present the papers say a great deal about excessive profits on supplies and munitions in war time, as revealed by the Nye Senate Investigating Committee. Much is also said about the disproportionate profits derived from war preparations in time of peace. The spirit of the National Defense Act, if fully applied, would check bath of these evils by systematizing all military preparation and making it a regular part of normal national life. War would be made less profitable and therefore less likely to occur—than in the past. Kindred steps would be the prevention of loans by American bankers to foreign belligerents, and a ban on the sale and delivery of American munitions equipment, and supplies to such parties. Thus, through the removal of several powerful incentives to war, the assurance of peace would become greater than ever before.

Once again the fire-department comparison seems appropriate. If there were some way of preventing fires from ever breaking out, or some better way of checking their ravages, we would not need such a department; but since no such ways exist, we coning to that department as the best known means of combating a constant peril. Even if we are working on a new and improved system, we are naturally forced to keep the old system in use until some successor is really perfected.

People called pacifists are constantly decrying war—and rightly. What is not right in the views of some of them is the notion that adequate preparedness tends to provoke or precipitate warfare. Ability to defend oneself certainly involves no temptation to attack others—but on the contrary makes peace more secure by removing from others the temptation to attack oneself. It is a matter of proved fact that every responsible officer of the United States Army from the Chief of Staff down, and every responsible member of the Congressional Committee on Military Affairs, is acutely conscious through experience of the disastrous and disorganizing effects of warfare, and anxious and determined to avoid that calamity in every possible way. The public does not sufficiently realize the large part which paper military and naval strength plays in the preservation of peace—how many times, for example, serious international disorder has been prevented by the timely appearance of an American battleship in the principal port of some excitable nation.

The advocates of National Defense know better than anyone else how the elimination of war would hasten economic progress to everyone's advantage. Not only is war a tragic financial drain during preparation and actual fighting, but also during the tremendously long aftermath when pensions, hospitalization, and similar expenses form a heavy national item and constant burden on every taxpayer. But until war actually can be superseded by the practice as well as preaching of brotherly love, and the Golden Rule, and the nations truly cease to feel envy, jealousy, greed, and inordinate ambition, or to fear outside aggression—until, that is, the coming of the long-wished millennium—it is only common sense that we do all we can to support, perfect, and perpetuate an adequate system of National

Defense as the best and indeed the only means of protecting our citizens and our country.

It is, therefore, our immediate civic duty to see that our defensive forces are kept up to the prescribed level of the Defense Act of 1920, below which it has been conclusively proved dangerous to let them fall. Though the Regular Army has recently been increased by 65,000 men, the general level of all national defense forces is sadly below the limit of safety. The Regular Army is now only 42% of the prescribed minimum; the National Guard only 40%; the Organized Reserves only 69%. I believe that every patriotic citizen should urge his Congressman to insist that these components be kept up to the minimum level provided for in the National Defense Act. Of what use is it to enhance and encourage business, or to beautify our cities and countryside, if we neglect the defense of those opportunities and possessions?

In closing, let me express the hope that we, and in turn our children and our children's children, down the path of time, so long as time shall last, may not neglect the responsibilities imposed by citizenship in a great nation. May we and they always be able to sing with pride and untroubled conscience that grand old anthem—

> "My country, 'tis of thee
> Sweet land of liberty,
>     Of thee I sing;
> Land where my fathers died,
> Land of the Pilgrim's pride,
> From every mountainside
>     Let freedom ring."

# The Last Days of H. P. Lovecraft:
# Four Documents

[1] Harry K. Brobst to R. H. Barlow, 2 March 1937

3-2-37

My dear Barlow:

Our old friend is quite ill—and so I am writing this letter for him. He has seemed to grow progressively weaker the last few days.

He says he will attempt to demolish your arguments when he can, and that Kline & Wright are thinking of issuing some of Howard's poetry.

I am honestly worried about his condition, and his aunt is very upset. He is still at 66 College, and has not been removed to the hospital.

The poor fellow is certainly in severe pain. The site of his trouble is some gastrointestinal condition.

I hope all is well with you—

Best wishes & kindest regards—Harry Brobst

[2] Annie E. Phillips Gamwell to R. H. Barlow, 12 March 1937

March 12, 1937

Dear Bobby—

I have intended to write you a gay little letter, long since, but now I am writing a sad little letter telling you that Howard is so pitifully ill & weak. I think you can imagine how frantic I am—but I try to keep of good cheer in his presence. Wednesday, March 10, the doctor said it would be better to go to the hospital & we went & with my inborn optimism I was looking for miracles but they have not come & the dear fellow grows weaker & weaker—nothing can be retained in his stomach. All the pain & trouble comes from intestinal & stomach distress.

Needless to say he has been pathetically patient & philosophical through it all. Howard gave me your letters to answer days ago but I simply couldn't write.

You are a dear good friend & I love & appreciate you because you love & appreciate my beloved nephew! I am going to spend this afternoon at the hospital as I have each day. Howard is at the same hospital that he courageously took me to, just a year ago. He was a bulwark of strength to me & I hope I can do as much for him.

Hastily but most sincerely your friend

Anne Gamwell

[3] Telegram from R. H. Barlow to Annie E. Phillips Gamwell, 14 March 1937

WOULD LIKE TO COME AND HELP YOU IF AGREEABLE ANSWER LEAVENWORTH TONIGHT

[4] Telegram from Annie E. Phillips Gamwell to R. H. Barlow, 10:23 p.m., 15 March 1937

HOWARD DIED THIS MORNING NOTHING TO DO THANKS

ANNIE P. GAMWELL.

## [R. H. Barlow: A Biographical Sketch]

*George T. Smisor*

Robert Hayward Barlow, the son of Colonel E. D. Barlow, U.S.A. retired, and Mrs. Bernice Leach Barlow, was born on May 18, 1918, in Leavenworth, Kansas. He was the second of two sons, the first, Colonel Everett Wayne Barlow, U.S.A. retired, having been born ten years prior to Robert. Robert seems to have been an exceptionally bright child, but lonely and dreamy. Before he finished grammar school, in De Land, Florida, where his family had previously moved, he engrossed himself in reading fantastic tales and weird fiction. Because he was a "queer" child, his mother tolerated his strange dreams and ambitions. When he was fourteen years old he wrote his first letter to Howard Philips Lovecraft, the dean of modern weird fiction, and until Lovecraft died in 1937, Barlow had received from him 105 letters and 54 postcards, some of the letters running to as many as 10,000 words. Barlow became Lovecraft's executor when he was 19 years old, and was so designated in Lovecraft's will, but many of the older weird fiction writers, intimate friends of Lovecraft, were angered over a mere youth becoming the great Lovecraft's executor. The one who became the most upset over the matter was Clark Ashton Smith, who wrote Barlow a short biting note in which he said he never wanted to see Barlow again and begged him never to communicate with him in any way. This note was a terrible blow to Barlow's sensitive nature, and he never got over it. In time, however, Barlow vindicated himself, but the blow was partly responsible for his turning his hopes of becoming a literary man to a career in anthropology.

During the years of his acquaintance with Lovecraft, he carried on an extensive correspondence with other poets and writers, such as George Allan England, August W. Derleth, Ernest E. [*sic*] Edkins, Frank Belknap Long, Jr., Catherine L. Moore (now Mrs. Henry Kuttner), E. Hoffman Price, Donald Wandrei, and Howard E. Wandrei. The contents of all his correspondence was devoted to problems of literature and writing.

As late as 1939, E. Hoffman Price wrote Barlow long letters trying to make him snap out of his dreaminess and face realities. "Is your problem unique?" he asks. "Are you one of a rare few who are too sensitive to endure reality? My dear sir, that is baloney! Your attitude is not an evidence of spiritual fineness; merely spiritual weakness and vacuity. I would hesitate to put it so bluntly were it not for that which follows: WE ALL PASS THAT STAGE WHICH NOW DISMAYS YOU. Some never emerge from it, alas . . . . When reality "bludgeons" you, strengthen your soul to resist. Nuts for shrinking into a corner and wistfully sniffing a lily!"

Later Price warns Barlow of too great dependence upon and too much admiration for Lovecraft: "Now, that story [Barlow sent him one of his own to criticize]: why bother with a pseudo Lovecraft? A genuine HPL is one thing. But I think a Genuine Barlow is infinitely better than an imitation HPL, even if it is a 99% perfect imitation, it still is a phony, and a confession of spiritual or imaginative vacuum."

During the years 1931 to 1938, Barlow seems to have spent little time in formal education, for he once confessed to me that he never went to high school, because it had nothing interesting to offer him. Instead he spent his time writing, setting up a small print shop, where he began printing *The Dragon Fly,* which contained largely his own compositions, learning the art of fine bookbinding, and dabbling in sketching and painting.

In 1936 Barlow studied at the Institute of Art in Kansas City, Missouri, and later at the Corcoran Gallery in Washington, D.C. In 1938, one of Barlow's ink and wash studies entitled "The Harem— Saturday Night", was listed as number 9 in an exhibition of midwestern art hung in the Kansas City Art Institute. He also won a first and second premium on two of his pieces of art at the Florida State Fair, Tampa, 1938.

In October 1933 Barlow began publishing in *The Fantasy Fan* his stories dealing with the "Annals of the Jinns." He also experimented a great deal with poetry, but had only a few pieces published in 1935. Most of his poetry appeared between 1939 and 1947.

In the winter of 1938–39 Barlow came to Woodstock, California, to work with Groo and Claire Beck in publishing small books. At this time they got out the *Commonplace Book* of Lovecraft, which is an extremely rare item today. Barlow hoped to found some sort of a transcendentalist colony which would be devoted to publishing fine pieces of literature, i.e., pieces dealing with the weird and fantastic. In the spring of 1939, the visions of a neat little colony were dissipated and Barlow went to San Francisco to live at the YMCA Hotel. Here he began writing various poems, reading Poe and the

Mound Builders, and spending considerable time visiting the Fine Arts Building. A little later he and Groo Beck took an apartment together and worked on the publication of *After Sunset* by George Sterling, a collection of Sterling's poetry.

Still not knowing what to aim for in life, Barlow went to a Barbara Mayer, psychologist, who in the course of their conversations advised him to try anthropology. Barlow then began taking classes at the junior college. It was at this time that he joined classes and groups of poetry enthusiasts and became acquainted with you [Lawrence Hart] and Rosalie Moore. Barlow, however, was quite interested in Mexican anthropology, for he had made a hurried trip to Mexico in the early part of 1938 and knew something of the country. At the beginning of summer, 1940, he was again in Mexico, and he and I were students together in a class in the Nahuatl language. Toward the end of summer school, after he and I had worked diligently with nahuatl, he exclaimed to me one day, "At last, I know what I want to be in life. I've never known until this summer what I wanted to devote myself to." Another time he said, "George, there's just so much to be done, and only you and Wigberto Jiménez Moreno [our teacher in nahuatl] and I to do it!" He had noticed how few real scholars there were at that time in Mexican studies.

Barlow stayed on in Mexico the following school year and studied at the Polytechnic Institute, taking courses in Indian languages and anthropology. He again attended the summer school in 1941, and by this time he had learned Spanish well enough to take a part in a one-act play called *Vacations,* written by Rodolfo Usigli, Mexico's great living dramatist. Barlow was "The man with the umbrella."

After this summer session of 1941, Barlow returned to the United States with us [my wife and me], and we left him at Berkeley, where during this year and the following summer he completed his requirements for the bachelor's degree. While at Berkeley, he entered his poems in contests on the Emily Chamberlain Cook prize and the Ina Coolbrith memorial prize. I printed the booklet of poems for him. I attended the university during the summer of

1942, and, at this time Barlow and I worked out a plan to publish a book, a translation from the nahuatl of a document relating to the founding of Nombre de Dios, Durango, Mexico, with complete notes. Barlow furnished the notes and did all the incidental research work. I translated the nahuatl into English, made the index, and printed the book. Then we worked out a plan to publish a journal called *Tlalocan,* which is still being published in Mexico. I printed the first volume of four numbers, and then Barlow had it printed here in Mexico for the second and part of the third volume.

At Berkeley, Barlow received a grant of $75 a month and later a $100 a month to do research in the Mexican field. This grant continued for some months after he had returned to Mexico in the fall of 1942. Barlow was very happy to get back to Mexico, for he seems to have had considerable difficulties at Berkeley about his courses and his manner of working. Soon after he arrived in Mexico, he wrote me: "I am just as happy in Mexico as I was unhappy in Berkeley."

Barlow continued his studies of anthropology and nahuatl language during the year of 1943. In 1944 he collaborated with Antonieta Espejo and Professor T. W. I. Bullock, under the general direction of Dr. Pablo Martínez del Río, in the excavation of the Aztec ruins at Tlaltelolco, and he began publishing monographs on the excavations which continued for a couple of years.

Barlow had so diligently continued his study of nahuatl that by 1945 he had practically mastered the spoken language, and because of his enthusiasm for things Indian and his knowledge of the written and spoken nahuatl, he was appointed by the Mexican government to become the director of the nahuatl project for the state of Morelos [teaching the Indians to read and write their own language]. Barlow not only paid frequent visits to villages of Morelos, but he also conducted classes in Mexico City for rural school teachers with nahuatl backgrounds. This experience led him later to begin the publication of little news- sheets in nahuatl for the Indians, and he was carrying on such types of publications at the time of his death.

During 1944 Barlow was receiving money from the Rockefeller Foundation to carry on his work in Mexican research. He was also studying at the National Institute of Anthropology, and soon became one of its teachers in nahuatl and pre-Columbian history. The grant, however, was discontinued early in 1945, and Barlow found himself in need of a job. For some six months in 1945 he was reference librarian at the Benjamin Franklin Library, a job he detested but which he performed so brilliantly that he was called the Library's walking encyclopedia, and all questions concerning Mexican history were referred to him. In spite of his lack of ready cash, he managed to buy himself a house in Atzcapotzalco toward of 1945, borrowing part of his money for the down payment at an interest rate of 5% a month!

On the 13th of March, 1946, Barlow was elected a member of the Sociedad Mexicana de Bibliografia. Then on April 14, 1946, he received his first Guggenheim fellowship, and with this financial assistance he was able to continue his research and the publication of articles and monographs. From time to time he gave lectures before various groups.

By 1948, Barlow had made such a reputation for himself in Mexican anthropology that he was asked to become the head of this department at Mexico City College, but he did not accept it immediately, for he really had no interest in tying himself up in school teaching and administration. His chief interests lay in personal research. It was during this year that he made his trip to Paris. He left by plane one afternoon for New York. He was a novel spectacle as he walked across the field to board the plane. He was dressed in his one and only suit, a sarape draped over his shoulder, and an Otomí cloth bag hanging at his side. However, he was disappointed in Paris, saying that he had arrived in that city of light ten years too late. He also hated the French language and refused to speak it, preferring to speak German wherever he could, which of course did not make too good an impression upon Francophiles. When he returned to Mexico he said very little about this trip.

He then accepted the chairmanship of the department of anthropology at Mexico City College, but still devoted long hours to research. Affairs never went smoothly for him at the College. He was so much of an individualist that it was impossible for him to follow a fixed College routine, and by the summer of 1950 his nerves were shattered. At this time the Carnegie Institute of Washington was trying to get Barlow to accept a fellowship to go into the study of Maya language and culture and eventually to take the place of Sylvanus G. Morley who had died shortly before. Barlow had visited Yucatán, the center of Mayan culture, and had hoped that the trip would calm his nerves, but when he returned to Mexico City he refused to teach classes at the College. He then made a trip to Washington, D.C., to talk over the matter of the fellowship, and was laying plans to go into Maya studies in earnest. He had a Maya boy in his household [he also had one who spoke nahuatl, also a secretary, a printer, and a cook], and he was progressing quite rapidly in the language. When he locked himself in his room the afternoon of January 1, 1951, where he swallowed twenty-six Seconal tablets, he pinned up on the outside of the door a paper written in Maya: "Do not disturb me. I want to sleep a long time." He was found dead on the afternoon of January 2 by his secretary Antonio Castaneda.

Barlow lived on a nervous tension all his life. He had to keep his mind busy or he was unhappy. He himself says in an introduction to an autobiography which he never finished, "And I don't [have an ounce of enjoyment] except in the smooth fulfillment of my varied compulsions. When I have a period of free time and the choice of activity, I am most discontent. At these times I am prone to do something irrelevant which ought to be pleasurable—read anything lying at hand, or most often rush out of the house to consume the time in looking at new books in bookstores, or more rarely going to the legitimate theatre. *At these times of 'free choice' I am most wretched.* Pleasure for me is a calm fulfilling the pattern of work, writing something or learning something, which I have convinced myself 'must' be done. But fulfilling the work-pattern, since it is the most rewarding of my activities, is the most difficult. I invent a thousand sham-pleasures to keep me otherwise occupied, or I exhaust myself so that no activity can be thought of, but only blank sleep.

"A mood which alternates with this urge to work like the literary blacksmith described in *The Flowering of New England*—that individual who smithied 12 hours or 14, and pursued his literary life at dawn and midnight—is the mood of gregariousness. A chasm of loneliness opens alongside my paths of study, and a pebble is enough to betray my foot. I delight in the presence of many people; I can end a conversation only by effort, can never get rid of a visitor, and when I have seduced people by wining and dining them into cheering the house with their voices, I hope they will never leave."

Between 1942 and 1950, Barlow published over a hundred works, some large and some small, but most of them original personal investigations in Mexican ancient history.

# R. H. Barlow and *Tlalocan*

*George T. Smisor*

Robert Hayward Barlow ended his career as an anthropologist at an age when most students are beginning theirs. He was born May 18, 1918, at Leavenworth, Kansas, and died at his home in Azcapotzalco, D. F., Mexico, January 2, 1951. He devoted the last ten years of his life to research in fields of Mexican history, anthropology and linguistics, and wrote, usually in Spanish, more than a hundred and fifty scholarly articles which were published in Mexican, American and French scientific journals. His loss will be deeply felt in these fields, but his numerous studies will maintain their importance as reference works for years to come. Many of these studies appeared in *Tlalocan*, a journal of which he was both the soul and the driving force and in which appeared his first serious contributions. But while giving a historical sketch of *Tlalocan*. we must also present a brief resume of Barlow's life in order to appreciate the growth of that brilliant and forceful intellect which impelled him to attain enviable fame as an anthropologist and linguist.

Barlow was a very precocious, sensitive and lonely child. Before he finished grammar school, he showed inquisitive interest in poetry and story writing, in sketching and painting, in printing and publishing, activities far removed from those of his family, who lived a professional army life. These artistic activities, however, laid the foundation for his future interest in anthropology.

In 1931 when Barlow had just graduated from grammar school, he began a correspondence with Howard Phillips Lovecraft, the dean of weird fiction writers, which continued until Lovecraft died in 1937, after having appointed Barlow his literary executor. Soon Barlow was corresponding with a number of poets and writers on subjects of literary criticism and problems in an author's life. In the following year Barlow began writing a series of episodes called the *Annals of the Jinns,* all relating to a mythical race of ancient times, living by a haunted black tower on the winding river Olaee near the hamlet of Droom. The *Annals* were supposedly found in musty manuscripts which had lain for centuries in the black tower and were written in a strange language of long ago. As one reads these *Annals* it is easy to comprehend the eager interest Barlow had at that early age for archaic races and curious languages.

For the next six years Barlow lent himself to writing stories and poems, to studying art and painting to dabbling with bookbinding and printing, but these activities (he performed them all better than average) left him unsatisfied, for he felt that none of them offered him a proper career by which he could earn a modest living. One must recall that these were the years of the Great Depression.

After a hurried trip to Mexico in the spring of 1938 Barlow returned to California to work in a small private press at Lakeport. He was still undecided about his future. One day he visited Miss Barbara Mayer, a leader of the National Youth

Administration, who had the perception to understand Barlow's problems. It was she who suggested to him that he study Anthropology and make that his life's work. She even suggested Mexican Anthropology, introduced him to leading California professors in this field, and encouraged him to pursue such courses in the local junior college. In the summer of 1940 he was again in Mexico, registered as a student of the National University Summer School. There in the class in Náhuatl language, taught by Prof. Wigberto Jiménez Moreno, I met Barlow for the first time.

We were both serious students and both overawed by Mexico's vast ancient culture, apprehended at that time by only a few world scholars. Pre-Columbian ruins, weird stone images and carvings, clay figures and pottery had been known for centuries. Many of the movable objects were gathered into collections and appeared in impressive displays in museums, but their very existence raised still unanswered questions, such as: What kind of people made these objects? Why did they make them? In what type of society did they live? What were their religious beliefs? What was the history of these many tribes, their conquests and defeats? What languages did they speak? Our introduction to Náhuatl opened our eyes to the immense quantity of early manuscripts written by or under the supervision of friars who began arriving in Mexico soon after the Conquest. A serious study of these manuscripts, scattered in archives throughout Mexico and in various cities of the world, would surely provide part of the answers to the questions above. The problem, therefore, as we saw it at that time, was to make these documents available to students of Mexican history through their publication. It was then that *Tlalocan* was conceived, but we did not know it until two years later.

During that summer I often went to Barlow's apartment to study Náhuatl with him. This studying together gave me the opportunity to see Barlow's keen, nimble, and retentive mind at work. He had an intellectual driving force that never seemed to relax, that picked me up and carried me along with it, as it likewise did later many others. He had a facility of expression that brought to life long-dead happenings. This happy facility was a carry-over from his years of reading and writing fantasy fiction and composing poetry. But there was nothing fantastic in this carry-over. He now insisted on accuracy of fact with brilliance of expression. At last he had discovered the career that appealed to him. He once said to me that summer, "This is the first time in my life I knew what I wanted to be. I'm going to devote myself to Mexican Anthropology."

After completing a year at the Polytecnic Institute and another summer session, Barlow returned with my wife and me to Berkeley, where he began work in earnest in the department of Anthropology under Dr. A. L. Kroeber and soon became a Research Associate in Anthropology. I went back to my position as a printing teacher in the Sacramento City Schools, but we corresponded with each other and discussed many plans for beginning the publication of Náhuatl texts. During the year Barlow unearthed a long Indian *Memorial* written in Náhuatl, one of the many miscellaneous manuscripts in the Bancroft Library, which described in detail the founding of the city of Nombre de Dios in Durango in 1562. Barlow prepared the footnotes and appendices; I made the English translation from the Nahuatl with the help of Chimalpopoca Spanish text, the index, and with the permission of the school authorities, I set up and printed the book under the imprint of The House of Tlaloc, which Barlow and I chose as the name of our publishing venture. Only 130 copies of *Nombre de Dios, Durango* were printed and distributed, and it has now become a very rare item.

In spite of the impressive-looking book we turned out, we were not satisfied with this type of publication for issuing manuscript material. We then hit upon the idea of publishing a journal which we called *Tlalocan* (meaning Tlaloc's Heaven), to average ninety-six pages per number, four numbers per volume, but numbers would be issued, not regularly, but whenever we could get them out, and subscribers would be charged so much a volume. *Tlalocan, a Journal of Source Materials on the Native Cultures of Mexico,* has been well received by students of Mexican history since the appearance of the first number in 1943, but its publication from time to time meant a tremendous amount of extra work and money from our own pockets to support it, since subscribers were few, because it dealt with a narrowed field of study and because, unfortunately, we began its publication during the war years.

Barlow returned again to Mexico in the fall of 1942 after receiving his A. B. degree and continued to receive the grant from the University of California for a few months. Now all our editorial work on *Tlalocan* had to be carried on by correspondence. Censorship of the mails caused delays and difficulties. One time I sent Barlow a copy of a manuscript in Nahuatl relating to Philip II of Spain, but the censor returned it, saying that nothing could be sent to Mexico in code. After explaining to the censor the nature of the document and assuring him that there was no imminent danger of Philip II invading the United States, he reluctantly allowed the document to go on through to Barlow.

We were fortunate to have made such friends as Rafael García Granados, Wigberto Jiménez Moreno, and Federico Gómez de Orozco in Mexico, and Paul Radin and Carl Sauer in Berkeley, all of whom became our editorial advisers. For our first issue Paul Radin permitted us to begin publishing his *Cuentos y Leyendas de los Zapotecos,* which he had collected in 1912 in Oaxaca but had never published; Angel Ma. Garibay K., canon of the church of Guadalupe and ardent Náhuatl scholar, prepared the text and translations of *Huehuetlatolli* (old sayings of the Aztecs); Barlow furnished a bibliography on 18th Century *Relaciones Geograficas;* and I prepared a few book reviews besides setting up, proofreading, printing and mailing the issue.

In 1945, after completing the first volume, I left my position in Sacramento and came to Mexico to become head of the Microfilm Laboratory in the Benjamin Franklin Library, a position I owe to Barlow, who had recommended me highly to the Director of the Library. This new position kept me so occupied that I was unable to collaborate with Barlow in publishing *Tlalocan*. He, however, made arrangements with Allan Farson, a printer of Indian texts, to print the journal, and Barlow then assumed the entire responsibility for editing, publishing and mailing the numbers. Volume II appeared between 1945 and 1948. With the first number of Volume III, Barlow had obtained financial assistance from the late George A. Hill Jr. and the San Jacinto Museum of History Association, which also assumed the responsibility of distributing copies in the United States.

Besides working on *Tlalocan* during these seven years, which took only a portion of his time, Barlow learned to speak Náhuatl more fluently than any foreigner in Mexico today. So well did he handle the language and understand the psychology of the Indian that the Mexican Government appointed him in 1945 as director of the Náhuatl project for the State of Morelos in Mexico's literacy campaign. A year before he died he began the study of Maya, and was progressing very rapidly in this language. Barlow was so interested in indigenous Mexico that his secretary, Lieutenant Antonio H. Castaneda, wrote to me after his death, "Vivió entre nosotros saboreando nuestros idiomas con dulzura, y amó tanto al indio mexicano que convivia con él a gusto pleno; pero al mismo tiempo que saboreaba sus idiomas, sus platillos y sus costumbres, lo estimulaba hacia el progreso que había de redimirlo de las condiciones en que vive. . . . Yo me considero altamente privilegiado por haber estado al servicio de ese genio en ciencia y en bondad. Mi agradecimiento como Mexicano hacia él será imperecedero, porque en verdad genios extranjeros como él que se dedicó en cuerpo y alma a todo lo mexicano, son muy raros en mi país."*

---

*"He lived among us, savoring our languages with sweetness, and loved the Mexican Indian so much that he lived with him at ease; but at the same time that he savored his languages, his dishes and his customs, he encouraged him towards the

Barlow did most of his research work through grants in aid. After the University of California research grant terminated, Barlow received a fellowship from the Rockefeller Foundation through 1944. Then on April 14, 1946, he received his first Guggenheim fellowship. Later he was an associate of Carnegie Institution's Division of Historical Research to study the Maya language and culture of Yucatan. Many of his articles in *Tlalocan* were the results of his investigations through the assistance of these grants. But Barlow also gave lectures before scientific societies, taught classes at the Instituto Nacional de Antropología e Historia, and for two years prior to his death was chairman of the Department of Anthropology at Mexico City College.

Happily *Tlalocan* will continue to appear from time to time in the future with the collaboration of the San Jacinto Museum of History Association. A very capable editor has been selected, Dr. Ignacio Bernal, present chairman of the Department of Anthropology at Mexico City College. Dr. Bernal will be ably assisted by Fernando Horcasitas Pimentel, professor of Spanish Literature, who acted as secretary for *Tlalocan* under Barlow for the past two numbers.

Although I have been unable to assist in the publication of *Tlalocan* for some years, I have always had a keen interest in its progress, and now, after recovering from the shocking blow of Barlow's sudden death, I am happy that *Tlalocan* can continue under such capable and enthusiastic leadership.

*April 5, 1951*

progress that had to redeem him from the conditions in which he lives. . . . I consider myself highly privileged to have been at the service of that genius in science and goodness. My gratitude as a Mexican to him will be imperishable, because in truth foreign geniuses like him who dedicated himself in body and soul to everything Mexican, are very rare in my country."

# Robert Barlow

*Rosalie Moore*

With his scholarly bearing, large spectacled eyes, and precise manners, strict as a beetle, Robert Barlow was often such a person that you did not want, in his presence, to do anything that was not perfectly accurate, use the vague word, or keep any of your pretentions toward the conventional falseness.

He had also a forbearance which allowed you time for making the right relation, and a great deal of warmth and sympathy which furnished a sort of climate in helping you find it.

Sometimes, like the rest of us, he simply made mistakes of judgment, or burbled inaccuracies, and because they were stumbles or errors (and anyone with his brilliance of range was bound to make them) he would barely forgive himself: then, after a while, do so—although not until he had pounded unforgiveably on some bar, told an unpleasant anecdote, or executed some other saleable tantrum in self- revenge.

I have seen Robert Barlow also commit himself to the most joyfully abandoned behavior, launch into a speech or a wild dance like a short Dionysius; yet in some way this was done as a matter of policy, forgiving himself in advance.

This was the character of the man who wrote these poems, as we knew him in the Activist group. If you could say only one thing about him you would say he was a gentleman and a sort of pedant. But if you were allowed to say two, you would say that he was a breaker of forms. Actually, it was deeper than that. Barlow was an essentialist, and if he couldn't get to the center of a thing, he broke it.

However, Barlow did seem to gain an ability to evaluate the whole process during his Activist period, and to realize that feeling the censure of one's inaccuracies was all a part of the learning process. As he began to work with more skill in poetry, his confidence grew, and he stopped throwing the punitive tantrum which had been so hard to put up with. He changed from the unpredictable and difficult colleague, making an accurate personal alignment which lasted as long as we knew him.

## Robert Barlow and the Mexicans

*Rosalie Moore*

It was at a party that one seemed to see Robert Barlow at his most brilliant. The day that I resumed acquaintance with him in Mexico, talking together in the narrow book-and-bone infested study of his pink concrete house in Azcapatzalco, I thought "he seems very ill at ease—perhaps Mexico has changed him, perhaps I shouldn't have looked him up at all." But many rimes after that at parties I saw clearly that he was still our friend, and still the same Barlow.

Panic seemed to provide an expansive medium in which Barlow could swim about like some exotic fish, being himself all over the place—perhaps because this was a situation in which he could always get away. No one could ever quite follow him where his mind and wit would go. And when this would happen, when he would get away as it were, he would seem both exultant and lonely.

The difficulty was that it was not easy to get Barlow to make like a fish in this way, because he would never come to a party, if he planned to—or seldom. We invited him to many while we were in Mexico, and he always came the next night. He came in response to our invitation (though late) because he was very courteous and because he was our friend; also, I felt, he actually liked parties but could not bring himself to do anything so conventional as to keep an appointment precisely. It is, in fact, a Mexican convention not to keep an appointment precisely, so that he may have been assuming a conventional role in the Mexican view. At any rate it is certain that he was a kindly person who cared very much what people thought about him, and this made him very angry and the anger used to explode in amusing expletives and dances.

A number of our American friends were interested in meeting Barlow the archeologist (he was one of the best in Mexico at the time of his death) or Barlow the poet, or Barlow the eccentric—(although to my mind his eccentricity was what you might call ornamental rather than intrinsic). So we planned for a party, keeping our fingers crossed. We wrote to Barlow that we had invited some Latin American poets who spoke almost no English, and were counting on him to interpret for us. Thar night, on schedule, he came.

The Latin Americans were extremely police and charming as they always are, speaking in their halting English and refusing our hot rum drinks with a disturbing smile. It was winter in Mexico City and very cold, and we thought hot drink would be nice. This was a mistake.

Barlow was sitting rather stonily beside a friend of one of the poets, a nice looking fellow, also Mexican, who was some sort of a scientist. Barlow listened to the police small-talk of the Mexican group, not entering in, but staring straight ahead. He refused the rum drink also, and I remembered too late that I had never seen him drink anything but a certain brand of imported Spanish sherry, waving all else aside with his standard remark, "I disapprove of the minor vices."

Our American friends sat around the room stiffly, trying to think of the few things they could ask the Mexican guests which the Mexican guests would be able to answer.

Suddenly Barlow got up with a bone-rattling abruptness and saying something loudly in Náhuatl strode into the kitchen. He turned on the tap full force (in itself, a sin in Mexico a everyone is always saving water) and started to drink glass after glass right out of the tap—another defection; you are supposed to drink only Agua Pura out of a disinfected bottle. Moreover Barlow let the water faucet run, between glassfuls, and when this particular tap was on, it created a quake-like rumble that could be heard throughout the apartment.

Bill, my husband, went to Barlow in the kitchen and put his hand on his shoulder. "Temperance, temperance. You are going to pay for this tomorrow," he said.

"I know!" Barlow bellowed . . . "Do YOU know that—that

FELLOW in there is making remarks about Americans? Nasty snide remarks? In Andalusian, under his breath?"

Bill turned off the tap. "But you are an expatriate. I didn't know you cared what anybody said about Americans."

"You don't get the point," Barlow replied. "THIS fellow is undoubtedly a biologist. I can't endure biologists."

By the time they came back to join the others, the party had somehow lose its glaze. Everybody was talking and laughing the Americans and Mexicans were communicating with each other, by signs, by languages, by gestures, by boy-scout wigwags. Sometimes they looked as if they were acting out charades, but they were having a good time. They started to compete with each other reading their poetry out loud—that is, the Mexican poets, at my invitation, started to read and compete. It was very delightful.

Suddenly I found myself in a situation where there were no barriers—at least in so far as poetry is concerned. I found that the Latin-American poets were speaking my language about poetry, even if I could not speak their actual language very well. Through the hodge-podge of English, Spanish, charades and hand waving, I could tell this. There was no need to define terms, no need to explain what poetic tradition you belonged to. Everything we fight for and explain and defend they take for granted, and proceed from there.

"Naturally," Barlow said at this point; "I've been telling you this for years but you wouldn't come down." (To Mexico, he meant.)

At this point one of the poets read a poem that sounded, in the Spanish, particularly impressive; those who understood were very moved by it, and even those who did not understand. I said, "If I could only understand . . . I *must* be able to really bear it." There was the poem still alive in the room from just having been read by the poet, and I couldn't understand it.

That was when Barlow took the poem away from the author and stood in the middle of the room, making gestures and translating it—image by image, picture by picture, the clear way it was written—without hesitation or stop.

Barlow had given the impression of the poem's having been created by him as he went along, and indeed in a way it was. We spoke of writing the translation down at once before it was forgotten, but Barlow refused.

After this incident, Barlow translated many Latin American or Náhuatl poems for us—always at parties—but I never could get any of these written, except one or two little songs in Náhuatl which I put down myself one night at some friends' apartment while a girl was playing a guitar and singing "Good Night Irene" at the top of her lungs.

But to get back to the party at our apartment, one of the Americans said to us on leaving, "Barlow is all you say. I don't like him, but he is everything you said he was. He is the poet Shelley and Walter Mittie [*sic*] and the Emperor Hirohito and some old bones dancing on an Aztec dyke."

"Why don't you like him then?"

"Oh, I don't know . . . maybe because he did all that on tap-water."

It was true that Barlow did seem to bring some sort of aliveness to bear on a situation, and though some people did not share our reaction, to us it always seemed most human (comfortable). It seemed to indicate some sort of awareness that unfortunately Barlow, like our guest, could bear to dispense with.

## A Note on Robert Barlow

*Lawrence Hart*

We learned early in January of the death of Robert Barlow in Mexico City on January 1, 1951. He worked in the Activist group from about 1939 until 1943, when he left for Mexico City: in a sense, he continued, for we remained in correspondence with him. However, almost all of his best poems were written during this period of close group work in San Francisco.

I think he may have been one of the most intelligent and able men I have ever met: witty and extraordinarily courteous and considerate. And he seemed so contemporary in his attitudes that it is only in retrospect that he almost appears—with his volatile genius, his exile, and the continual overtones of felt but not defined tragedy—to be following the model of the romantic poet of the time of Shelley and Byron.

In spite of his remarkable ability in almost every field which he entered, Robert Barlow seems to have spent much of his life in running away from any success as soon as it began for him. At his death it was found that Lovecraft had appointed Robert Barlow, then only nineteen, executor of his estate in his will. Barlow later met Thomas Hart Benton, showed a great talent as a painter, and was taken by Benton as a pupil. Departing from this also, he came to San Francisco, where he because one of the earlier Activist poets and began to work in archaeology at the University of California.

He received a Guggenheim award for research in archaeology and went to Mexico to become the head of the department of archaeology at the University [*sic*] of Mexico City. Finally, (his last career), he began to do some extraordinary work among the Mexican Indians, travelling or sending representatives among the villages, gathering Nahuatl poetry and songs. Also he educated some of the Nahuatl Indians, taught them to work in his print shop, [using an alphabet he adapted to the Nahuatl tongue] and in general carried on a surprising career as a sort of minor culture hero among the Indians of that region. He ended his life on January 1, [1951] by suicide. On that afternoon he locked himself in his room, took twenty-six capsules of seconal, leaving pinned upon his door in Mayan pictographs. "Do not disturb me. I want to sleep a long time."

His poetry was sometimes remarkably brilliant, and, if there are few poems which are sufficiently disciplined throughout, the whole impedimenta of the archeology of the Mexican Indians is brought into his work in such a way as to give it a romantic flavor which was almost as strong an esthetic quality as the poetry itself. The poetry, if uneven, was frequently sudden in its beauty, as in his poem "The Lights of San Francisco":

> Scarce is the border over run of this blue forest,
> Scarce is the violent wing of the saber loosened . . .

[Note: Text is from *Poetry*, augmented with text from *Accent*.]

# A Study of Robert Barlow:
# The T. E. Lawrence of Mexico

*Clare Mooser*

In the spring of 1948, a young American joined the faculty of Mexico City College (now the University of the Americas) as chairman of the department of anthropology. His name was Robert Hayward Barlow, and his brief tragic life—ending by suicide in 1951 when he was 33 years old—was destined not only to influence the lives of those few who knew him personally,* but also to create a whole body of myth and mystery for those contemporaries to whom he was little more than a name, a face, perhaps a danger, or simply a set of facts. His successors have inherited the Barlow legend, and with it a picture of an extraordinary personality—a scholar, artist, and scientist—a solitary genius committed passionately to a solitary task for which there was "never enough time."

Now, nearly twenty years after his death, and thirty years after he first came to Mexico to settle down in the outlying district of Azcapotzalco, the details of Barlow's life and work can be quickly catalogued. They form perhaps the least interesting part of the total man, since they do not offer any conclusive explanation for Barlow's amazing versatility in a number of scientific and artistic fields, or his apparently universal acclamation ass a major talent during his lifetime by Mexicans and American's alike. The contradictions in his

---

*I am deeply grateful to E[dward] H[owell] for his comments and reminiscences, many of which were to serve as major guidelines for the ideas in this paper.

nature, too, do nothing to diminish the mystery. Fanatically anti-American culture, he often pretended not to speak English to Americans who could not speak Spanish; and—to carry this perversity to its logical end—spoke only Náhuatl at times to Mexicans. One is early reminded of the young T. E. Lawrence, who felt it necessary to employ a similar disguise by dressing pointedly in Arab style on a number of social occasions with his British compatriots.

Author, poet, painter, teacher, anthropologist and—perhaps most important—linguistic expert in the Nahua and Maya languages—Barlow worked with a feverish haste and unbounded energy, leaving behind him more than 100 published articles, pamphlets, notebooks, and full-length works, most of them concerned with Mexican culture before and after the conquest. When a friend once remarked that he was overtiring himself, Barlow burst into tears. "After I am dead, which will be soon, who is going to work in this codex? It may be 200 years before anyone looks at it again!" Many of his unpublished papers—those written in Mexico—were classified by anthropologists Charles Wicke and Fernando Horcasitas and are now in the *Archivo Barlow* of the library of the University of the Americas. It is possible that still others are in the possession of the family of the late Dr. Pablo Martínez del Río, distinguished historian, prominent personality, and one of Barlow's few intimate friends. These documents are largely scientific; Barlow, according to one source, hated any connection between his anthropological research and his literary productions

To this writer's knowledge, only one photograph has ever appeared of Barlow: a blurred and badly-printed likeness, probably a passport picture, published in the MCC *Collegian* of 1949. Avoiding photographers on all occasions, Barlow apparently felt that the thick glasses, the high balding forehead, the general air of sensitivity and reserve were in some way strikes against him. Those who read novels in faces will be disappointed by this one, for it eludes the single impression which, like a Rembrandt portrait, can lure the observer behind the mask and into its secret world. Neither heroic nor romantic, tragic nor diabolic, Barlow's face—with its traces of humor around the mouth and its air of mild intellectual detachment—is as maddeningly elusive as the rest of him.

Of the available facts, gathered from scattered newspaper stories, his own writings, some reminiscences by Mexican anthropologists and archeologists, and the sizeable body of rumor that has accumulated around him, we know that Barlow, born in Kansas in 1918, came to Mexico at the age of 20. A summer course at the National University (he was 4F for U.S. Army service) seems to have consolidated his enthusiasm for this strange land; he was not to leave it again except for short periods of time designated for specific research or study. Of his life in the States, it has been subsequently learned that Barlow, as virtually a young boy in his teens, was a disciple and close personal friend of the now-famous H. P. Lovecraft, probably the most successful American writer of gothic horror stories since Edgar Allan Poe. Ignored as a pulp journalist in his lifetime, Lovecraft was the creator of an entire mythology centered around another race who at one tie inhabited the world and who, in practicing black magic, lost their foothold and were expelled, yet "live on outside, ever ready to take possession of this earth again."

There seems to be little doubt that Lovecraft's morbidly fascinating tales, with their mixture of half-baked science and imaginative myth, had a permanent effect on his young admirer. Barlow founded a science fiction club in California when he was still in his teens, and after Lovecraft's death in 1937 he left the United States for a country of ancient civilization in which it is indeed possible to imagine the roots of Lovecraft's "Cthulhu" mythology.

After the death of Lovecraft, Barlow was named his literary executor, a fact remarkable because of Barlow's extreme youth: he was 19 in comparison to Lovecraft's mature 47 [sic]. In the collection of "Lovecraftiana" donated by CC to Brown University when Barlow died, there are evidently glowing references to his precocious disciple as a "young genius"—all the more unusual since

Lovecraft was surrounded by a circle of talented friends of his own generation, many of whom were writers themselves. The enthusiasm of the older man, bridging an age gap of almost thirty years, speaks for itself as a tribute to the qualities Barlow must have possessed even as a young boy. Although he formally turned over his literary trusteeship to publishers August Derleth and Donald Wandrei, Barlow is certain to have had a hand in the permanent collection of Lovecraft's work issued by the mysterious publishing company of Arkham House (named after the Massachusetts town around which Lovecraft Based his stories) which in 1939 burst upon the world with his completed writings—hitherto only printed in science fiction or pulp magazines—to establish him permanently in American literary circles as an undisputed master of the macabre. At the present time, Arkham House has a number of Barlow's unpublished works in its files, among which are six poems, four of them "in tribute to H. P. L."

The existence of these poems combined with Barlow's sudden appearance in Mexico hint of a possible emotional connection with Lovecraft's death. Why was a 19-year-old boy chosen to be the literary executor of one of the most significant American writers of the century? In any case, Barlow's break with the United States was final, and he seems to have declared his intention—a rather unusual one considering his age and the unknown element of Mexico in the 1930s—to settle down permanently here. after a house in Azcapotzalco (which was mortgaged before he died as he could not make ends meet), Barlow's first step was to set about mastering Náhuatl as both a spoken and a written language. (This was considered, even among Mexican scholars, a rare achievement, and prior to his Náhuatl courses at MCC Barlow taught a system of spoken Náhuatl in his Mexican Escuela Nacional de Antropologia.) His servants were Indians from remote regions of the Republic who spoke no Spanish; and it is said that within three months Barlow had a working vocabulary in Náhuatl and Maya. His determination, combined with a high intelligence and a strong sympathy for the

Indian groups (perhaps they were a symbol for him of Lovecraft's lost peoples, the "Great Ones") is again reminiscent of the linguistic talent and romantic search for an identify of T. E. Lawrence, working twenty years before Barlow in a desert of his own making.

Yet somewhere in the roots of Barlow's strongly pro-Indian attitude lay a fatal romanticism. Along with the giant strides he took in restoring the Indian languages (and therefore cultures) to their legitimate place in the over-all culture of Mexico, there was a tendency toward exaggeration in his nature which led to extreme and at times flamboyant manifestations of enthusiasm. His fear of the camera was in a sense superficial since, ironically enough, it was probably based on the primitive superstition that appearance an reality are one, and that taking a casual snapshot was equivalent to stealing a man's soul. And Barlow seems to have respected his superstitions. Although he was no believer in the traditional Christian god, it is interesting to note that he was often much disturbed by natural phenomena such as ghosts. His conviction of a life after death was firm: at the time of his suicide he left a message in Náhuatl to an Indian associate, speaking about the possibility of their meeting in another life. In the year before his death Barlow came up with the idea of a series of costume parties to be held in his Azcapotzalco home, Casa de Tlaloc—parties in which he required that all of his guests, as well as himself, appear dressed as Aztec gods. Although only one such parity ever took place, Barlow, ordinarily ill at ease at any social gathering, might well have reasoned that behind the mask of an ancient god he could claim his right to assume another, greater self—a sell which he lacked the courage to assert under ordinary circumstances. Theoretically a sophisticate, this pioneer in anthropology nonetheless preferred disguise.

In 1941 Barlow went to the University of California, where he studied for his B..A. degree and taught on the Berkeley staff. While in Berkeley he won the Ina Galbraith [Coolbrith] award for poetry. His only other absence from Mexico occurred in 1948 when he traveled to Europe to supplement his already vast knowledge by studying Mexican manuscripts in the Paris and London Libraries. Working on Guggenheim and Rockefeller Foundation fellowships, Barlow completed the research for his book, *The Empire of the Culhua-Mexica,* which, in press since 1942, was finally published in 1949 and has been hailed as a masterpiece of scholarship.

In 1948, Barlow became the chairman of the department of anthropology of MCC, then headed by Dr. Henry L. Cain and Dr. Paul V. Murray. A study of the *Collegian* during the post-war decade gives a vivid picture of those brilliant days—days in which every student was an individual, every professor a personality. Those were the days of strong individualism, when academic degrees were rated second place to creativity and imagination; when Mexico—outside the capital—was still a wild and savage and, largely inaccessible to the casual tourist; when Mexico City Collect, still a young institution, had managed to attract a dazzling faculty of Mexican, Lain American and Spanish scholars: Pablo Martínez del Río, Ignacio Bernal, Wigberto Jiménez Moreno, Pedro Armillas, Fernando Horcasitas, Luis Wickmann, Justino Fernández, Pedro Bosch Guimpera, José Caos, Edmundo O'Gorman. It is easy to understand how Barlow was caught up in the intellectual current of the times; how, without even a B.A. degree, he was accepted with enthusiasm and admiration by men who were the giants of their age. Excitement generates excitement; and Barlow, in 1948, was ready for the flames which were eventually to consume him.

His rate of production at the College became steadily more intense, embracing a variety of projects. The courses in Náhuatl which he formulated single-handedly for the University represent only a small part of his work during those last years. perhaps his most important contribution was the founding of *Mesoamerican Notes,* an anthropological bulletin published irregularly and edited by Barlow, which gained so much attention from its first printing that it has continued to appear up to the present time. The first two issues came out in 1950, hand-set and printed by Barlow personally on a tiny press in his own home. The magazine is a fascinating mixture of detailed scholarly research with literary and artistic subjects. Issue No. 2, for example, contains a series of descriptions, edited by Fernando Horcasitas, of "La Llorona," the famous Mexican archetype of the woman eternally damned for killing her own children. The research into sources and origins is admirably thorough; but the human interest value of the myth is a powerful poetic force, changing the study from a simple compilation of facts to a universal human drama.

After Barlow's death, there was a lapse in publication of the magazine, but the third issue finally appeared under the editorship of John Paddock, present director of the Instituto de Estudios Oaxaqueños. In his introduction to the *Notes,* Paddock comments: "Although I had not known Barlow, I felt then and still feel that the fearsome task was an honor."

In the summer of 1950, Barlow was given a leave of absence by the College for ill health. It may have been at this time that his tremendous productivity and ability for concentration began to backfire, causing in him a nervous condition which paved the way for his suicide on January 1 of the following year. it may be, too, that his Rousseau-esque belief in the Mexican Indian as a naturally "good" and uncorrupted cultural being turned suddenly bitter and negative; it had been observed that toward the end he was badly exploited by the very Indians who lived in his house. At any rate, on the first of January 1951, after a fashionable (and for Barlow untypical) New Year's Eve party the night before, an 18-page letter in Spanish never completed, was found in Barlow's bedroom next to his body. it was addressed to Pablo Martínez de Río and spoke of his insomnia and other problems. This letter has been burned. On the door, outside, was a note in May saying: " wish to sleep for a long time," or words to that effect. The two Mayans who lived in his house at that time read it and did not enter.

Barlow's body was cremated and his ashes were buried in the Desierto de los Leones next to a tree. Only Martínez del Río, his friend and executor, was present. In the last analysis, any "personal" explanation for Barlow's suicide must belong to the past and to the dead. But the personal can never exist independently outside the context of the general; and it is the general motivation for his action—the seeds of which were surely in him for many years—which awakens the imagination and sympathy of those who never knew him.

Perhaps there is a fatal appeal in the combination of youth and brilliance, cut off so prematurely at the height of Barlow's career. Or perhaps his strange, self-imposed exile in Mexico, his search for other, better worlds, ended in a kind of profound disillusionment which he was unable to reconcile with his dream. We can suppose that Barlow was at a crucial point in his development, a psychological crisis which all idealists and artists eventually face: the clash of personal ethics with the brutal facts of real life. The imbalanced man will compromise; but there are always some who are unable to survive the shock of collision.

T. E. Lawrence was one such, for he died a spiritual death when he was 32, unable to make the final identification with his beloved Arabia, yet at the same time forced into believing that he could find himself under another name and another life in England. As a result of this deception, Lawrence lived on pointlessly for nearly twenty years in an alien land: his own. Lawrence, too, imagined he had found a culture and a people he could claim his own; yet despite the brilliance of his will-power and the intensity of his purpose in attempting to unite, psychologically and physically, the wandering tribes of Arabia, he was to live to recognize his own double failure—failure from the outside, since his political efforts were eventually over-ruled; and more damaging, failure from within himself, as he came to a gradual disillusionment with the unending mysteries of these strange peoples he so wished to love.

Barlow, also an outsider by choice, also a linguist, a man of disguises, an idealist and poet, avoiding his own country as Lawrence avoided England, might have found similarly that the peoples he embraced did not and could not reflect the darkest images of his own soul. Love—the deepest spiritual identification with another being or beings—was to remain a solitary inward process; and Mexico, for all his hopes and all her temptations and imitations, could not—like Ulysses' Siren—offer any cure for his loneliness except the ultimate one of death.

It is not difficult to picture the young Barlow, magnetized by the brilliant visions of Lovecraft, visions of other races, glimpses into lost gigantic civilizations, spending his youth in a conscious or unconscious pursuit of an equivalent ideal. When he could not discover it in the ancient cultures he so passionately studied, the whole structure of his personality broke down. Shy, introverted, leading the life of a semi-recluse in his Azcapotzalco home, respected by many but known to few, Barlow could not accept a compromise. He died leaving the world a mystery to solve, one as fragmented, elusive and intensely personal as his poetry. In the slim volume of verse which he published in 1947 there may be more of an answer than all the romantic speculations a curious world can make:

> "Today I went for a walk in Hell,
> Explored the red precincts,
> Because of the fine weather and your eyes.
> There was an alley I had never seen,
> With houses that must be old
> Leaning their chins over the ember pavement,
> Whispering aged lecheries together.
> There were doors cluttered with ribs and cheek bones,
> With the visible stench carding over them.
> Because of your philosophical attitudes and your knees
> I was admitted by all the servants.
> I thought I knew every charred signpost, every monument of the
>     place,
> From the proper bonfires of the well-to-do
> To the ragged flame of poets and social reformers,
> Drawing a bitter persistent thread through the nostrils.
> I did not know I could get lost like a stranger,
> Ponder, wander mapless through Hell."

# BIBLIOGRAPHY

## Books

*Poems for a Competition.* Sacramento: Fugitive Press, 1942.

*View from a Hill.* Azcapotzalco: [no publisher given], 1947.

*Accent on Barlow: A Commemorative Anthology.* Edited by Lawrence Hart. San Rafael, CA: Lawrence Hart, [1962].

*The Annals of the Jinns.* West Warwick, RI: Necronomicon Press, 1978.

*The Night Ocean* (as by H. P. Lovecraft). West Warwick, RI: Necronomicon Press, 1978, 1982.

*A Dim-Remembered Story.* West Warwick, RI: Necronomicon Press, 1980.

*Obras de Robert H. Barlow.* Mexico City: INAH; Puebla, Mexico: UDLA, 1987f.

*The Battle That Ended the Century and Collapsing Cosmoses* (with H. P. Lovecraft). West Warwick, RI: Necronomicon Press, 1992.

*On Lovecraft and Life.* Edited by S. T. Joshi. West Warwick, RI: Necronomicon Press, 1992.

*The Hoard of the Wizard-Beast and One Other* (with H. P. Lovecraft). West Warwick, RI: Necronomicon Press, 1994.

*Eyes of the God: The Weird Fiction and Poetry of R. H. Barlow.* Edited by S. T. Joshi, Douglas A. Anderson, and David E. Schultz. New York: Hippocampus Press, 2002. Translated as *La noche del océano y otros cuentos,* tr. Montero. Madrid: Distinta Tinta, 2018 (fiction and select poems only, as by Robert H. Barlow, without attribution to the editors of the first edition).

*The Dragon-Fly and Leaves.* Edited by S. T. Joshi. Seattle: Sarnath Press, 2020.

# Fiction

"Annals of the Jinns"

    I. The Black Tower. *Fantasy Fan,* 1, No. 2 (October 1933): 28. *Kadath* No. 1 (1974).

    II. The Shadow from Above. *Fantasy Fan,* 1, No. 3 (November 1933): 39.

    III. The Flagon of Beauty. *Fantasy Fan,* 1, No. 4 (December 1933): 57–58.

    IV. The Sacred Bird. *Fantasy Fan,* 1, No. 5 (January 1934): 75.

    V. The Tomb of the God. *Fantasy Fan,* 1, No. 6 (February 1934): 91–92. In Lin Carter, ed. *Kingdoms of Sorcery.* New York: Doubleday; Science Fiction Book Club, 1976. 91–92.

    VI. The Flower God. *Fantasy Fan,* 1, No. 9 (May 1934): 139–40, 144.

    VII. The Little Box. *Fantasy Fan,* 1, No. 10 (June 1934): 153, 157.

    VIII. The Fall of the Three Cities. *Fantasy Fan,* 1, No. 12 (August 1934): 181–84.

    IX. The Mirror. *Fantasy Fan,* 1, No. 6 (February 1935): 91–93.

    The previous items are reprinted in facsimile in Charles D. Hornig, ed. *The Fantasy Fan: September, 1933–February, 1935.* [n.p.: Lance Thingmaker, 2010.]

    X. The Theft of the Hsothain [*sic*] Manuscripts. *Phantagraph,* 4, No. 5 (August 1936): 6–8.

    XI. An Episode in the Jungle. *Phantagraph* 6, No. 1(May 1937). The poorly printed issue was destroyed; only one set of four pp. with RHB's stories survived.

"The Artizan's Reward." *Polaris* 1, No. 4 (September 1940): 11–17. *Crypt of Cthulhu* No. 60 (Hallowmas 1988): 39–40.

"At Night." A.Ms. (S).

"The Battle That Ended the Century" (with H. P. Lovecraft). T.Ms./A.Ms. (JHL). First appearance as an unsigned mimeographed document, distributed anonymously through the mail. *Acolyte* 2, No. 4 (Fall 1944): 9–12. In H. P. Lovecraft. *Some-*

*thing about Cats and Other Pieces.* Sauk City WI: Arkham House, 1949. 165–69. In Glenn Lord. *The Last Celt: A Bio-Bibliography of Robert Ervin Howard.* West Kingston, RI: Donald M. Grant, 1976. 359–63 (as by H. P. Lovecraft). In H. P. Lovecraft. *Miscellaneous Writings.* Ed. S. T. Joshi. Sauk City, WI; Arkham House, 1995. 66–71, In *Medusa's Coil and Others: The Annotated Revisions and Collaborations of H. P. Lovecraft,* Volume 2. Ed. S. T. Joshi. Welches, OR: Arcane Wisdom, 2012. 264–68. In H. P. Lovecraft. *Collected Fiction: A Variorum Edition,* Volume 4. Ed. S. T. Joshi. New York: Hippocampus Press, 2022. 518–22.

"Birthday." *Scarlet Cockerel* No. 7 (1938/9?). John H. Dow's "Bibliography of the *Scarlet Cockerel*" states that there were four different versions or states of the issue; see *Fossil* No. 185 (n.d. but c. December 1965): 2. What Dow calls issue 7a was a proof (1937); 7b apparently was a printed issue (June 1937). Babcock later issued another set of proofs (7c, March 1938) that did not contain the story, nor did the final of September 1938–April 1939). The text herein derives from what must have been galley proofs, found among RHB's papers (S) after his death. The printed version (in 7b) has not been seen.

"The Bright Valley." T.Ms. (S).

"The Burrow." A.Ms. (S).

"The Cavern of Fear." T.Ms./A.Ms. (S).

"Chant." Unpublished. First title: "The Legend of He That Was Chosen." T.Ms. (private hands).

"The City in the Desert." T.Ms. (JHL).

"Collapsing Cosmoses" (with H. P. Lovecraft). A.Ms. (JHL). *Leaves* No. 2 (1938): 100–101. In *Medusa's Coil and Others: The Annotated Revisions and Collaborations of H. P. Lovecraft,* Volume 2. Ed. S. T. Joshi. Welches, OR: Arcane Wisdom, 2012. 548–50. In H. P. Lovecraft. *Collected Fiction: A Variorum Edition,* Volume 4. Ed. S. T. Joshi. New York: Hippocampus Press, 2022. 500–502. In *The Dragon-Fly and Leaves* 237–29.

"Cousin Anna." T.Ms. (S).

"The Daughters of Darkness." A.Ms. (S).

"The Deplorable Voyage." T.Ms./A.Ms. (JHL).

"A Dim-Remembered Story." *Californian* 4, No. 1 (Summer 1936): 72–87.

"A Dream." *Dragon-Fly* No. 1 (October 15, 1935): 1–6. *Crypt of Cthulhu* No. 60 (Hallowmas 1988): 43–4. In *The Dragon-Fly and Leaves* 17–19.

"The Excursion." *California Pelican* 48, No. 5 (December 1941): 28.

"The Experiment." *Unusual Stories* 1, No. 1 (May–June 1935): 35–40. *Perry Rhodan* No. 42 (March 1974): 142–54. *Crypt of Cthulhu* No. 60 (Hallowmas 1988): 14–16. In Forrest J Ackerman, ed. *Perry Rhodan #42: Time's Lonely One.* New York: Ace, 1974. 142–46. In Forrest J Ackerman ed. *Ackermanthology: 65 Astonishing Rediscovered Sci-Fi Shorts, Millennium Edition.* Los Angeles: General Publishing Group, 1997; Rockville, MD: Sense of Wonder Press, 2000. 85–88 (as "Experiment").

"Eyes of the God." T.Ms. (private hands). *Sea Gull* No. 37 (May 1933): 5–6. *Crypt of Cthulhu* No. 60 (Hallowmas 1988): 41 (as "Eye of the God").

"The Fidelity of Ghu." T.Ms. (JHL).

"Fine Bindings." T.Ms. (S).

"A Fragment." *Californian* 3, No. 3 (Winter 1935): 73. *Crypt of Cthulhu* No. 60 (Hallowmas 1988): 32. [Last two paragraphs of "The Night Ocean."]

"From the Book of Garoth." *Perspective Review* (Summer 1935): 6–8, 10 (chs. 10–12 [partial]; as "The Adventures of Garoth"). Balance of ch. 12 and entirety of chs. 14, 16, and 18 from T.Ms. (S); [untitled chapter] from T.Ms. (JHL).

"The Fugitives." A.Ms. (S).

"A Glimpse of Euterpe" *California Pelican* 48, No. 6 (January 1942): 16–17.

"The Hat." T.Ms. (S).

"The Herbivorous God." T.Ms. (S).

"The Hoard of the Wizard-Beast" (with H. P. Lovecraft). In *The Hoard of the Wizard-Beast and One Other* (includes facsimile of T.Ms.). In *Medusa's Coil and Others: The Annotated Revisions and Collaborations of H. P. Lovecraft,* Volume 2. Ed. S. T. Joshi. Welches, OR: Arcane Wisdom, 2012. 242–49. In H. P. Lovecraft. *Collected Fiction: A Variorum Edition,* Vol. 4, ed. S. T. Joshi. New York: Hippocampus Press, 2022. 500–05.

"Hunter's Trophy." A.Ms. (S).

"I Hate Queers." Nonextant?

"An Immortality." T.Ms. (S).

"The Inhospitable Tavern." *Perspective Review* (Autumn 1934): 3, 12.

"The Last Prophecy." T.Ms. (S).

"A Legend." A.Ms. (S).

"Loneliness." T.Ms. (private hands).

"A Memory." *Californian* 3, No. 3 (Winter 1935): 48–55. *Crypt of Cthulhu* No. 60 (Hallowmas 1988): 25–31.

"The Misfortunes of Butter-Churning." *Voyageur* 3, No. 1 (Fall 1934): 2–3.

"My First Cacomixtli." *California Pelican* 48, No. 4 (November 1941): 20.

"The Night Ocean" (with H. P. Lovecraft). T.Ms. (with HPL's revisions in pen) (S). *Californian* 4, No. 3 (Winter 1936): 41–56. (see also "A Fragment.") *Weird Tales* 48, No. 2 (Spring 1981): 9–42. In Stefan Dziemianowicz, Martin H. Greenberg, and T. Liam McDonald, ed. *Sea-Cursed: Thirty Terrifying Tales of the Deep.* New York: Barnes & Noble, 1994. 515–32. In In *Medusa's Coil and Others: The Annotated Revisions and Collaborations of H. P. Lovecraft,* Volume 2. Ed. S. T. Joshi. Welches, OR: Arcane Wisdom, 2012. 385–414. *Lovecraft Annual* No. 8 (2014): 60–110 (includes facsimile of T.Ms.). In H. P. Lovecraft, *Collected Fiction: A Variorum Edition,* Volume 4. Ed. S. T. Joshi. New York: Hippocampus Press, 2022. 632–58.

"Nightfall." A.Ms. (S).

"Origin Undetermined." *Leaves* No. 2 (1938): 134–45. *Crypt of Cthulhu* No. 60 (Hallowmas 1988): 3–13. In *The Dragon-Fly and Leaves* 292–310.

"The Priest and the Heretic." *Sea Gull* No. 53 (September 1935): 4. *Crypt of Cthulhu* No. 60 (Hallowmas 1988): 42.

"Pursuit of the Moth." *Dragon-Fly* No. 2 (15 May 1936): 33–40. In *The Dragon-Fly and Leaves*.

"The Questioner." *Polaris* 1, No. 4 (September 1940): 19. *Crypt of Cthulhu* No. 20 (Eastertide 1984): 51.

"Return by Sunset." *Acolyte* 1, No. 4 (Summer 1943): 7–14. *Crypt of Cthulhu* No. 60 (Hallowmas 1988): 17–24

"The Root-Gatherers." *Polaris* 1, No. 2 (March 1940): 7–9.

"School of Art." Nonextant?

"The Slaying of the Monster" (with H. P. Lovecraft). In *Hoard of the Wizard-Beast and One Other* (includes facsimile of T.Ms.). In *Medusa's Coil and Others: The Annotated Revisions and Collaborations of H. P. Lovecraft,* Volume 2. Ed. S. T. Joshi. Welches, OR: Arcane Wisdom, 2012. 240–41. In H. P. Lovecraft. *Collected Fiction: A Variorum Edition,* Volume 4. Ed. S. T. Joshi. New York: Hippocampus Press, 2022. 498–99.

"The Summons." *Californian* 3, No. 2 (Fall 1935): 28–32. *Crypt of Cthulhu* No. 60 (Hallowmas 1988): 33–38.

"The Swearing of an Oath." *Polaris* 1, No. 3 (June 1940): 19.

"The Temple." *Perspective Review* (Spring 1935): 3–5.

"'Till A' the Seas'" (with H. P. Lovecraft). T.Ms. (JHL). *Californian* (Summer 1935): 3–7. *Arkham Collector* No. 4 (Winter 1969): 90–101. *Crypt of Cthulhu* No. 17 (Hallowmas 1983): 33–39. In Lovecraft's *The Horror in the Museum and Other Revisions*. Sauk City, WI: Arkham House, 1970. 95–103. Rev. ed. 1989 (ed. S. T. Joshi). 421–29. In *Medusa's Coil and Others: The Annotated Revisions and Collaborations of H. P. Lovecraft,* Volume 2. Ed. S. T. Joshi. Welches, OR: Arcane Wisdom, 2012. 269–80. In H. P. Lovecraft. *Collected Fiction: A Variorum Edition,* Volume 4. Ed. S. T. Joshi. New York: Hippocampus Press, 2022. 536–47.

*The Sombreron.* A play by B[ernardo] Ortiz de Montellano, trans. by RHB. *Number Magazine: A Quarterly of Modern Poetry* 1, No. 3 (Autumn 1950*): 11–24. In *AB.*

## Poetry

*Poems for a Competition.* Emily Chamberlain Cook Prize in Poetry, twenty-sixth award—1942. Sacramento: Fugitive Press, 1942. *Contains:* "Date Uncertain"; "Nostalgia"; "For D."; "Lines to Diana"; "The Gods in the Patio"; "The School Where Nobody Learns What"; "For Leon Trotzky and Huitzilopochtli"; "Sacre du Printemps"; "In Black and White"; "Explanation to M."

*View from a Hill.* Azcapotzalco: [no publisher given], 1947. *Contains:* I. For D: "From This Tree"; "Air for Variations"; "New Directions"; "To a Friend on Sailing"; "To One Rescued"; II. Fresco of priests & beans: "On a Feather Poncho"; "The Chichimecs"; "Stela of a Mayan Penitent"; "Tepuzteca, Tepehua"; "The Conquered"; III. For Rosalie: "blotted a beetle"; "Table Set for Sea-Slime"; IV. Five Years: "First Year: Sebastian"; "Second Year: Dream While Paris Was Threatened"; "Third Year: About a Mythical Factory-Area"; "Fourth Year: Letter to My Brother"; "Fifth Year: Viktoria"; V. For E & for W: "'Que Quieres? Mis Costillas?' (For E.)"; "Chili sin Carne (For W.)"; VI. View from a Hill: "To the Builders of a Dam"; "View from a Hill"; "Recantation"; "On the Lights of San Francisco"; "A Escoger"; "In Order to Clarify"; "We Kept on Reading 'Tuesday'"; VII. For Barbara Mayer: "On Leaving Some Friends at an Early Hour."

*A Stone for Sisiphus.* 1949; unpublished. T.Ms. (S). *Contains:* "Sonnet to Siva"; "Anniversary"; "Invocation"; "Evening"; "The Coming Fructification by Night of Our Cyrus"; "Of the Names of the Zapotec Kings"; "Framed Portent"; "Orientation to the West."

---

*The Autumn 1950 issue did not appear until c. April 1951, and so it has no date on the cover as previous issues did.

*Accent on Barlow: A Commemorative Anthology.* Edited by Lawrence Hart. San Rafael, CA: Lawrence Hart, [1962]. *Contains:* "Robert Barlow" by Rosalie Moore and Lawrence Hart; "Respect Not the Leaf"; "To One Rescued"; "Mourning Song"; "View from a Hill"; "Admittance"; "The Gods in the Patio"; "The Chichimecs"; "In Order to Clarify"; "Tepuzteca Tepehua"; "Air for Variations"; "For D."; "To the Builders of a Dam"; "Of the Names of the Zapotec Kings"; "Sacre Du Printemps"; "On the Lights of San Francisco"; "Date Uncertain"; "Sonnet to Siva"; "Lines to Diana"; "Mythological Episode"; "Metropolitan Fable"; "Explanation to M"; "The Conquered"; "Recantation"; "For Rosalie"; "The School Where Nobody Learns What"; "The City"; "Letter to My Brother"; "Warning to Snake Killers"; "About a Mythical Factory Area"; "The Coming Fructification by Night"; "Sebastian"; "'¿Que Quieres? Mis Costillas?'"; "On a Feather Poncho"; "Stela of a Mayan Penitent"; "For Leon Trotzky and Huitzilopochtili"; "Rainy-Day Pastime"; "Orientation to the West"; "Nostalgia"; "We Kept on Reading 'Tuesday'"; *The Sombreron* by B. Ortiz de Montellano, translated by Barlow; plus other poems by Robert Brotherson; Waltrina Furlong; Emily Pausch; Betty Turnoy; Lois Moyles; John Hart; Adele Levi; Jeanne McGahey; Marie Graybeal; Fred Ostrander; Rosalie Moore; Marie Wells; Don Wobber; Leonard Horwitz; and James T. Wright.

"A Escoger." In *VH.*

"Admittance." *Number Magazine: A Quarterly of Modern Poetry* 1, No. 3 (Autumn 1950): 4. *Circle* 1, No. 2 (1944): [15] (under "Four Poems"). In *AB.*

"Air for Variations." *Forum* (Spring 1940): 16 (as part of "For D."). In *VH, AB.*

"Alcestis." T.Ms. (S).

"Altamira." T.Ms. (JHL, S).

"Anniversary." T. Ms. (S). In *SS.* In H. P. Lovecraft and Divers Hands. *The Shuttered Room and Other Pieces.* Sauk City, WI: Arkham House, 1959. 210.

"The Barlow Tributes." In H. P. Lovecraft and Divers Hands. *The Shuttered Room and Other Pieces.* Sauk City, WI: Arkham House, 1959. 206–11. [Contains: "H. P. L." (q.v.); "Anniversary"; "Letter for Last Christmas."]

"Beyond Zimbabwe." See "Bouts Rimés."

"blotted a beetle." In *VH, AB.*

"Bouts Rimés." *Crypt of Cthulhu* No. 44 (Yuletide 1986): 68. In H. P. Lovecraft. *The Ancient Track: Complete Poetical Works of H. P. Lovecraft.* Ed. S. T. Joshi. San Francisco: Night Shade, 2001. 79. Rev. ed. New York: Hippocampus Press, 2013. 95. [Written in collaboration with H. P. Lovecraft. RHB devised the end-rhymes; Lovecraft then wrote the rest of the lines to fit. The title literally means "end-rhymes." Comprises "Beyond Zimbabwe" and "The White Elephant."]

"Burlesque." T.Ms. (S).

"The Chichimecs." In *VH, AB. New World Journal* 1, No. 1 (Fall 1975): 32 (under "A Fresco of Priests and Beans").

"Chili sin Carne (For W.)." In *VH.*

"The City." T.Ms. (S). In *AB.*

"Colors." T.Ms. (S).

"The Coming Fructification by Night of Our Cyrus." T.Ms. (S) (as "Theological Problem"). *Berkeley: A Journal of Modern Culture* No. 4 (July 1948): 4 (as "Theological Problem"; under "Two Poems"). In *SS.* In *AB* (as "The Coming Fructification by Night").

"The Conquered." In *VH, AB.*

"Cycle from a Dead Year." T.Ms. (S).

"Dark Echo." A.Ms. (private hands).

"Date Uncertain." *Quarterly Review of Literature* 4, No. 1 (1947): 14–15. In *PC, AB.*

"Dawn Delayed." T.Ms. (S). *Cubicle* 4, No. 3 (Winter 1939): [12].

"Dirge for the Artist." T.Ms. (S). *Couleur de Rose* No. 4 (Christmas 1938): [8] (untitled).

"Dream-Battle." A.Ms. (private hands).

"Evening." T.Ms. (S). In *SS.*

"Explanation to M." *New Rejections* No. 2 (April 1942): 32. *Number Magazine: A Quarterly of Modern Poetry* 1, No. 3 (Autumn 1950): 2. In *PC, AB*.

"Fifth Year: Viktoria." *Circle* 1, No. 2 (1944): [15] (as "Viktoria"; under heading "Four Poems"). In *VH*.

"First Year: Sebastian." In *VH*. *Number Magazine: A Quarterly of Modern Poetry* 1, No. 3 (Autumn 1950): 8 (as "Sebastian"). In *AB*.

"For D." In *PC, AB*.

"For D." Series comprising "1."; "2. Air for Variations"; and "3. To a Friend on Sailing" (but not the poem "For D." as above). *Forum* (Spring 1940): 16–17.

"For Leon Trotzky and Huitzilopochtli." *New Rejections* No. 2 (April 1942): 22. In *PC, AB*.

"Fourth Year: Letter to My Brother." T.Ms. (S) (as "Letter to My Brother"). *New Rejections* No. 3 (May 1943): 28 (as "Letter to My Brother"). In *VH*.

"Fragments" (Even as from the chaos of the wave). T.Ms. (S).

"Fragments" (Through my leafed and branchey mind). T.Ms. (S).

"Framed Portent." T.Ms. (S). *Circle* 1, No. 6 (Autumn 1945): 17. *Number Magazine: A Quarterly of Modern Poetry.* 1, No. 3 (Autumn 1950): 5 (as "Metropolitan Fable"). In *Ideas of Order in Experimental Poetry* 17, in a section titled "Ideas of Order in Experimental Poetry" (with contributions by Hart, Moore, and others). In *SS*. In *AB* (as "Metropolitan Fable").

"A Fresco of Priests and Beans." *New World Journal* 1, No. 1 (Fall 1975): 31–35. [*Contains:* "On a Feather Poncho"; "The Chichimecs"; "Stela of a Mayan Penitent"; "Tepuzteca, Tepehua."]

"From This Tree." *Forum* (Spring 1940): 6 (as part of "For D."). *Number Magazine: A Quarterly of Modern Poetry* 1, No. 3 (Autumn 1955): 25. In *VH*.

"Frustration." T.Ms. (S).

"The Gods in the Patio." T.Ms. (S). *Number: A Magazine of Modern Poetry* 1, No. 2 (Fall 1950): 19. In *PC, AB*.

"A Gull from a Cliff." T.Ms. (S).

"H. P. L." T.Ms. (S). In H. P Lovecraft and Divers Hands. *The Shuttered Room and Other Pieces.* Sauk City, WI: Arkham House, 1959. 206–10. [*Contains:* "March 1937"; "March 1938"; [Untitled] (The ocean vast from myriad darts of rain); [Untitled] (The night of iron, the day of foam is made,); "H. P. L." (The dimensionless sun, an hour since white with flame); "H. P. L. (March 15, 1940)."]

"H. P. L." (The dimensionless sun, an hour white with flame). See "H. P. L."

"H. P. L. (March 15, 1940)." See "H. P. L."

"The Heart." T.Ms. (S).

"In Black and White." *Aonian* 1, No 1 (Spring 1943): 1. In *PC.*

"In Order to Clarify." In *VH, AB.*

"Intimations of Mortality." T.Ms. (S).

"Invocation." T.Ms. (S). In *SS.*

"Isolde." T.Ms. (S).

"Letter for Last Christmas." T.Ms. (S). In H. P. Lovecraft and Divers Hands. *The Shuttered Room and Other Pieces.* Sauk City, WI: Arkham House, 1959. 211.

"Lines to Diana." In *PC, AB.*

"March." T.Ms. (S). *Couleur de Rose* No. 3 [c. June 1938]: [3–4] (untitled). *Leaves* No. 2 (1938): 119 (as by "Jonathon Lindley"). In *The Dragon-Fly and Leaves* 270.

"March 1937." See "H. P. L."

"March 1938." See "H. P. L."

"The Mask." *Number Magazine: A Quarterly of Modern Poetry.* 1, No. 3 (Autumn 1950): 6.

"Metropolitan Fable." See "Framed Portent."

"Mexico to the Tourists." T.Ms. (S). *New Rejections* No. 3 (May 1943): 28.

"[Miscellaneous Lines]." T.Ms. (S).

"Mourning Song." *Quarterly Review of Literature* 4, No. 1 (1947): 13–14. In *AB.*

"Mozart's G Minor." T.Ms. (S).

"Mythological Episode." T.Ms. (S). In August Derleth, ed. *Fire and Sleet and Candlelight*. Sauk City, WI: Arkham House, 1961. 13.

"N. Y." T.Ms. (S).

"New Directions." *Forum* (Spring 1940): 44 (untitled, but labeled "Poem" in the magazine's table of contents; as part of "For D."). In *VH*.

"Nostalgia." *New Rejections* No. 2 (April 1942): 32. *Quarterly Review of Literature* 4, No. 1 (1947): 13. *Number Magazine: A Quarterly of Modern Poetry*. 1, No. 3 (Autumn 1950): 5. In *PC, AB*.

"Of the Names of the Zapotec Kings." T.Ms. (S). In *SS, AB*.

"On a Feather Poncho (Nazca, c. 100 A.D.")." *Berkeley: A Journal of Modern Culture* No. 4 (July 1948): 4 (under "Two Poems"). In *VH, AB*. *New World Journal* 1, No. 1 (Fall 1975): 31 (under "A Fresco of Priests and Beans").

"On Leaving Some Friends at an Early Hour." *Forum* (Spring 1940): 17. In *VH*.

"On the Lights of San Francisco." T.Ms. (S). *New Rejections* No. 3 (May 1943): 29. *Number Magazine: A Quarterly of Modern Poetry* 1, No. 3 (Autumn 1950): 3 (as "The Lights of San Francisco"). In *VH, AB*.

"Orientation to the West." T.Ms. (S). *New Rejections* No. 3 (May 1943): 29. In *SS, AB*.

"Out of the Dark." T.Ms. (S). *Cubicle* 5, No 1 (Spring 1940): [24].

"The Papyrus of Nyarlathotep." T.Ms. (JHL).

"Poem." *Number Magazine: A Quarterly of Modern Poetry* 1, No. 3 (Autumn 1950): 7.

"Poema de Salida." T.Ms. (S).

"Prophecy." T.Ms. (S).

"¿Que Quieres? ¿Mis Costillas? (For E.)." T.Ms. (S) (as "For E. G."). *Number Magazine: A Quarterly of Modern Poetry* 1, No. 3 (Autumn 1950): 9 (as "(For E.) ¿Que Quieres? ¿Mis Costillas?". In *VH, AB*.

"Quetzalcoatl." T.Ms. (S).

"R. E. H." T.Ms. (S). *Weird Tales* 28, No. 3 (October 1936): 353. *Howard Collector* No. 10 (Spring 1968): 33. In *The Howard Collector*. New York: Ace, 1979. 220. *Revelations from Yuggoth* No. 2 (May 1988): 41. *Strange Worlds* No. 12 (2003): 56. *Sword & Fantasy* No. 3 (July 2005): 4.

"Rainy-Day Pastime." T.Ms. (S).

"Recantation." In *VH*.

"Reproach." A.Ms. (private hands).

"Respect Not the Leaf." T.Ms. (S). In *AB*.

"Sacre du Printemps." *Pacific* 2, No. 3 (April 1947): 17. In *PC, AB*.

"St. John's Churchyard" [acrostic on Edgar Allan Poe]. In Maurice W. Moe, ed. *Four Acrostic Sonnets on Edgar Allan Poe*. Milwaukee, WI: Privately printed, 1936 (as "Edgar Allan Poe"). *Science-Fantasy Correspondent* 1, No. 3 (March–April 1937): 16. In August Derleth, ed. *Fire and Sleet and Candlelight*. Sauk City, WI: Arkham House, 1961. 11 (as "Edgar Allan Poe"). In Sam Moskowitz, ed. *The Man Who Called Himself Poe*. Garden City, NY: Doubleday, 1969. 236. *Crypt of Cthulhu* No. 57 (1988): 28.

"The School Where Nobody Learns What." *Quarterly Review of Literature* 4, No. 1 (1947): 14. In *PC, AB*.

"Second Year: Dream While Paris Was Threatened." In *VH*.

"Shub-Ad." T.Ms. (S). In August Derleth, ed. *Fire and Sleet and Candlelight*. Sauk City, WI: Arkham House, 1961. 11–12.

"Song." T.Ms. (S).

"Sonnet" (Forbidden the languid rapture of your lips,). T.Ms. (S).

"Sonnet" (The sunlit fields wherethrough I walked all day). *Polaris* 1, No. 1 (December 1939): 8.

"Sonnet to Siva." In *SS, AB*.

"Sonnet IV." A.Ms. (JHL).

"Sonnet V." T.Ms. (S).

"Sonnet VI." T.Ms. (S).

"Sonnet VII." T.Ms. (S).

"Springtime." [N.p.: Privately printed, 1940.]

"Stela of a Mayan Penitent." *Contour* (Berkeley, CA) No. 3 (Summer 1948): 13. In *VH, AB. New World Journal* 1, No. 1 (Fall 1975): 33 (under "A Fresco of Priests and Beans").

"Strife." T.Ms. (private hands).

"Table Set for Sea-Slime." *Circle* No. 6 (1945): 17 (in a section titled "Ideas of Order in Experimental Poetry," with contributions by Hart, Moore, and others). In *Ideas of Order in Experimental Poetry* 17.

"A Tapestry." T.Ms. (S).

"Tepuzteca, Tepehua." *Circle* No. 6 (1945): 49 (with illustration, p. 48). In *VH, AB. New World Journal* 1, No. 1 (Fall 1975): 34–35 (under "A Fresco of Priests and Beans").

"Theological Problem." See "The Coming Fructification by Night of Our Cyrus."

"Third Year: About a Mythical Factory-Area." *Circle* 1, No. 2 (1944): [14] (as "About a Mythical Factory-Area"). In *VH, AB*.

"To a Companion." T.Ms. (S).

"To a Friend on Sailing." *Forum* (Spring 1940) 16–17 (as part of "For D."). In *VH*.

"To a Wayfarer." T.Ms. (S).

"To Alta, on Her Original American Sonnet." T.Ms. (S).

"To Bacchus." T.Ms. (S).

"To One Rescued." *Number Magazine: A Quarterly of Modern Poetry* 1, No. 3 (Autumn 1950): 7; 1, No. 8 (Autumn 1955): 24. In *VH, AB*.

"To Sleep." T.Ms. (S).

"To the Builders of a Dam." *Circle* 1, No. 2 (1944): [14] (under heading "Four Poems"). *Number Magazine: A Quarterly of Modern Poetry* 1, No. 3 (Autumn 1950): 3 (as "Dam"). In *VH, AB*.

"To W——." A.Ms. (private hands).

"The Unresisting." T.Ms. (S). *Leaves* No. 2 (1938): 119 (as by "Jonathon Lindley"). In *The Dragon-Fly and Leaves* 269–70.

[Untitled] (A lover I had in the starry night). A.Ms. (private hands).

[Untitled] (Curse you that are beautiful). T.Ms. (S).

[Untitled] (Here sun and scarlet flower declare). T.Ms. (S).

[Untitled] (I and Percy B. Shelley). In *SS*.

[Untitled] (I shall be gay this night as any fly). T.Ms. (S).

[Untitled] (I would weave my happiness into a song). T.Ms. (S).

[Untitled] (In aimless whirl two thousand million years). T.Ms. (S).

[Untitled] (Into the clear and jewelled heart of day). T.Ms. (S).

[Untitled] (Let us swell the peace with warmth,). T.Ms. (S).

[Untitled] (Like figures scattered on a noiseless clock). T.Ms. (S).

[Untitled] (Los años son un abismo de celaje). T.Ms. (S).

[Untitled] (Love came, and abode his time). T.Ms. (S).

[Untitled] (Mute though my mouth has been, yet have I heard). T.Ms. (S).

[Untitled] (Of course it is abominable). T.Ms. (S).

[Untitled] (Oh golden beach and blue-enamelled sea). T.Ms. (S).

[Untitled] (Our regal city, which for one long day glows fair). T.Ms. (S).

[Untitled] (Over me courses the mist, and the stars are obscured,). T.Ms. (S).

[Untitled] (She sought the hut wherein the gods abode,). T.Ms. (S).

[Untitled] (That night the birds had ceased their painful cries). T.Ms. (JHL).

[Untitled] (The copper sherry, rippling flame). T.Ms. (S).

[Untitled] (The crucibles of war; and pomp and might). T.Ms. (JHL).

[Untitled] (The morning ocean, glimmering with mist). A.Ms. (private hands).

[Untitled] (The night of iron, the day of foam is made,). T.Ms. (S). See "H. P. L."

[Untitled] (The ocean vast from myriad darts of rain,). T.Ms. (S). See "H. P. L."

[Untitled] (These are the leaves). A.Ms., T.Ms. (S).

[Untitled] (To what avail were path and garden cleared,). T.Ms. (S).

[Untitled] (Underneath this velvet floor). T.Ms. (S).

[Untitled] (Walkers in the meadow, walkers in the grass,). T.Ms. (S).

[Untitled] ("We caught him prowling in the dark,"). T.Ms. (S).

[Untitled] (Well I know the starless night awaiting). T.Ms. (S).

[Untitled] (Yet ever my gaze returns). T.Ms. (S).

"View from a Hill." In *VH, AB*.

"Warning to Snake Killers." T.Ms. (S). *Number Magazine: A Quarterly of Modern Poetry* 1, No. 3 (Autumn 1950): 4. In *AB*. In August Derleth, ed. *Fire and Sleet and Candlelight*. Sauk City, WI: Arkham House, 1961. 12–13.

"We Kept on Reading 'Tuesday.'" A.Ms. (S). *Accent* 3, No. 1 (Autumn 1942): 48. *Number Magazine: A Quarterly of Modern Poetry* 1, No. 3 (Autumn 1950): 2. In *VH, AB*.

"The White Elephant." See "Bouts Rimés."

"Who Will Not Know." T.Ms. (S).

"Winter Mood." T.Ms. (S). *Aonian* 1, No. 3 (Autumn 1943): 1.


## Nonfiction

"About H. G. Wells." *Fantasy Fan* 1, No. 9 (May 1934): 143–44 (as by "Daniel McPhail").

"Angel Hernandez, Artist." *Circle* 1, No. 7/8 (Winter 1946): 70. A drawing by Hernandez is on p. 71.

"Autobiography." T.Ms. (S). In *On Lovecraft and Life* 19–25. In *O Fortunate Floridian: H. P. Lovecraft's Letters to R. H. Barlow*. Ed. S. T. Joshi and David E. Schultz. Tampa, FL: University of Tampa Press, 2007. 407–17.

"Blake and the 'Songs of Innocence.'" *Southern Amateur* 1, No. 2 (December 1935): 7–8.

"The Burro in America." *American Notes and Queries* 2, No. 8 (November 1942): 117–18.

"A Check-List of Matthew Gregory Lewis (1775–1818)." *Acolyte* 2, No. 3 (Summer 1944): 7.

"A Check-List of the Published Weird Stories of Henry S. Whitehead." *Leaves* No. 2 (1938): 133. In *The Dragon-Fly and Leaves* 290–91.

"The Children of Axayacatl." T.Ms. (Kenneth W. Faig papers, JHL)

"Colophon or Epitaph." *Leaves* No. 2 (1938): [146]. In *The Drag-on-Fly and Leaves* 311–12.

"Fragment of a Letter to a Young Poet." T.Ms. (S).

"Henry S. Whitehead." In Whitehead's *Jumbee and Other Uncanny Tales*. Sauk City, WI: Arkham House, 1944. vii–xii.

"A Hitherto Unknown Map of the Pensacola Coastal Region, 1762." *Florida Historical Quarterly* 22, No. 1 (1943): 41.

"Journey to the Place of the Fish-Masters." T.Ms. (S).

Letter. *Astounding Stories of Super-Science* 11, No. 3 (January 1933): 427.

Letter. *Fantasy Fan* 1, No. 2 (October 1933): 31.

Letter. *Fantasy Fan* 1, No. 4 (December 1933): 50.

Letter. *Fantasy Fan* 1, No. 5 (January 1934): 76.

Letter. *Fantasy Fan* 1, No. 8 (April 1934): 114; 124.

Letter. *Fantasy Fan* 1, No. 12 (August 1934): 178.

Letter. *Fantasy Fan* 2, No. 2 (October 1934): 19.

Letter. *Sweetness and Light* 1, No. 3 (Fall 1939): 11.

"[Memories of Lovecraft]." A.Ms. (S). In August Derleth. *Some Notes on H. P. Lovecraft*. Sauk City, WI: Arkham House, 1959; Folcroft, PA: Folcroft Press, 1971; [Norwood PA]: Norwood Editions, 1976; Philadelphia: R. West, 1977; Darby, PA: Arden Library, 1980; West Warwick: Necronomicon Press, 1982. xxiv–xxxi. In H. P. Lovecraft and Divers Hands. *The Dark Brotherhood and Other Pieces*. Sauk City, WI: Arkham House, 1966. 316–22 (in August Derleth's "Final Notes"). In *On Lovecraft and Life* 11–18. In Peter Cannon, ed. *Lovecraft Remembered*. Sauk City, WI: Arkham House, 1998. 351–55 (as "The Barlow Journal"). In *O Fortunate Floridian: H. P. Lovecraft's Letters to R. H. Barlow*. Ed. S. T. Joshi and David E. Schultz. Tampa, FL: University of Tampa Press, 2007. 401–7.

"The Malinche of Acacingo." *Circle* 1, No. 10 (Spring 1948): 53 (drawing by RHB on p. 52).

"National Defense." With H. P. Lovecraft. *Californian* 3, No. 3 (Winter 1935): 79–82. As by E. D. Barlow. *Lovecraft Annual* 14 (2020): 8–14.

"Note." In George Sterling, *After Sunset*. San Francisco: John Howell, Publisher, 1939. [v].

"Obiter Dictum." *Dragon-Fly* No. 1 (15 October 1935): 27–28. In *The Dragon-Fly and Leaves* 30.

"Obiter Scriptum." *Leaves* No. 1 (Summer 1937): 60–64. In *The Dragon-Fly and Leaves* 167–75.

"Origin of 'Guarache.'" *American Notes and Queries* 2, No. 7 (October 1942): 108.

"Parícutin." Unpublished. T.Ms. (S).

"Pedro! Pedro!" *California Folklore Quarterly* 2, No. 1 (1 January 1943): 45. A letter.

"Pseudonyms of Lovecraft." *Acolyte* 1, No. 4 (Summer 1943): 18 (as by "R. E. Barlow").

"Restoration of Santiago de Tlaltelolco." *The Americas: A Quarterly Review of Inter-American Cultural History* 1, No. 3 (October 1944): 355–56. (Listed in Smisor as "Inaugural Mass at Santiago Tlatelolco.")

"[Statement about Poetry]." *Circle* No. 6 (1945): 18–19, in a section titled "Ideas of Order in Experimental Poetry" (with contributions by Hart, Moore, and others) that was also issued as a small booklet. In *In Ideas of Order in Experimental Poetry* 17.

"A Seditious Book." *Science Fiction Advance* 1, No. 1 (April 1938): 9.

"Three Letters [to Larry Farsaci] on H. P. Lovecraft." *Golden Atom* 1, No. 10 (Winter 1943): 31–32.

"*The Time Machine:* A Bibliographical Note." *Fantasy Fan* 1, No. 7 (March 1934): 109.

"The Wind That Is in the Grass: A Memoir of H. P. Lovecraft in Florida." In H. P. Lovecraft. *Marginalia*. Sauk City, WI: Arkham House, 1944. 342–50. In Peter Cannon, ed. *Lovecraft Remembered*. Sauk City, WI: Arkham House, 1998. 356–63. In *O Fortunate Floridian: H. P. Lovecraft's Letters to R. H. Barlow*. Ed.

S. T. Joshi and David E. Schultz. Tampa, FL: University of Tampa Press, 2007. xxix–xxxiv. In S. T. Joshi and David E. Schultz, ed. *Ave atque Vale: Reminiscences of H. P. Lovecraft*. West Warwick, RI: Necronomicon Press, 2018. 389–95.

## Editor

H. P. Lovecraft. *The Notes & Commonplace Book Employed by the Late H. P. Lovecraft Including His Suggestions for Story-Writing, Analyses of the Weird Story, and a List of Certain Basic Underlying Horrors, &c., &c., Designed to Stimulate the Imagination.* [Edited by R. H. Barlow.] Lakeport, CA: Futile Press, 1938. West Warwick, RI: Necronomicon Press, 1978. Glendale, CA: H. P. Lovecraft Historical Society, 2020.

George Sterling. *After Sunset.* [Compiled by R. H. Barlow.] San Francisco: John Howell, Publisher, 1939.

## Publisher

*The Dragon-Fly.* No. 1 (15 October 1935); No. 2 (15 May 1936). In *The Dragon-Fly and Leaves.*

*Leaves.* No. 1 (Summer 1937); No. 2 (1938). In *The Dragon-Fly and Leaves.*

*Tlalocan.* Ed. R. H. Barlow (1943–49; with George T. Smisor, 1943–46). Volume 1 (1943–44); Volume 2 (1945–48); Volume 3 (1949–57).

*Mexihcayotl.* December 1945–May 1946. In Nahuatl.

*Mesoamerican Notes.* Volumes 1–8 (1950–66). [RHB edited Volumes 1 and 2, (1950)]

Frank Belknap Long, Jr. *The Goblin Tower.* Cassia, FL: Dragon-Fly Press, 1935.

H. P. Lovecraft. *The Cats of Ulthar.* Cassia, FL: Dragon-Fly Press, 1935.

## Stillborn Projects

Barlow, R. H. *Fragments*. (See Appendix; a table of contents for a booklet of Barlow's fiction.)

———. *Leaves* 3 and 4.

———. *A Memory & a Dream*. (See Appendix; a table of contents for a booklet of Barlow's fiction.)

Edkins, Ernest A. *Poems*.

Howard, Robert E. *Echoes from an Iron Harp*.

———. *The Gates of Nineveh*.

Long, Frank Belknap. *A Man from Genoa*. [rpt.]

Lovecraft, H. P. *The Ancient Track and Other Poems*.

———. *The Colour out of Space and Others*.

———. *Fungi from Yuggoth*.

———. *Fungi from Yuggoth and Other Verses*.

———. *The Shunned House*. Printed by W. Paul Cook (1928) but not bound. The unbound sheets were sent to Barlow for binding. After Barlow's death, they ultimately arrived at Arkham House, which bound and sold 100 copies in 1961.

Merritt, A. *The Moon Pool and Other Stories*.

Moore, C. L. *Shambleau and Other Stories*.

Smith, Clark Ashton. *Incantations*.

———. *The Jasmine Girdle*. Both published in Smith's *Selected Poems* (1971).

Toldridge, Elizabeth. "Collected works."

Wandrei, Howard. An untitled edition of photographs of Wandrei's drawings.

Whitehead, Henry S. *Caneviniana*. Issued by Paul Freehafer as *The Letters of Henry S. Whitehead*. [Los Angeles:] Fantasy Amateur Press Association, [December 1942]. Printed from eight stencils prepared by RHB.

# Other

Adams, Jr., H. Leon. *Katunob: Occasional Publication in Mesoamerican Anthropology* No. 116. Robert Hayward Barlow: An Annotated Bibliography with Commentary. Greeley, CO: Museum of Anthropology, University of Norther Colorado, 1981.

Berruti, Massimo. *Dim-Remembered Stories: A Critical Study of R. H. Barlow*. New York: Hippocampus Press, 2011.

Faig, Jr., Kenneth W. *R. H. Barlow: An Account of the Life and Career of the Most Controversial Member of the Lovecraft Circle.* Columbia, SC: Dragonfly Press, 2000. In Faig's *The Unknown Lovecraft*. New York: Hippocampus Press, 2009. 194–234 (as "R. H. Barlow").

———. "Robert H. Barlow as H. P. Lovecraft's Literary Executor: An Appreciation." In Faig's *The Unknown Lovecraft*. New York: Hippocampus Press, 2009.

Hart, Lawrence. "A Note on Robert Barlow." *Poetry* 78, No. 2 (May 1951): 115–16. Rev., *AB* 8–9 (under "Robert Barlow").

Joshi, S. T. "R. H. Barlow and the Recognition of H. P. Lovecraft. *Crypt of Cthulhu* No. 60 (Hallowmas 1988): 45–51, 32. In Joshi's *Lovecraft and a World in Transition: Collected Essays on H. P. Lovecraft.* New York: Hippocampus Press, 2014. 439–47.

Lovecraft, H. P. "Correspondence between R. H. Barlow and Wilson Shepherd of Oakman, Alabama—Sept.–Nov. 1932." *Lovecraft Studies* No. 13 (Fall 1986): 68–71. In *CE* 5.211–15.

Moore, Rosalie. "Robert Barlow." *AB* 7–8.

———. "Robert Barlow and the Mexicans." *Number Magazine: A Quarterly of Modern Poetry.* 1, No. 3 (Autumn 1950): 27–30.

Mooser, Clare. "A Study of Robert Barlow: The T. E. Lawrence of Mexico." *Mexico Quarterly Review* 3, No. 2 (1968): 5–12.

Shea, J. Vernon. "R. H. Barlow: Lost Little Boy." T.Ms., John Hay Library, Brown University, Providence. 15 pp., Unpublished.

Smisor, George T. "Barlow Biography." *Number Magazine: A Quarterly of Modern Poetry* 1, No. 3 (Autumn 1950): 25–26. Unsigned.

———. "Bibliography of the Literary Publications of Robert Hayward Barlow." T.Ms. (S).

———. "[R. H. Barlow: A Biographical Sketch]." Contained in a letter by Smisor to Lawrence Hart, 13 March 1951. Held privately. "Barlow Biography" above was abstracted from this piece.

———. "R. H. Barlow and *Tlalocan*." *Tlalocan* 3, No. 2 (1952): 97–102.

# INDEX OF POETRY TITLES

# INDEX OF FIRST LINES

CPSIA information can be obtained
at www.ICGtesting.com
Printed in the USA
BVHW042131120423
662273BV00012B/327